THE
UNIVERSE
IN **100** KEY DISCOVERIES

THE
UNIVERSE
IN 100 KEY DISCOVERIES

GILES SPARROW

Quercus

Contents

Introduction

The history of astronomy is one of constant discovery – an ongoing revolution driven by technological improvements, theoretical breakthroughs, and humanity's unquenchable desire for knowledge about our place in the Universe. It is the oldest of the sciences, with origins that stretch far back into prehistory. We can only guess at the beliefs held by the earliest stargazers, from rare but unmistakable traces in the archaeological record. Cuneiform tablets from ancient Babylon, now more than 3,000 years old, provide the first written evidence for astronomy, but these meticulous records, most likely kept for astrological purposes, do little to illuminate ancient ideas about our place in the wider Universe. The first evidence for all-encompassing cosmological theories emerges in the last few centuries BC, among the philosophers of classical Greece.

From the centre to the edge

From this time on, however, the progressive reinvention of our own place in the Universe forms a strong thread through the history of astronomy. From Ptolemy to Copernicus to Hubble, our planet has been downgraded from the centre of everything to the status of a small world orbiting an average star in a galaxy that is itself just one among hundreds of billions.

But it would be wrong to assume from the above that such discoveries have somehow degraded the status of humanity in the Universe. The fact that such an insignificant world has given rise to intelligent life raises profound questions about the nature of the cosmos itself, and the more complex our understanding of the Universe becomes, the more we should pride our species on its ability to grasp these complexities.

A changing discipline

Of course the nature of astronomy has changed enormously over the centuries. The musings of priests and astrologers always coexisted with practical applications such as navigation, timekeeping and cartography, and the technological breakthroughs of the 17th century, coupled with the increasing importance of global trade, saw astronomy become the first 'professionalized' science, with the establishment of national observatories across Europe and beyond.

Nevertheless, astronomy has always had a strong appeal for amateurs, and many of the great breakthroughs of the 18th and 19th centuries were made through the committed efforts of ardent enthusiasts. Even today, while astronomy has become an increasingly complex and academic subject filled with many specialisms, it remains one of the few sciences where amateurs can make significant discoveries – and thanks to the proliferation of powerful telescopes, imaging tools and computer technology, the scope for amateur contributions is still increasing. Thanks to distributed computing projects, it's now possible to make a useful contribution even without using a telescope – for instance sifting through data from planet-hunting satellites, or classifying images of complex galaxies in the distant Universe.

The past few decades have also been revolutionary for professional astronomers, as longstanding technological barriers have given way and unleashed a wealth of new data and discoveries. New multiple-mirrored and computer-controlled telescopes are far larger and more precise than their predecessors, producing sharper, brighter images from ground-based observatories. Unimpeded by the atmosphere, satellite observatories create pin-sharp images in visible light, and gather up other forms of radiation, from the infrared to the ultraviolet, that are impossible to use from Earth's surface. Computerized CCDs and other sensors allow these radiations to be detected with ever greater sensitivity, and manipulated and analyzed in new ways. Finally, spaceprobes can send back images directly from the worlds of our solar system, and even return physical samples of material from comets and other bodies.

New challenges

The sheer amount of information produced by these new theories can seem overwhelming at times, and is transforming astronomy at an ever-faster pace. Exciting new fields that have recently opened up for study include the dynamic history of our solar system (see page 100), the complex variety of extrasolar planets (see page 288), and the turbulent early days of the Universe itself (see page 68). Even long-standing ideas, such as the steady expansion of the cosmos driven by the Big Bang, have been revolutionized by evidence for a mysterious 'dark energy' that influences the structure of space itself (see page 400).

Indeed, at times it seemed as if the rate of astronomical discovery was outpacing my writing of this book. Doubtless this was just a selection effect, brought on by concentrated trawling of press releases, university websites and scientific journals, but I hope that this snapshot of the current state of astronomy captures a unique and exciting time in its long history – one in which the answers to many long-standing questions came within reach, and new and even more ambitious challenges appeared to take their place.

GILES SPARROW

Uncentering Earth

DEFINITION THE CONCEPTUAL SHIFT AWAY FROM AN EARTH-CENTRED VIEW OF THE UNIVERSE TO ONE CENTRED ON THE SUN.

DISCOVERY ARISTARCHUS OF SAMOS ESTIMATED THE DISTANCE TO THE SUN AROUND 250 BC, AND CONCLUDED IT WAS SO LARGE THAT IT, NOT EARTH, MUST BE THE CENTRE OF THE COSMOS.

KEY BREAKTHROUGH IN 1514 AND 1543, NICOLAUS COPERNICUS RESTARTED DEBATE ABOUT THE HELIOCENTRIC THEORY.

IMPORTANCE WHILE COPERNICUS'S OWN VERSION OF THE HELIOCENTRIC THEORY WAS FLAWED, IT PAVED THE WAY FOR THE LATER DISCOVERIES OF KEPLER, GALILEO AND NEWTON.

For most of recorded history, mankind has assumed that Earth was the centre of the Universe. Despite some early doubters, it was only in the 16th century that we began the long journey to an appreciation of our true place in the Universe.

The idea that Earth is at the centre of everything seems self-evident. Unaware of our planet's daily rotation, let alone its motion through space, it is only natural that our ancestors assumed that the Sun, Moon, stars and planets were, as they appeared, circling our fixed location. The astronomer-priests of the first civilizations were more concerned with predicting the motions of celestial objects for astrological purposes than they were with constructing a coherent model of the Universe itself. So far as we know, the ancient Greek philosophers were the first to consider Earth's place in the cosmos, from around the fifth century BC onwards.

In the mid-fourth century BC, an important step forward came with Aristotle's argument that Earth was a huge sphere suspended in space, rather than the flat disc floating on an infinite ocean that earlier thinkers had believed. By around 200 BC, Eratosthenes of Cyrene had even worked out an ingenious way of measuring Earth's circumference, based on the shadows cast by the midday Sun at different latitudes.

A true cosmology, however, still had to address other problems – the movements of Sun and stars, the changing phases of the Moon, eclipses and, most troubling of all, the wandering motions of the planets Mercury, Venus, Mars, Jupiter and Saturn. To explain these, most Greek philosophers advocated a system of circular orbits or crystalline spheres onto which these

OPPOSITE A long-exposure image reveals the stars pinwheeling around the South Celestial Pole above La Silla Observatory in Chile. Today we view the movement of the stars as a key clue to Earth's rotation, but ancient astronomers believed the stars were moving around a fixed Earth.

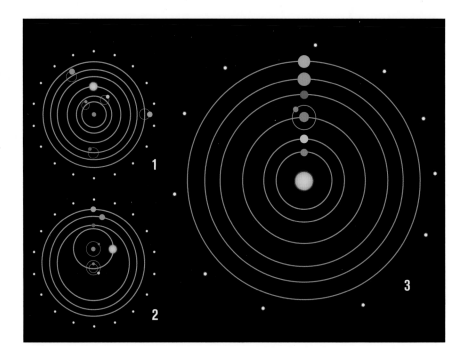

objects were attached, with the stars as lights on a fixed outer sphere, or perhaps pinpricks in that sphere letting in the light of heaven itself. Some had their doubts, however – in the third century BC, Aristarchus of Samos used trigonometry to estimate the distance to the Sun. He underestimated hugely, but still concluded that the Sun was so large that it must be the true centre of the Universe, with Earth circling it just as the planets did.

Hipparchus and Ptolemy

Unfortunately for astronomy, Aristarchus's ideas were widely rejected as outlandish, and the overwhelming weight of opinion remained behind the idea of an Earth-centred or geocentric Universe. However, the system was not without its problems. In particular, philosophers were dogmatically attached to the idea of circular motion at uniform speed – a kind of cosmic clockwork to which the planets resolutely refused to conform. Attempts to predict their movements using circular orbits around Earth met with failure, and around the middle of the second century BC, Hipparchus of Nicaea introduced the idea of epicycles – smaller circles that held the planets, moving around on the main 'referent' circles.

Epicycles helped to account for problems such as the looping or 'retrograde' motion of the outer planets (see page 15), but even this model could not provide a passable match for reality. An apparent solution only came in the mid-second century AD, when the astronomer and geographer Ptolemy of Alexandria introduced a new concept called the 'equant point' – a fudge that allowed him to preserve the principle of uniform motion around a point in space, while dropping the awkward need for the motion to be uniform relative to Earth itself. Ptolemy's breakthrough finally allowed theory to match observation to a reasonable degree, and his works on astronomy, now known by the Arabic title of the *Almagest*, became the last word on the subject for more than a millennium. The geocentric world view was enthusiastically adopted in Europe by the rising Christian church, while Islamic scholars, too, largely subscribed to the Ptolemaic model.

The Copernican revolution

As the centuries wore on, however, and techniques for astronomical measurement improved, doubts about the Ptolemaic Universe grew. It became increasingly clear that it did not offer a perfect tool for predictions beyond the short term, and its complex workings also began to seem inelegant. With the beginnings of the Renaissance in the late 1400s, scholars in a range of fields from medicine to geology began to realize that perhaps ancient wisdom was not always the last word.

In 1514, Nicolaus Copernicus, a Polish priest with a passion for astronomy, circulated a handwritten book called the *Commentariolus* (*Little Commentary*) in which he comprehensively challenged the geocentric view of the Universe, putting forth seven statements that instead suggested a Sun-centred or heliocentric Universe in which the movement of objects in Earth's skies are caused by their movement around the Sun, coupled with Earth's daily rotation.

'Philosophers were dogmatically attached to the idea of circular motion at uniform speed – a kind of cosmic clockwork to which the planets resolutely refused to conform.'

Over the next two decades or more, the Copernican theory spread through scholarly circles. Copernicus had always intended to follow the *Commentariolus* with a longer work, but he was only spurred to produce it in 1539, when Georg Joachim Rheticus, a professor from the University of Wittenberg, produced an enthusiastic account of his theories. The result was *De revolutionibus orbium coelestium* ('*On the revolutions of the heavenly spheres*'), a fuller statement of Copernicus's ideas backed up with comprehensive arguments and proofs.

The book was published when Copernicus was on his deathbed and, despite its later status as an icon of the scientific revolution, was not well received. The Copernican theory replaced the ancient models of uniform circular motion around Earth or (in Ptolemy's version) around equant points, with one of uniform circular motion about the Sun. The idea of celestial spheres and a finite Universe was maintained, and it soon became clear that this was little better at describing the reality of planetary motions.

Half a century later a less measured cleric, the heretical Italian friar Giordano Bruno, broke the limits of the Copernican view with his suggestion that the stars were suns in their own right, orbited by planetary systems of their own. Other heresies saw him burnt at the stake in 1600, unaware that, within a decade, the old order of the Universe would be overthrown once and for all.

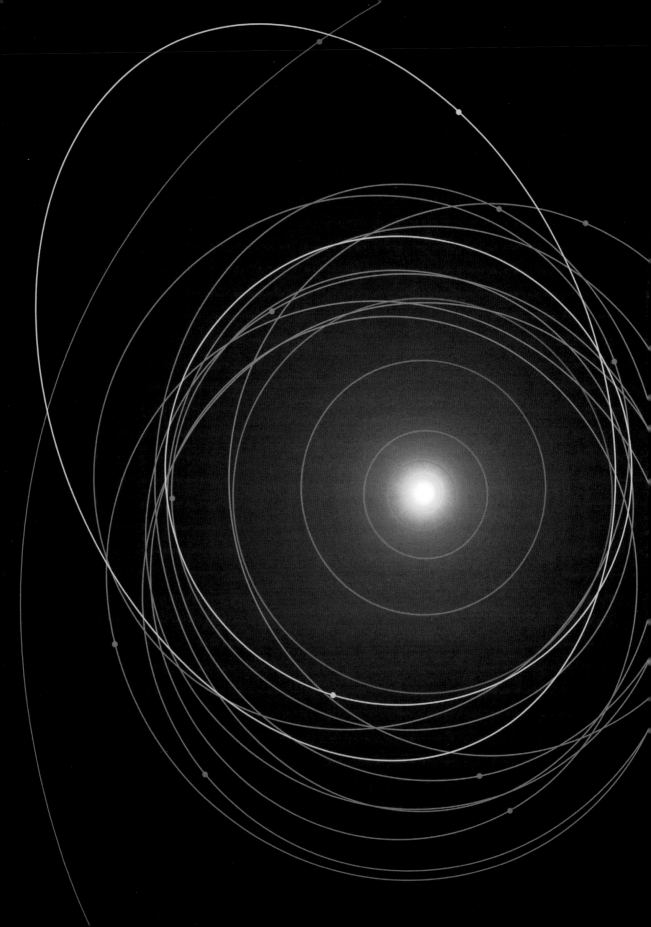

Elliptical orbits

DEFINITION THE THEORY OF ORBITS THAT FINALLY CONFIRMED THE HELIOCENTRIC VIEW OF THE SOLAR SYSTEM, AND ULTIMATELY THE TRUE NATURE OF THE UNIVERSE.

DISCOVERY TELESCOPIC OBSERVATIONS BY GALILEO AND OTHERS PRODUCED DIRECT EVIDENCE THAT THE PTOLEMAIC VIEW OF THE UNIVERSE WAS WRONG.

KEY BREAKTHROUGH IN 1609, JOHANNES KEPLER SUGGESTED THAT THE PLANETS ORBITED ON ELLIPSES RATHER THAN CIRCLES.

IMPORTANCE A TRUE UNDERSTANDING OF EARTH'S MOTION AROUND THE SUN HAS BEEN VITAL TO COUNTLESS LATER DISCOVERIES.

In the early 1600s, two parallel revolutions saw the old geocentric view of the cosmos overturned, and the seeds of modern astronomy established. Then, towards the end of the same century, the theory of universal gravitation put the capstone on this new view of the Universe.

The transformation of astronomy that took hold in the early 17th century is usually attributed to two factors – the early telescopic observations of Italian physicist Galileo Galilei and the theoretical breakthroughs of German astronomer Johannes Kepler. While this is a simplification, it is undeniable that these two led the way in establishing a new cosmology.

Galileo views the heavens

Around 1608, Dutch lensmakers discovered that by aligning two lenses along the length of a tube, they could produce magnified images. Galileo, a respected professor of mathematics and experimentalist at the University of Padua, determined to build an instrument of his own, and first turned it to the heavens in late 1609. What he saw convinced him that many established theories about the Universe were wrong. Far from being a perfect sphere, the Moon was a varied world of mountains and craters. The Milky Way dissolved from a band of light into a stream of countless stars. Most crucially, four starlike points of light dancing around Jupiter could only be its own satellites, and Venus exhibited distinct phases like those of our Moon. Contrary to received wisdom, there were objects in the Universe that did not revolve around Earth, and Venus, at least, appeared to circle the Sun.

Galileo published reports of his observations in his 1610 book *The Starry Messenger*. While he refrained from comment on their implications at the

OPPOSITE Among the major planets of the solar system, Mercury and Mars have the most elliptical orbits. However, the orbits of smaller dwarf planets such as Ceres, Pluto and Eris, often have more clearly eccentric shapes.

time, he personally viewed his discoveries as a resounding confirmation of the heliocentric model of the Universe first proposed by Copernicus almost a century earlier. However, working in Italy under the nose of a powerful Catholic Church that viewed such ideas as heresy, he had little choice but to keep silent for the moment.

Kepler describes the planets

By a remarkable coincidence, in the same year as Galileo's momentous discoveries, Johannes Kepler published the breakthrough that secured the theoretical groundings of the heliocentric system, shattering the old view of a Universe of orderly celestial spheres forever. Using the meticulous observations collected by his sometime tutor, collaborator and occasional rival, the great Danish astronomer Tycho Brahe, Kepler realized that problems such as the retrograde motion of Mars were best described if the orbits of the planets were not only heliocentric, but also somewhat elliptical. (An ellipse is a more generalized form of a circle, longer along one axis than the other, and with two foci to either side of the centre on the long axis.)

'Contrary to received wisdom, there were objects in the Universe that did not revolve around Earth, and Venus, at least, appeared to circle the Sun.'

In his *New Astronomy* of 1609, Kepler argued that planets orbited on ellipses with the Sun at one focus, and that the speed with which a planet moved on its orbit varied depending on its distance from the Sun. At a stroke, these laws of planetary motion resolved many long-standing problems of astronomical prediction, and in 1619, Kepler added a third law, linking the square of a planet's orbital period to the cube of its 'semi-major axis' (its average distance from the Sun), which allowed relative orbital periods to be compared.

Working in the more receptive environment of Protestant northern Europe, Kepler faced few of the problems experienced by Galileo, and his theories were rapidly accepted by the scholarly establishment. A change to a more lenient papacy in Italy encouraged the Italian to risk putting his own thoughts into writing as *Dialogue concerning the two chief world systems*, published in 1623. But while limited discussion of the Copernican view as a purely mathematical model was permitted, any suggestion that it actually represented the reality of the Universe was still regarded as heretical, and Galileo's lectures persistently overstepped this line. In 1632, he found himself brought before the Inquisition, forced to recant, and placed under a house arrest for the rest of his life – an injustice that the Church took centuries to live down.

But while the rise of the Copernican/Keplerian view was now inevitable, some important questions remained – most notably *why* the planets obeyed Kepler's laws of motion, and indeed, why they moved at all. The French philosopher Descartes, around 1644, suggested that they might be pushed around by vortices in space, but failed to come up with a coherent explanation of why such vortices would produce the observed relationships.

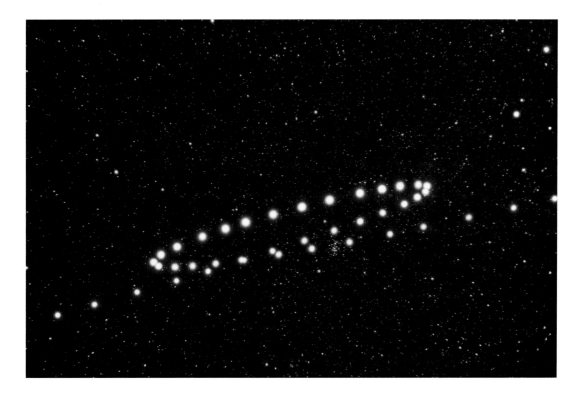

Newton unifies the cosmos

Ultimately, this breakthrough fell to the English scientist and polymath Isaac Newton, who around 1666 realized there was no reason why the force known today as gravity (whose general properties were established by Galileo a century before) should lose its influence beyond the surface of Earth. The same force that made an apple in his garden fall to the ground should also act on the Moon in orbit around Earth. Years later, Newton set to work on his extraordinary masterwork, the *Principia mathematica* (finally published in 1687), in which he set down three laws of motion and one of 'universal gravitation'. The laws of motion described how objects remain at rest or in a state of uniform motion unless acted on by a force; how such a force affects their acceleration depending on their mass; and why every action produces an equal and opposite reaction. The law of gravitation, meanwhile, describes a force between massive objects that is directly proportional to their masses, and inversely proportional to the square of the distance between them (so that the strength of gravity between two objects diminishes by a factor of four when the distance between them is doubled).

Together, these laws perfectly describe Keplerian orbits, though later developments would show that Newton's laws were not the last word on gravity (see page 45). However, the mathematical techniques established by Newton in order to reach his conclusions, and the very principle of deriving a theory from observation that can then be used to make testable predictions, helped establish a 'scientific method' that is still used to this day.

ABOVE A series of images of Mars taken over several weeks reveal a loop in the sky. This retrograde motion, caused as the fast-moving Earth 'overtakes' its slower-moving neighbour, is displayed by all the planets that orbit beyond Earth, but most obvious in the case of Mars.

3 | Measuring stellar distances

DEFINITION TECHNIQUES FOR MEASURING THE ENORMOUS
DISTANCES FROM THE SOLAR SYSTEM TO OTHER STARS.

DISCOVERY IN 1838, FRIEDRICH BESSEL MADE THE FIRST
SUCCESSFUL MEASUREMENT OF STELLAR DISTANCE USING
THE PARALLAX METHOD.

KEY BREAKTHROUGH THE HIPPARCOS SATELLITE, LAUNCHED IN 1989,
BROUGHT FAR GREATER ACCURACY TO PARALLAX MEASUREMENTS.

IMPORTANCE AN ACCURATE KNOWLEDGE OF THE DISTANCE TO STARS
IS VITAL TO UNDERSTANDING THEIR TRUE PROPERTIES AND OUR
PLACE IN THE COSMOS.

How do we measure the distance to objects that are far beyond our physical reach? In order to understand the true distribution of stars and other objects within our galaxy and beyond, astronomers push a principle familiar from everyday life to its absolute limit.

The realization that the stars in the night sky were unimaginably distant counterparts of our own Sun came hand in hand with the Copernican Revolution, and the discovery that the Sun, rather than Earth, was the centre of our solar system (see page 11). The idea had been raised by ancient Greek philosophers and medieval Islamic astronomers, but the first person to consider it seriously in European thought was the Italian friar and astronomer Giordano Bruno (famously burnt at the stake for his heretical beliefs in 1600). By the late 17th century, the idea had gained widespread acceptance, but astronomers were still confronted with one major issue – the lack of stellar parallax.

Parallax is familiar to most people as a result of stereoscopic vision – it is simply the effect by which nearby objects appear to shift against a more distant background when viewed from two different angles. For humans, it is a vital, though subconscious, tool for hand–eye coordination and distance measurement, but for Enlightenment astronomers it presented something of a problem – if Earth really was moving on a vast orbit around the Sun, then why were the directions of the stars not changing through the year? Astronomers such as Tycho Brahe used this as an argument against the Copernican system, but once the other evidence became overwhelming, the lack of parallax was taken correctly as an indication that the stars were even more distant than had previously been imagined.

OPPOSITE Star clusters such as the Pleiades offered an early clue to the physical variety among the stars. Since it was safe to assume that such close groups were genuine clusters at about the same distance from Earth, astronomers realized that differences in the appearance of cluster members must reflect true variations between stars.

The challenge of parallax

Throughout the 18th century, attempts to measure parallax were frustrated. The principle was simple enough: by measuring the shift in apparent position of nearby stars against the more distant background, as seen from opposite sides of Earth's orbit 300 million km (186 million miles) apart, it should be possible to use simple trigonometry to estimate the distance to the stars themselves. Working out which stars might be nearby involved some guesswork, but the identification of certain stars that moved relatively swiftly across the sky (displaying high 'proper motion') offered a useful clue.

English astronomer James Bradley made an important step towards parallax measurement in the 1720s, by identifying other major effects on the apparent position of the stars that can swamp the effects of parallax itself. However, the precision of Bradley's instruments was still far too poor to measure parallax itself, and it was only in the 1830s that several talented observers returned to the problem in earnest. German astronomer Friedrich Wilhelm Bessel had already spent decades improving on Bradley's work in order to rule out every other possible effect on the measured positions of the stars, and in 1838 he announced that he had successfully measured the parallax of the double star 61 Cygni as 0.314 arcseconds. (An arcsecond is 1/3,600th of a degree or roughly 1/1,800th the diameter of the full Moon). In modern measurements, this indicated that 61 Cygni was 10.4 light years away – a close match to the modern figure of 11.4 light years. Bessel's work was rapidly followed by estimates for other nearby stars – Alpha Centauri and Vega – and astronomers began to use the parsec (the distance at which a star would exhibit a parallax of 1 arcsecond, equivalent to 3.26 light years) as a unit of distance.

'Hipparcos was able to measure parallax to milliarcsecond levels, extending accurate measurement to tens of thousands of stars within around 1,600 light years of Earth.'

Nevertheless, measuring parallax was still an exhausting procedure, and only a few dozen more distances were established through the 19th century. It was only with the advent of sensitive astrophotography in the 20th century that astronomers were able to measure stellar positions away from the telescope eyepiece, and large numbers of parallaxes could be collected for the first time. Nevertheless, the effects of parallax were so tiny that they could still be measured only for the closest stars.

But despite the limitations, parallax offered a vital first step on the cosmic distance scale. Armed with the distance to a star, astronomers were able to work out its intrinsic brightness or luminosity, and when they compared luminosity and colour or other spectral features to one another, they discovered important patterns in the distribution of stars (see page 265). Once astronomers were able to recognize these patterns, they could use the principle in reverse, going from the spectral type and *apparent* brightness of a star to an estimate of its intrinsic luminosity and, hence, its distance.

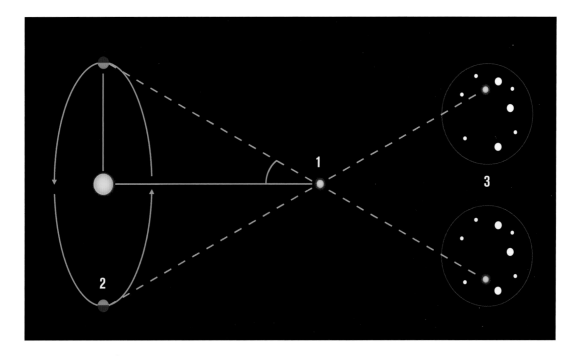

Parallax in the Space Age

Parallax remains the only way to measure the distance to a star with absolute precision – other methods are always prone to error thanks to unpredictable effects such as the absorption of light by interstellar dust. By 1989, advances in computer imaging and satellite technology allowed the launch of the first space 'astrometry' mission, the European Space Agency's Hipparcos (the High-Precision Parallax Collecting Satellite). From its elliptical orbit ranging from hundreds to thousands of kilometres above Earth, this sensitive telescope could avoid the blurring effects of the atmosphere and measure stellar positions with pinpoint accuracy. Hipparcos was able to measure parallax to milliarcsecond levels (thousands of an arcsecond), extending accurate measurement to tens of thousands of stars within around 1,600 light years of Earth, but of course this is still only a tiny fraction of the entire Milky Way galaxy.

Scheduled for launch in 2012, the European Space Agency's Gaia mission will see another giant leap for the parallax technique. Over a planned five-year mission, it will measure the properties of a billion stars – recording their spectra, proper motions and, of course, parallaxes to a precision of a few millionths of an arcsecond. Data from the satellite should allow astronomers to construct a three-dimensional starmap stretching as far as the centre of the Milky Way, including hundreds of millions of stars that were previously far too faint for parallax measurements. What's more, its spectral measurements will identify the Doppler shifts of the target stars (see page 51), revealing their radial motions towards or away from Earth, and therefore providing an amazing view of our galaxy in motion.

ABOVE The parallax method of finding stellar distances relies on measuring the apparent change in position of a nearby star (1). As Earth (2) moves from one side of its orbit to the other throughout the year, the star seems to shift against the more distant background (3).

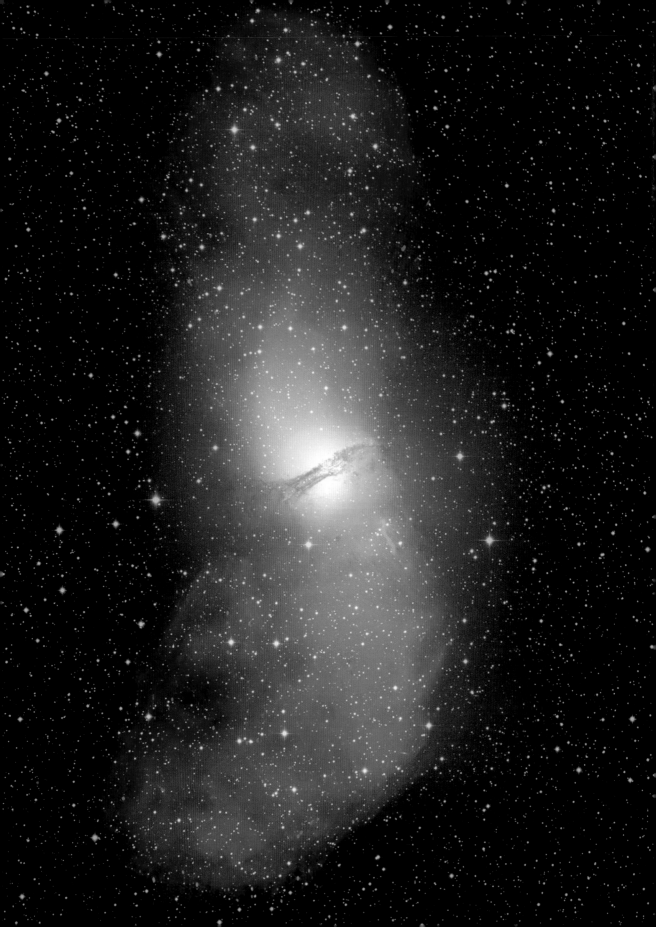

4 The invisible Universe

DEFINITION THE WIDE RANGE OF RADIATIONS WITH WAVELENGTHS BEYOND THE NARROW RANGE OF VISIBLE LIGHT.

DISCOVERY WILLIAM HERSCHEL IDENTIFIED THE EXISTENCE OF INFRARED RADIATION IN 1800.

KEY BREAKTHROUGH IN 1864, JAMES CLERK MAXWELL PUBLISHED HIS DESCRIPTION OF LIGHT AS AN ELECTROMAGNETIC WAVE.

IMPORTANCE RADIATIONS BEYOND THE RANGE OF VISIBLE LIGHT REVEAL A HUGE AMOUNT ABOUT HIGH- AND LOW-ENERGY PROCESSES AT WORK IN THE UNIVERSE.

The nature of light was a long-standing puzzle for early physicists, but no one could have imagined that light was just one part of an electromagnetic spectrum that stretched far beyond the visible. Today, these high- and low-energy radiations offer new ways of seeing the Universe.

In England around 1670, Isaac Newton began a series of investigations into the nature of light. By splitting it through prisms and lenses, he showed for the first time that colour was an intrinsic property of light, and that white light was a mix of many colours. Further experiments with mirrors convinced him that the light was a stream of particles or 'corpuscles'. Newton published his theories in 1675, and expanded them in his 1704 work *Opticks*.

But some scientists of the time had other ideas. Newton's rival Robert Hooke published a theory of light as a wave in 1665, and in the late 1670s, Dutch astronomer Christiaan Huygens began his own experiments. Evidence such as the refraction and diffraction (bending and spreading out) of light, as well as the ability of light beams to pass through each other unaffected, convinced him that light was a wave, propagating through a 'luminiferous aether' that filled the Universe. Huygens published his theory in 1690, and over the following century its predictive power won over many scientists. Finally, in the early 1800s, English scientist Thomas Young came up with an experiment that conclusively disproved the corpuscular theory, showing interference between light waves spreading out from a pair of narrow slits.

New types of light

By this time, scientists had also begun to realize there were forms of 'light' beyond what they could see. The first breakthrough was made by German-

OPPOSITE A spectacular multi-wavelength image reveals the complex nature of galaxy NGC 5128, better known as the radio source Centaurus A (see page 369). Gamma ray emissions from hot gas around the galaxy's centre are shown in purple, while radio-emitting lobes appear orange.

born astronomer William Herschel, the discoverer of Uranus. While using a prism to measure the temperatures associated with different colours of sunlight, he noticed a marked increase in temperature from violet light to red. This led him to test the apparently unilluminated region beyond the red end of the spectrum, which proved to be the hottest of all. Herschel named the new type of radiation, which we now know as infrared, 'calorific rays'.

A year later, taking inspiration from Herschel's discovery, German chemist Johann Wilhelm Ritter found invisible rays at the other end of the spectrum. His experiment involved testing the ways in which different colours of light affected the darkening of silver salts: it showed that violet light darkened them more than red, and invisible 'chemical rays' beyond the violet end of the spectrum affected them most of all.

Meanwhile, scientists were still struggling to understand the true nature of light. In 1817, French physicist Augustin-Jean Fresnel suggested that light waves were transverse rather than longitudinal (more akin to water waves than sound waves) because they could be polarized (affected by slits parallel to the angle of their vibrations).

Electromagnetic radiation

In 1845, British scientist Michael Faraday made the crucial discovery that the polarization of light could be affected by a magnetic field. This inspired Scotsman James Clerk Maxwell, who, in 1864, published his interpretation of light as an electromagnetic wave – a pair of interlinked electric and magnetic waves aligned at right angles, reinforcing each other as they travel through space. Maxwell's wave equations described how the characteristics of light and invisible radiations are governed by linked properties of wavelength and frequency. They showed that greater energies were required to generate higher-frequency, shorter-wavelength waves, and also predicted the precise value of the speed of light.

'[Herschel] noticed a marked increase in temperature from violet light to red. This led him to test the apparently unilluminated region beyond the red end of the spectrum, which proved to be the hottest of all.'

By placing infrared, visible light and ultraviolet on a continuous spectrum, the equations showed there was no physical reason why waves could not exist with much higher or lower frequencies, provided there were processes with appropriate energy to create them. When Heinrich Hertz discovered microwaves (short-wavelength radio waves) in 1888, they fitted neatly into the spectrum below the infrared, but the behaviour of X-rays (discovered by Wilhelm Röntgen in 1895) and gamma rays (found by Paul Villard in 1900) seemed so dissimilar to light that they were not immediately linked to electromagnetism – it was only later that they were recognized as extensions of the spectrum to energies beyond the ultraviolet.

Observing the invisible

Earth's atmosphere absorbs most invisible radiation from space, leaving just a few windows where visible light and a few other bands, including the near-infrared and some radio waves, can reach the surface. As early as 1932, American engineer Karl Jansky realized that a daily cycle of radio interference was linked to the position of the Milky Way. However, the true flowering of invisible astronomy had to wait until the dawn of the Space Age. From the late 1940s onwards, rocket-borne sensors and, eventually, satellites revealed that the sky was alive with X-ray and ultraviolet radiation coming from objects far hotter and more energetic than the Sun.

Meanwhile the large dish antennae built for tracking satellites also proved to be ideal for studying astronomical radio sources in more detail, linking them to objects such as cool clouds of interstellar gas. The infrared was the most challenging region to explore – it can reveal warm objects that are not hot enough to glow in visible light, such as brown dwarf stars (see page 277), planets and interstellar dust, but it is easily swamped by the warmth of telescopes and detectors themselves. As a result, the first infrared space telescope was not launched until 1983. The InfraRed Astronomical Satellite (IRAS) observed the sky for just a few months before its liquid helium coolant was exhausted, but it paved the way for a new type of astronomy.

5 The chemistry of the cosmos

DEFINITION EMISSION AND ABSORPTION LINES IN THE SPECTRA
OF STARS AND OTHER OBJECTS CAN BE USED TO IDENTIFY THEIR
CHEMICAL COMPOSITION.

DISCOVERY DARK LINES IN THE SOLAR SPECTRUM WERE IDENTIFIED
BY JOSEPH VON FRAUNHOFER IN 1814.

KEY BREAKTHROUGH IN 1859, GUSTAV KIRCHOFF PROVED THE LINK
BETWEEN ASTRONOMICAL SPECTRA AND THE LIGHT EMITTED BY
LABORATORY CHEMICALS.

IMPORTANCE SPECTROSCOPY REVEALS AN ENORMOUS AMOUNT
ABOUT THE CHEMISTRY AND PHYSICAL PROPERTIES OF STARS.

The techniques of spectroscopy allow astronomers to analyse the chemical make-up of stars, planets, galaxies and nebulae. Furthermore, as atoms interact with light, they leave signatures that can help trace other physical processes as well.

In one of history's more amusing moments of scientific short-sightedness, French philosopher Auguste Comte loftily declared in 1835 that 'On the subject of stars ... we shall never be able by any means to study their chemical composition.' In just a few short years, he would be proved wrong, and although he could not know it, the crucial discovery that eventually revealed the chemistry of the stars had already been made.

Lines across the Sun

In 1814, German instrument-maker Joseph von Fraunhofer repeated an experiment carried out by Isaac Newton many years before – passing a narrow strip of sunlight through a prism and studying the image it projected onto a wall. To his surprise he found that, if the slit was narrow enough and the beam of sunlight focused tightly through a lens prior to being split, the resulting rainbow spectrum was crossed by a multitude of dark lines.

Fraunhofer gave the darkest lines letter designations (others have since been named after their discoverers, or the processes that produce them). He also pioneered the development of the diffraction grating, a plate engraved with a large number of narrow lines that diffracts light, causing it to spread out and create a spectrum far wider and clearer than that produced by a prism. His 'Fraunhofer lines' ultimately proved to be the key to understanding not only the chemistry of the Sun, but that of the wider cosmos as well.

OPPOSITE A solar spectrum, in which different wavelengths and colours of light are widely dispersed by a diffraction grating, reveals a forest of dark lines corresponding to energy absorbed by atoms and molecules in the atmospheres of both the Sun and Earth.

In 1832, Scottish physicist David Brewster identified the twin sources of the Fraunhofer lines. Observing the spectrum of the setting Sun, he noticed that certain lines grew more intense towards sunset, and correctly attributed these to the absorption of certain colours of light in Earth's atmosphere (since the sunlight has to pass through a thicker layer of atmosphere as it sets). The rest, he realized, must be due to similar absorption of light in the atmosphere of the Sun itself.

Explaining the lines

The key to understanding Fraunhofer's lines came from the chemist's laboratory. In 1859, German physicist Gustav Kirchoff repeated an earlier experiment by Fraunhofer, in which he passed sunlight through a flame coloured by simple salt. He noticed that one particular line grew significantly stronger and darker. When light from the flame alone was analysed with a spectroscope, this same 'D line', today associated with sodium, appeared as a bright 'emission line' against a dark background.

The discovery that Fraunhofer's absorption lines matched emission lines that could be produced in a laboratory paved the way for chemical analysis of the Sun's atmosphere. Kirchoff and his chemist colleague Robert Bunsen continued to investigate the emission lines of various elements, and in 1868, Swedish physicist Anders Ångstrom published an analysis of the solar atmosphere based on photographs of the Sun's spectrum. That same year, French astronomer Jules Janssen and Britain's Norman Lockyer observed the solar spectrum during an eclipse and identified emissions from an unknown element that was soon named helium. It proved to be the second most common element in the Universe.

'To his surprise Fraunhofer found that, if the slit was narrow enough and the beam of sunlight focused tightly through a lens prior to being split, the resulting rainbow spectrum was crossed by a multitude of dark lines.'

Meanwhile in 1861, British amateur William Huggins, a pioneer of astronomical photography, began to use long exposures to make spectroscopic studies of much fainter and more remote celestial objects, showing for the first time that stars had similar chemical compositions to the Sun. In 1864, he turned his spectroscope on the Cat's Eye Nebula in the constellation of Draco, and found that, rather than the usual 'continuum' spectrum with dark lines, its light was limited to just a few bright emission lines. Huggins correctly concluded that the Cat's Eye was a glowing cloud of gas (see page 321), and astronomers soon discovered many more 'emission nebulae' in the sky. Not all nebulae were like this, however – many others did produce a continuum, crossed by forests of faint absorption lines. These objects, many of which showed a spiral structure, would prove to be something entirely different (see page 29).

Secrets of the stars

As if spectroscopy were not a useful enough tool for discovering the chemistry of different objects, it also allows astronomers to find out about

other properties. Spectral lines can be affected by phenomena such as strong magnetic fields (the Zeeman effect, see page 94), and the temperature of the material producing them. Perhaps most useful of all, however, is the key that spectral lines provide for analysing Doppler shifts in starlight. The Doppler effect, a shift in the wavelength of light from objects moving towards or away from Earth (see page 51), would be unmeasurable if it were not for the ability to locate spectral lines that have shifted out of their expected positions.

Huggins successfully used this technique to measure the motion of the star Sirius in 1868. Since then, it has allowed us to measure the paths of stars and other objects through space, to find objects such as spectroscopic binary stars (see page 301), to measure the rotation of our galaxy and others and, ultimately, to discover the expansion of the Universe itself (see page 49).

ABOVE Cosmic chemistry can also be studied through large-scale differences in the emission properties of celestial objects. This false-colour image from the Spitzer Space Telescope shows the Helix Nebula at three different infrared wavelengths, with red representing the coolest material (thought to be dust in the immediate vicinity of the central star). Relatively cool gas is shown in green, and hotter gas in blue.

6 Our galaxy and others

DEFINITION THE REALIZATION THAT OUR GALAXY IS JUST ONE
AMONG MANY BILLIONS IN THE VASTNESS OF SPACE.

DISCOVERY WILLIAM HUGGINS IDENTIFIED SOME DISTANT GALAXIES
AS STARRY MASSES FROM AROUND 1864.

KEY BREAKTHROUGH EDWIN HUBBLE USED CEPHEID VARIABLE STARS
TO DIRECTLY MEASURE THE DISTANCE TO GALAXIES IN 1925.

IMPORTANCE ESTABLISHING THE TRUE SIZE OF THE UNIVERSE IS
VITAL TO UNDERSTANDING OUR PLACE WITHIN IT.

While the scale of the Milky Way galaxy, 100,000 light years in diameter, is far beyond human comprehension, the reality is that even our immense spiral star system, containing perhaps 200 billion individual suns, is just a speck of sand on the beach of the wider cosmos.

As telescopes improved in the 18th and 19th centuries, they were able to observe a greater range of objects, including diffuse patches of light in the sky. Astronomers such as the Frenchman Charles Messier compiled the first catalogue of these objects in 1774, and the British astronomers William and John Herschel devoted a great deal of time to studying these objects and analysing their structure. Some of them proved to be loose clusters of stars, others were dense balls of tightly packed stars. However, there were also tenuous wisps of diffuse light, sometimes with stars clearly embedded inside them, and sometimes but bubble-like structures or swirling spiral patterns. In the 1880s, Danish-Irish astronomer J.L.E. Dreyer compiled the influential New General Catalogue of non-stellar objects, in which he categorized these objects into groups such as open and globular star clusters and diffuse, planetary and spiral nebulae.

Probing spiral nebulae

From the late 19th century, astronomers used photography to capture the light of these objects in long exposures, revealing far more detail than that visible directly through the eyepiece. From 1864, astronomer William Huggins combined photograph and spectroscopy (see page 25) to collect spectra from the various types of nebulae. Many of the nebulae turned out to have emission spectra, producing light at just a few specific wavelengths, but the majority proved to have absorption spectra, with a continuous spectrum

OPPOSITE The band of the Milky Way is a prominent feature under dark skies, and today we know that it is formed from dense star clouds in the plane of our galaxy. But it is less than a century since astronomers confirmed that our galaxy was just one among many.

of light crossed by dozens of dark lines. This suggested that the diffuse nebulae were made from glowing gas, while the spirals and ball-shaped or elliptical nebulae contained stars.

Some astronomers suggested that the spiral nebulae, in particular, were solar systems in the process of formation, but others suggested they were either in orbit around the Milky Way, or they were distant galaxies in their own right. One suggestive fact was that the spirals tended to lie in relatively empty parts of the sky, away from the plane of the Milky Way.

The 'Great Debate'

From around 1909, Vesto Slipher of the Lowell Observatory in Flagstaff, Arizona, began extensive studies of the spectra of nebulae. In 1912, he made an important breakthrough, discovering that the absorption lines of spiral nebulae such as the Andromeda Nebula, the brightest in the sky, were shifted from their normal positions towards the red end of the spectrum. Slipher interpreted these 'redshifts' as a Doppler effect, showing that the spiral nebulae were moving away from us at high speeds. This discovery paved the way for Edwin Hubble's later discovery of cosmic expansion (see page 49), but it was also further evidence that the spiral nebulae lay outside

BELOW The Andromeda Galaxy is the most prominent 'spiral nebula' in the sky, and the easiest external galaxy to observe. The box encloses the first Cepheid variable observed by Edwin Hubble, variations in which revealed the spiral's true distance of more than 2 million light years for the first time.

of the Milky Way. In 1913, Slipher also showed that nebulae were slowly rotating, by identifying slight differences in the redshifts of their approaching and receding edges.

By the early 1920s, a schism developed between astronomers who believed in a compact Universe, not much larger than the Milky Way itself, and those who believed in a larger cosmos stretching away for unimaginable distances. The evidence on both sides of the argument was discussed in an influential debate between astronomers Harlow Shapley and Heber D. Curtis at the Smithsonian Museum in 1920, but the 'Great Debate' would only be settled five years later, thanks to the work of astronomers Henrietta Swan Leavitt, Ejnar Hertzsprung and Edwin Hubble.

'A schism developed between astronomers who believed in a compact Universe and those who believed in a larger cosmos stretching away for unimaginable distances.'

Measuring the distance

Leavitt helped to establish a cosmic distance scale using a class of variable stars known as Cepheids – yellow supergiants that change their brightness over periods varying from days to months. In 1912, Leavitt identified and measured the variations of several Cepheids within the Large Magellanic Cloud (LMC), allowing her to assume that the stars were all at more or less the same distance, and therefore that the differences in their apparent (average) brightness reflected differences in their actual luminosities. This revealed a period–luminosity relationship: the brighter a star was, the longer its period.

Soon after this, Swedish astronomer Ejnar Hertzsprung independently determined the distance of several relatively nearby Cepheids in the Milky Way, helping to fix the distance scale. Hertzsprung went on to estimate Leavitt's Cepheids in the LMC. It turned out to be an astonishing 160,000 light years away, confirming that the cloud lay far beyond the Milky Way.

In the 1920s, Edwin Hubble used the 2.5-metre (100-inch) Hooker Telescope at Mount Wilson Observatory in California to survey some of the brightest spiral nebulae and to identify Cepheids within them. He published his results in 1925, showing that they were typically millions, even tens of millions, of light years away. Hubble went on to make further discoveries that would transform our view of the Universe and our place within it (see page 51). The Hubble Space Telescope (HST), named in his honour, has continued to build on his work.

Hubble established beyond doubt that our galaxy was just one of many, and today astronomers believe there are as many galaxies in our Universe as there are stars in the Milky Way. Thanks to the work of the HST and other observatories, both in orbit and on Earth, we are constantly learning more about the origins and structure of these star cities.

The structure of matter

DEFINITION THE ESSENTIAL NATURE OF MATTER, RANGING FROM ATOMS DOWN TO ELEMENTARY PARTICLES INTERACTING THROUGH FUNDAMENTAL FORCES.

DISCOVERY THE FIRST SUBATOMIC PARTICLE, THE ELECTRON, WAS DISCOVERED IN 1897.

KEY BREAKTHROUGH IN 1964, MURRAY GELL-MANN PROPOSED THE EXISTENCE OF ELEMENTARY PARTICLES CALLED QUARKS.

IMPORTANCE UNDERSTANDING THE DEEP STRUCTURE OF MATTER HELPS ASTRONOMERS TO EXPLAIN A HUGE RANGE OF LARGE- AND SMALL-SCALE PROCESSES AT WORK IN THE UNIVERSE.

Over more than a century, the long scientific journey to the heart of the atom has revealed an elegant structure underlying all matter in the Universe, with a small number of subatomic particles – imbued with elementary properties – interacting with each other through four fundamental forces.

Although Greek philosopher Democritus first speculated that all matter might be composed of tiny particles as early as the fourth century BC, the reality of these atoms only became clear through a series of breakthroughs in the 18th and 19th centuries. By the 1860s, Russian chemist Dmitri Mendeleev had devised an ingenious system for ordering different elements according to their mass and chemical reactivity – the periodic table.

Inside the atom

However, it was only with the discovery of particles within the atom that scientists began to understand why different elements react in the ways they do. The first of these particles, the electron, was identified by British physicist J. J. Thomson in 1897. This lightweight particle carried a negative electrical charge, and Thomson found it within cathode rays emitted from heated electrodes. It soon became clear that the number of electrons associated with a particular atom was key to its reactivity – exchange or sharing of electrons can create chemical bonds, while the addition or removal of electrons from individual atoms can produce electrically charged ions.

However, since electrons carried a negative charge and atoms were essentially neutral, the next question was where the atom's positive charge resided. For a while, Thomson's 'plum pudding' model, in which electrons floated freely in a general mass of positive charge, reigned supreme, but

OPPOSITE A computer visualization from the Large Hadron Collider's Compact Muon Solenoid (CMS) experiment captures a collision between two protons travelling at high speed. The collision converts the mass of both protons into energy, which in turn generates a blizzard of subatomic particles.

in 1909, New Zealand physicist Ernest Rutherford and his colleagues fired radioactive particles at a sheet of thin gold foil and showed that while most passed straight through, occasionally one would bounce straight back. This indicated that atoms were largely empty space, with most of their mass and positive charge concentrated in a central nucleus, orbited by the electrons.

By 1932, the nucleus was known to consist of protons (each with an equal but opposite charge to the electron, and thus making the entire atom electrically neutral) and neutrons (uncharged particles with almost identical mass to the proton, and usually found in roughly equal numbers to the protons).

'All known hadrons can be produced by combinations of six "flavours" of quark. Conveniently, these are paralleled by six leptons.'

Meanwhile in 1913, Danish physicist Niels Bohr applied the new idea that electromagnetic radiation travelled in photons (see page 37) to the problems of atomic structure, showing that the distinctive spectra of emission and absorption associated with each element could be explained if electrons occupied specific shell-like 'orbitals' at set distances from the nucleus. Each electron would therefore have a specific energy level within the atom: injection of energy through photons of specific wavelengths could boost it to a higher 'orbital' while, conversely, its descent to a lower orbital would release energy as distinctive photons. In 1925, Austrian physicist Wolfgang Pauli explained the origin of the orbitals through an exclusion principle that prevents electrons with identical quantum properties from existing in the same system at the same time.

Making sense of the particle zoo

Investigations of atomic structure accelerated in the 1930s and 1940s thanks to the Second World War and the race to harness atomic energy. The most important tools for such investigations proved to be particle accelerators – devices that use electromagnetic fields to accelerate atoms and other particles to extreme speeds, then smash them into each other in order to examine the fragments released. Not all the particles detected in this way are components of the raw material in the conventional sense – energy released by the collisions can be converted directly into other rare particles in accordance with Einstein's $E = mc^2$. As a result, the number of known subatomic particles multiplied rapidly, creating a confusing particle zoo.

Within this menagerie, physicists began to distinguish between particles that were affected by different fundamental forces. All particles, it seems, are influenced by electromagnetism and (to a tiny extent) gravitation, but there are also forces that operate only over subatomic distances: the weak and strong nuclear forces. Heavyweight particles, called hadrons (including the proton and neutron), are affected by all four forces, while lightweight leptons (such as the electron) are immune to the strong force.

The situation only became clearer in the 1960s, when American physicist Murray Gell-Mann and others showed that the properties of the various hadrons could be explained if each was composed of two or three smaller particles called quarks. Ultimately, all known hadrons can be produced by combinations of six 'flavours' of quark – up, down, strange, charm, top and bottom. Conveniently, these are paralleled by six leptons – the electron, muon, tau, and their corresponding neutrinos (see page 89). These are believed to be the elementary particles of matter, collectively known as fermions. Forces are transmitted between these massive particles by massless carrier particles called bosons, the best known of which is the photon, carrier for the electromagnetic force. Other bosons include the gluon, which transmits the strong force, and the W and Z particles that carry the weak force.

This standard model of matter and forces has withstood many tests since the 1960s, but many questions linger. Theorists still strive to resolve puzzles such as why the different forces act in the way they do, whether they can be united in a single 'Theory of Everything', and why the elementary particles exhibit their measured properties. Meanwhile, experimentalists hope that ambitious accelerator projects such as the Large Hadron Collider, completed on the Franco-Swiss border in 2008, will help them to detect new and elusive particles predicted by theoreticians.

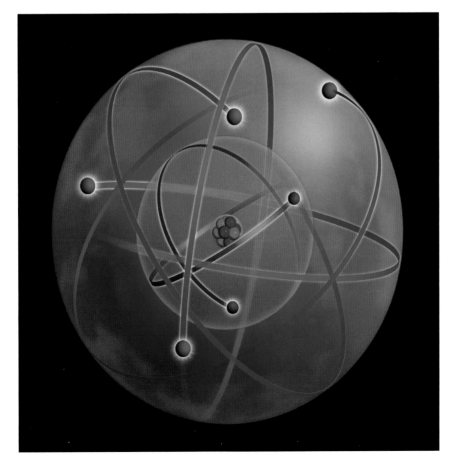

LEFT An illustration of atomic structure shows how each atom is composed of a concentrated nucleus composed of protons and neutrons (centre) orbited by electrons in orbital shells that determine their energy. The number of protons in an atom's nucleus determines its 'atomic number' and therefore its identity as an element, while the number of protons plus neutrons determines its atomic mass. This illustration shows the structure of a carbon-12 atom, with six protons, six neutrons and six electrons.

8 Quantum theory

DEFINITION A THEORY THAT DESCRIBES THE UNUSUAL BEHAVIOURS OF PARTICLES AND RADIATION ON EXTREMELY SMALL SCALES.

DISCOVERY ALBERT EINSTEIN WAS THE FIRST TO TREAT PHOTONS AS REAL OBJECTS IN 1905. LOUIS VICTOR DE BROGLIE SUGGESTED THAT PARTICLES HAVE WAVELIKE PROPERTIES IN 1924.

KEY BREAKTHROUGH IN 1927, WERNER HEISENBERG DISCOVERED THE UNCERTAINTY PRINCIPLE THAT RULES THE SUBATOMIC WORLD.

IMPORTANCE THE QUANTUM NATURE OF REALITY FUNDAMENTALLY CHANGES OUR UNDERSTANDING OF NATURAL PHENOMENA.

Quantum theory is a key element in our modern view of the Universe. While it typically operates on the scale of the very small, its description of the ways in which matter and energy interact are vital to understanding the nature of the broader cosmos.

The quantum revolution of the early 20th century grew out of a crisis in the late 1800s, during which scientists became increasingly aware that various aspects of classical physics, and, particularly, the behaviour of electromagnetic radiation, did not add up. For instance, the wavelike properties of such radiations were undeniable (see page 23), but the medium that was supposed to carry it, the 'luminiferous aether', did not appear to exist. The invention of the incandescent lightbulb allowed astronomers to measure 'black body radiation' – the range of wavelengths produced by a non-reflective emitter of light (such as a star) with any given temperature, but no one could produce a theoretical model that matched reality. Meanwhile, the photoelectric effect – a release of electrons when some metals are bombarded with light was found to be inconsistent: large amounts of red light failed to produce an electric current, while far smaller amounts of blue light would.

Particles of light

In 1900, German physicist Max Planck found an ingenious solution to the black body problem. Reasoning that the energy released by a light source originates in vibrations of its atoms, he assumed that these vibrations occur at discrete frequencies, much like the harmonic modes of a violin string. Radiation that is released as an atom changes its mode would therefore also have a distinct energy, frequency and wavelength. Planck's model produced

OPPOSITE A computer simulation shows vortices within a Bose–Einstein condensate (BEC), a state of matter that can only be explained through quantum theory. BECs form when atoms are cooled very close to absolute zero, and all fall into the same quantum energy state, behaving as a frictionless 'super-atom'.

a description that matched experimental measurements, but no one thought at the time that it also revealed a fundamental truth about the nature of light. This breakthrough came from Albert Einstein who, in a 1905 paper, offered a solution to the problem of the photoelectric effect. By assuming that light itself is broken down into discrete packets or 'quanta', each of which has its own wavelike properties of energy, frequency and wavelength, he revealed why a small quantity of high-energy blue photons could produce a current where much larger quantities of low-energy red photons had failed.

The existence of quanta of light, known today as photons, has huge importance to modern astronomy. The spectral lines used to identify chemicals in distant stars, galaxies and nebulae are ultimately caused by photons of light that are produced or absorbed as electrons change their orbits around atomic nuclei, as described by Niels Bohr and Wolfgang Pauli (see page 34). Electronic CCD detectors rely on the photoelectric effect to collect rare photons arriving from distant galaxies and to produce images that would be impossible with conventional film. Planck's model of black body radiation also describes phenomena ranging from the surfaces of stars to the afterglow of cosmic creation itself. Another major advantage of light's ability to travel in photons, of course, was that it finally did away with the need for a light-propagating aether.

Wavelike matter

But quantum physics encompasses far more than just the nature of light. In 1924 French physicist Louis Victor de Broglie made an outrageous suggestion: if light waves sometimes exhibit the behaviour of particles, then might particles of matter occasionally behave like waves? De Broglie even produced a theoretical means of calculating the wavelengths of particles, which proved to be inversely proportional to their mass and therefore vanishingly small for anything above the subatomic scale. Within a few years, however, scientists at two separate laboratories had been able to show that, in certain experiments, electrons can indeed diffract and interfere with one another just like light.

But what does it mean to say that a particle has a wavelength? Austrian physicist Erwin Schrödinger considered that the wavelength must represent the distribution of the particle's energy in space, and in 1926 he developed a means of calculating this property, known as the 'wavefunction'. Physicists have disagreed about the true meaning of the wavefunction ever since – Schrödinger believed that it was a fundamental revelation that all particles are essentially waves of energy, while others such as Germany's Werner Heisenberg argued that the wavefunction was no more than a means of describing the probability of a particle occupying a particular location at a particular time.

Uncertainty rules

Consideration of the wavefunction mean led Heisenberg to another important discovery: a wave concentrated at a well-defined point cannot reveal its wavelength, and a wave with a measurable wavelength cannot be precisely confined in space. This is Heisenberg's uncertainty principle: it renders it impossible to measure various paired or conjugate properties of a particle with absolute precision. For example, the more accurately we measure a particle's position, the less accurately we can know its momentum and energy. From a cosmological point of view, this is significant since it renders the entirety of spacetime susceptible to random fluctuations – short-lived 'virtual particles' (or more precisely, particle–antiparticle pairs – see page 65) can pop into existence for the briefest instant and sometimes exert a surprising amount of influence. Similarly, even in the uniform fireball produced by the inflationary phase of the Big Bang (see pages 57 and 61), there would be tiny quantum fluctuations in the temperature and density of matter that allowed the creation of our present, structured Universe. Even in more mundane astrophysical processes, the uncertainty principle makes its presence felt, permitting various types of nuclear reaction and radioactive decay that would be impossible according to conventional physics.

Taken to its extreme, the wavelike nature of matter raises fundamental scientific and philosophical questions about the nature of reality, and various theories have been put forward to describe the way in which the microscopic quantum world interacts with the classical physics of the macroscropic world (the more traditional area of interest for astronomers).

BELOW Electron microscopy is a standard tool of modern science, used to create stunning images of very small structures such as these bacteria. Its principle relies on a quantum property – the ability of electrons to display wavelike behaviour in certain circumstances.

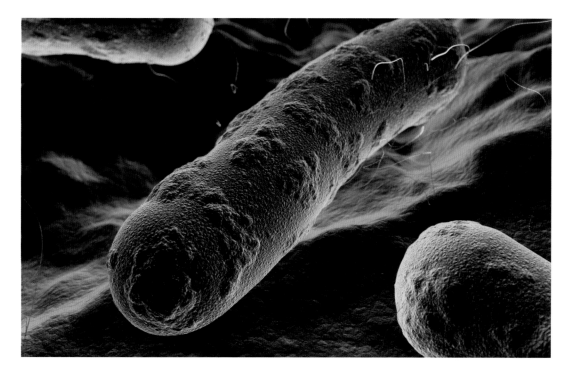

9 The speed of light

DEFINITION THE REALIZATION THAT LIGHT TRAVELS AT THE SAME
SPEED, REGARDLESS OF THE MOTIONS OF SOURCE AND OBSERVER.

DISCOVERY THE FIXED SPEED OF LIGHT WAS CONFIRMED BY THE
MICHELSON—MORLEY EXPERIMENT CARRIED OUT IN 1887.

KEY BREAKTHROUGH ALBERT EINSTEIN'S SPECIAL THEORY OF
RELATIVITY EXPLORED THE IMPLICATIONS OF THE SPEED OF LIGHT
FOR PHENOMENA SUCH AS MASS AND ENERGY.

IMPORTANCE THE FACT THAT THE SPEED OF LIGHT IS FIXED FORMS A
CORNERSTONE TO OUR UNDERSTANDING OF THE UNIVERSE.

The discovery that light in a vacuum moves at a fixed speed, regardless of the motions of source and observer, goes against all common sense. Accommodating this remarkable fact involved a reworking of our understanding of the Universe from first principles.

The first person to attempt a scientific measurement of the speed of light was Italian physicist Galileo Galilei, in 1638. Galileo's experiment was limited and inaccurate, but it allowed him to establish that light travelled a great deal faster than sound. However it was another of his discoveries, the Galilean satellites of Jupiter, that finally confirmed the finite speed of light.

Early measurements

By the 1660s, the orbital periods of the Galilean moons of Jupiter were well known. Telescopes had improved to a state where they could reveal the passage of the moons and their shadows across the face of Jupiter, as well as eclipses when the moons disappeared behind the planet. In the 1660s, Italian astronomer Gian Domenico Cassini set out to study these events from the Paris Observatory, while Ole Rømer made similar measurements from the Uraniborg Observatory in Denmark. Cassini soon noticed unexpected deviations from the predicted times of events, and realized they were caused by changes in the time that light takes to reach Earth as the distance to Jupiter changes. Rømer later put some exact figures on these variations, estimating the speed of light at around 75 percent of the modern value.

Despite this, some scientists remained sceptical about the finite speed of light until the 1720s, when English astronomer James Bradley used it to explain the aberration of starlight – a minute change in the observed position of

OPPOSITE A rainbow spectrum of light emerges from the ends of a fibre-optic cable. Colour is simply the way that human eyes perceive light waves of different energies, and is therefore intrinsically linked to a wave's frequency and wavelength. High-frequency, short-wavelength electromagnetic waves appear blue, while low-frequency, longer waves appear red.

stars from one side of Earth's orbit to the other. This allowed him to make an improved estimate of the speed of light, within 1 percent of the modern 299,792 km/s (186,282 miles per second).

But as measurement techniques improved through the 19th century, scientists noticed something strange: the speed of light was always the same, regardless of the motions of source or observer. Contrary to everyday experience, light does not reach us sooner when its source is moving towards us, or later when we are moving away from its origin. In 1865, as part of his model of light as an electromagnetic wave (see page 23), James Clerk Maxwell showed that all electromagnetic radiation propagates through vacuum at a fixed speed.

But in what frame of reference was this speed fixed? Most scientists agreed that a wave could only propagate in a medium, just as sound waves move through air or water waves cross a pond. The mysterious medium of light, which must fill the vacuum of space, was named the luminiferous aether, and was assumed to provide the absolute standard of rest for the Universe. In 1887, American scientists Albert Michelson and Edward Morley devised an ingenious experiment to measure predicted changes in the speed of light moving in different directions, caused by Earth's motion through the aether.

When the Michelson–Morley experiment produced no evidence of such changes, physicists began to speculate that the aether theory might be wrong.

The relativistic Universe

In 1905, Albert Einstein published a series of landmark papers that triggered a revolution. In essence, he reimagined physics around just two postulates: the principle of relativity, and the principle of invariant light speed. The principle of relativity states that laws of physics should appear exactly the same way for all systems in comparable frames of reference (i.e. those not experiencing acceleration), while the principle of invariant light speed states that light always propagates through empty space with the same velocity. The speed of light must also be the ultimate speed limit of the Universe, otherwise we would be able to see and react to events before they happened, and the rules of causality would be broken.

The resulting special theory of relativity showed how objects moving at relativistic speeds (approaching light-speed) experience strange phenomena such as time dilation (in which time appears to slow down) and Fitzgerald-Lorentz contraction (in which their length appears to change). Even more strangely, as an object approaches the limit of the speed of light c, further acceleration increases its mass rather than its speed. In other words, mass and energy are interchangeable – the origin of the famous equation $E = mc^2$. Explaining light's ability to propagate through a vacuum at fixed speed, meanwhile, relied on another of Einstein's breakthroughs – the theory of quantized light (see page 37).

'As measurement techniques improved in the 19th century, scientists noticed something strange: the speed of light was always the same regardless of the motions of source or observer.'

Strange though these predictions seem, they have been proven in countless experiments, and today's spaceprobes and satellite networks are built to take relativistic effects into account. Special relativity also formed a strong foundation for many breakthroughs of 20th century physics and cosmology including, in 1915, Einstein's own general theory of relativity (see page 45).

However, recent developments have shown that Einstein's theory may not tell the whole story. Since the 1980s, some cosmologists have become intrigued by the idea that c may be slowing down. A faster speed of light in the early Universe offers a solution to several problems in describing its present appearance, and in 1998, a team of astronomers from the University of New South Wales announced tentative evidence, based on studies of distant quasars, for ancient changes to the fine-structure constant that is intimately connected to the speed of light. Another study in 2004 suggested that the constants could have changed as recently as 2 billion years ago. However, the idea remains highly controversial, as do the headline-making 2011 reports from Gran Sasso in Italy (see page 91) of neutrinos apparently travelling faster than light.

10

Spacetime

DEFINITION THE DEEP CONNECTION OF SPACE AND TIME
DIMENSIONS IN A FOUR-DIMENSIONAL 'SPACETIME MANIFOLD'.

DISCOVERY HERMANN MINKOWSKI INTRODUCED SPACETIME AS A
TOOL FOR UNDERSTANDING SPECIAL RELATIVITY IN 1907.

KEY BREAKTHROUGH EINSTEIN'S GENERAL THEORY OF RELATIVITY
DESCRIBED HOW LARGE GRAVITATIONAL FIELDS, AS WELL AS
RELATIVISTIC MOTION, CAN CAUSE SPACETIME TO BEND AND WARP.

IMPORTANCE UNDERSTANDING THE FABRIC OF THE UNIVERSE IS
VITAL TO INTERPRETING THE BEHAVIOUR OF OBJECTS WITHIN IT.

In the decade following the publication of the theory of special relativity, Albert Einstein continued to work on the consequences of his theory. Within a decade, this resulted in a new idea that transformed the way we look at both space and time – the theory of general relativity.

1905 is often described as Einstein's *annus mirabilis* (year of wonders). Within the space of a few months, he published four papers that set the stage for much of 20th and 21st century physics. His explanation of the photoelectric effect (see page 37) finally resolved long-standing questions about the nature of light by describing its ability to behave as both a wave and a particle. His work on Brownian motion, the strange and unpredictable movement of large particles suspended in fluids, proved the existence of invisible atoms and molecules beyond all reasonable doubt, and his papers on special relativity and mass-energy equivalence (see page 43), along with the photoelectric effect, helped pave the way for the rise of quantum physics.

Generalizing relativity

Despite this, Einstein was unsatisfied – in particular by the limitations that applied to special relativity. He felt sure that relativistic principles should also be applicable to non-inertial situations – that is, those in which objects or observers are experiencing acceleration or deceleration. Einstein therefore began to consider the possibility of a more generalized relativity theory.

The key to general relativity lay in the equivalence principle, discovered by Einstein in 1907 when he realized that the laws of physics for an observer in free fall, unaffected by gravity, would be the same as those for one in a non-accelerated or inertial frame of reference. Crucially, the converse is

OPPOSITE A series of timelapse images captures the majesty of a total solar eclipse – a rare occasion on which it is possible to observe stars close to the Sun in the sky, and the shifts in their apparent position caused as light passes through the region of space warped by our star's gravity.

also true: the influence of any gravitational field is physically equivalent to a force of constant acceleration.

Laying the foundations for special relativity, Einstein had already shown that beams of light will appear to bend in any rapidly accelerating situation, so he predicted that they would also bend in strong gravitational fields. Pursuing the implications of his hypothesis further, Einstein found that strong gravity would produce similar effects to relativistic motion, including distortions of appearance, mass and time. In order to describe the effects of general relativity, Einstein enthusiastically adopted an idea first promoted by his old teacher Hermann Minkowski, in a 1907 response to the special theory.

Combining space and time

Minkowski's theory of spacetime described a connected manifold with three 'space-like' dimensions and one 'time-like' dimension. In everyday situations spacetime manifests itself through the normal characteristics of three-dimensional 'Euclidean' space and the apparently unrelated flow of time.

BELOW Gravitational waves are an as-yet-unproven prediction of general relativity – distortions of spacetime generated by extreme cosmic events and objects, rippling across the Universe. This simulation models the gravitational waves generated by a pair of superdense black holes (see page 338) in the process of merging together.

However in relativistic situations, the space-like dimensions can contract and the time-like dimension can expand in accordance with equations known as the Lorentz transformations (developed by Dutch physicist Hendrik Lorentz and others in the late 19th century).

Einstein reasoned that if the effects of relativistic speeds could be described as distortions of spacetime, then so could those caused by gravitational fields. Massive objects warp spacetime in their surroundings, and this affects the inertial motion of objects passing close to them. The effect can be visualized by imagining spacetime as a rubber sheet with two space-like dimensions across the sheet, and a time-like dimension downwards. When a large mass is placed in the middle of the sheet, it creates a dent, or 'gravitational well', that deflects the paths of objects passing close to it. Focusing on the distortion of the three space-like dimensions alone, the effect is rather more like the pinching of an hourglass with the mass at its narrowest point.

'The space-like dimensions can contract and the time-like dimension can expand in accordance with equations known as the Lorentz transformations.'

Proving general relativity

Einstein published his theory of general relativity in 1915, at the height of the First World War, and publishing restrictions meant that it took some time to spread around the world. In order to demonstrate the theory's potential, Einstein himself showed how it could be used to explain a long-running astronomical puzzle about gradual changes in Mercury's orbit. Despite this, the theory was not widely accepted until 1919, when British astronomer Arthur Eddington led an expedition to the west African island of Príncipe to test its predictions.

Since general relativity explained gravitation as a distortion of spacetime rather than a force acting on objects with mass, Einstein argued that extreme gravitational fields should affect the path of massless light waves. Eddington's team measured the positions of stars close to the Sun during a total solar eclipse – the only occasion when they can be seen – and showed that the starlight had been deflected on its journey past the Sun in exactly the way suggested by general relativity. While some cast doubt on the accuracy of these measurements, the results were confirmed by similar observations with more advanced equipment during later eclipses.

General relativity and four-dimensional spacetime are powerful concepts that shape our models of the cosmos itself, making their presence felt in extreme events throughout the Universe. Gravitational lenses, black holes and the cosmology of the Big Bang itself (see pages 393, 338, and 57) are all proof of the crucial nature of Einstein's discovery. Nevertheless, Einstein was not immune to mistakes; in order to account for what seemed at the time to be a static Universe, unaffected by the gravity of objects within it, he introduced a factor called the cosmological constant. Within a decade, advances in astronomy had rendered it completely redundant.

11

The expanding cosmos

DEFINITION THE REVELATION THAT THE DISTANCE BETWEEN
GALAXIES IS STEADILY INCREASING AS THE UNIVERSE EXPANDS.

DISCOVERY THE EXPANSION WAS IDENTIFIED BY EDWIN HUBBLE
USING REDSHIFT MEASUREMENTS OF DISTANT GALAXIES.

KEY BREAKTHROUGH COMPLETION OF THE HUBBLE KEY PROJECT
IN 2001 PRODUCED THE FIRST ACCURATE MEASURE OF THE RATE
OF EXPANSION.

IMPORTANCE COSMIC EXPANSION PLAYS A CRUCIAL ROLE IN OUR
MODERN VIEW OF THE UNIVERSE, AND LAYS THE CORNERSTONE
FOR THE BIG BANG THEORY.

The discovery in the 1920s that space itself is expanding changed our view of the Universe forever, and it led directly to the Big Bang theory of cosmic origins. But recent discoveries have shown that the picture is more complex, and are changing our models of the Universe once again.

By the early 20th century, geological evidence had thoroughly overturned long-standing theories of a relatively young Earth, battered into its present shape by relatively recent prehistoric catastrophes. In their place came a model of an ancient planet that had been moulded by gradual, inexorable forces over hundreds of millions of years or more. In the astronomical community, meanwhile, astronomers were rethinking their ideas about the lifespan and fuel sources of stars (see page 265), and cosmological ideas had swung from one extreme to another: if the Universe was so unimaginably ancient, then what evidence was there to say it had ever been 'born' at all – perhaps it had always existed?

Fitting theory to reality

However, the new interpretation of spacetime inspired by Einstein's theory of relativity tended to produce models of a dynamic, rather than static Universe, constantly evolving on the largest scale thanks to the gravity of the objects within it. By 1922, Russian cosmologist Alexander Friedmann had even developed a set of equations that suggested the Universe should be expanding. It was against this background that Einstein introduced the cosmological constant into his field equations – a 'fudge' designed to generate a static Universe in line with observations of the time. Einstein would later ruefully describe this constant as his greatest mistake.

OPPOSITE The Hubble Ultra-Deep Field (see page 73) reveals thousands of galaxies in one small region of the sky, the furthest of which are more than 10 billion light years away and rushing away from Earth at a substantial fraction of the speed of light.

Around this time, astronomers were engaged in fighting out the 'great debate' around the nature of spiral nebulae and the scale of the Universe – a debate that was ultimately settled by Edwin Hubble's measurements of the true distance to nearby galaxies (see page 29). But Hubble's work inevitably led to another discovery that was even more startling – confirmation that the Universe as a whole was expanding.

The discovery relied on measurements of galactic redshifts – the stretching of the wavelengths of light coming from distant galaxies, caused by the Doppler effect. These shifts and their general significance had been discovered as early as 1912 by Vesto Slipher, working at Lowell Observatory in Flagstaff, Arizona. Measuring the spectra of the contentious spiral nebulae, Slipher had discovered that the tell-tale dark absorption lines, which normally revealed the chemical signatures of stars (see page 25) made no sense whatsoever. It soon became clear that they were in fact shifted out of position by large amounts, suggesting that distant nebulae in different parts of the sky were all moving away from us at tremendous speeds.

'Cosmological expansion is considered a key piece of evidence for the Big Bang theory. If things are moving apart they must have been much closer together in the distant past.'

In 1929, Hubble and Milton Humason published the results of a comparison between the distances of galaxies and the redshifts in their light. The result showed a clear proportionality – the further away an object lies, the larger its redshift and the faster it must be moving away from Earth. The only plausible explanation for this result, tying in with the equations of general relativity, is not that our galaxy is peculiarly unpopular, but instead that the entire Universe is expanding and carrying all galaxies away from each other (rather like raisins in a baking cake). If space is expanding at a fixed rate, then it makes sense that the gap between distant galaxies grows faster than that between nearby ones. It is important to realize that it is the expansion of space itself that drives the galaxies apart, rather than a physical movement across space – hence light that left distant galaxies billions of years ago has had to cross an ever-increasing span of space in order to reach us and only arrived now despite the fact that the galaxy may have been much closer to our location when its light departed on its journey.

Pinning down the numbers

The rate of this cosmological expansion, typically measured in kilometres per second per megaparsec (where a megaparsec is equivalent to 3.26 million light years) soon became known as the Hubble Constant (H_0) but it remained infamously difficult to measure. This was partly because most galaxies remained far beyond the reach of Hubble's Cepheid-based method for measuring intergalactic distances, and partly because localized gravitational effects within groups and clusters of galaxies (see page 385) tend to muddy the effects of the expansion. Hubble himself wildly overestimated the value of H_0 at around 250 km/s/Mpc, and the first reasonably accurate

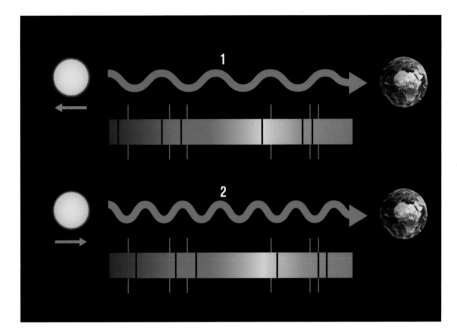

LEFT The Doppler effect is a perceived stretching (1) or compression (2) of waves coming from a distant source, produced when the source is moving away from, or towards, an observer. It is best measured in light through the shift in spectral lines (shown as dark lines against a continuum spectrum in this illustration) compared with their expected stationary positions (white lines).

estimate, of roughly 75 km/s/Mpc, was published by American astronomer Allan Sandage in 1958. Nevertheless, measurements of H_0 continued to vary wildly, and the principal aim of the Hubble Space Telescope (HST), launched in 1990, was to extend the range of Cepheid measurements across much greater distances and to finalize an accurate value for the constant. Completed in 2001, the 'Hubble Key Project', led by Wendy L. Freedman of the Carnegie Observatories, delivered a value of 72 ± 8 km/s/Mpc, remarkably close to that obtained by Sandage. Since then, astronomers have found ingenious ways of re-measuring the constant using instruments aboard satellites such as the Chandra X-ray Observatory, WMAP (see page 55) and with other instruments aboard the HST itself, all with results that have been in general agreement to within a small percentage.

Along with the cosmic microwave background radiation (see page 53), cosmological expansion is considered a key piece of evidence for the Big Bang theory (see page 57). The logic that if things are moving apart they must have been much closer together in the distant past is inescapable and appealingly intuitive: while some alternative cosmological models can produce an eternal cosmos that still has expansion built in, these theories tend to fall down when explaining other aspects of the Universe.

Just as importantly, once cosmological expansion was generally accepted, redshift became a useful proxy for other distance measurements. Even before an exact value of the H_0 was established, it was possible to use measures of redshift (known as z) to work out whether galaxies were, on balance, closer or more distant, and even to estimate the ratios of distance between them (since a galaxy with twice the redshift should be twice as far away).

12 Cosmic microwave background radiation

DEFINITION A LOW-ENERGY GLOW FROM ALL PARTS OF THE SKY THAT IS CRUCIAL EVIDENCE FOR THE BIG BANG.

DISCOVERY THE CMBR WAS FIRST IDENTIFIED BY ARNO PENZIAS AND ROBERT WILSON IN 1964.

KEY BREAKTHROUGH FROM 1989 TO 1992, THE COBE SATELLITE MAPPED THE MICROWAVE BACKGROUND, DISCOVERING RIPPLES LINKED TO THE FORMATION OF LARGE-SCALE COSMIC STRUCTURE.

IMPORTANCE THE CMBR PROVIDES US WITH INFORMATION ABOUT CONDITIONS SHORTLY AFTER THE BIG BANG ITSELF.

A faint glow coming from all around the sky is one of the strongest pieces of evidence for the Big Bang theory. But astronomers are discovering that this background radiation also offers a valuable tool for exploring the nature of the early Universe.

The story of the discovery of the cosmic microwave background radiation (CMBR) is one of the most famous in the history of astronomy – in 1964 Arno Penzias and Robert Wilson, two physicists working at Bell Labs, New Jersey, were testing a new and highly sensitive horn antenna intended for radio astronomy observations. However, they found that the system was registering a faint but persistent background signal. After investigating every possible source of radio noise (including radioactivity from pigeon droppings), Penzias and Wilson concluded that the signal was natural, and was coming from all over the sky.

Although the two radio-astronomers did not know it, cosmologists had predicted just such a signal as a natural consequence of the Big Bang, in which the Universe was heated to unimaginable temperatures and compressed into a tiny point in space. After billions of years, the remnants of this radiation should now come from every part of the sky – beyond the most distant stars and galaxies, from the very edge of the observable Universe itself. Word of Penzias and Wilson's findings soon reached Princeton physicist Robert Dicke, who was able to confirm that this was the long-sought after radiation.

The CMBR glows with short-wavelength radio waves in the microwave range, and its radiation indicates a temperature of –270.4°C (–454.7°F) – just 2.73°C (4.9°F) above absolute zero, the coldest possible temperature. This

OPPOSITE A spherical projection shows minute variations in the CMBR measured by the Wilkinson Microwave Anisotropy Probe (WMAP) during its first phase of observations in 2003.

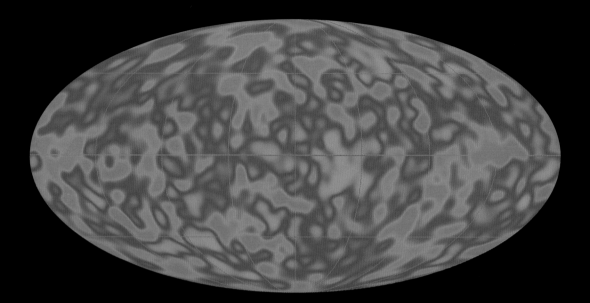

apparently low temperature is the result of a phenomenal redshift stretching the wavelength of radiation on its way to Earth, caused by the Doppler effect (see page 51) as the source of the CMBR moves away from us at very nearly the speed of light. The radiation marks the 'last scattering surface' of the Universe – the moment when the Universe became transparent roughly 400,000 years after the Big Bang itself – hence it forms a wall that blocks our view of the moment of creation itself (which should otherwise theoretically be visible).

Wrinkles in time

The discovery of the CMBR was hailed as a massive triumph for the Big Bang cosmology, but it immediately presented astronomers with a problem. The glow from across the sky appeared featureless and uniform, as was to be expected if it came from an era when radiation pressure kept the distribution of subatomic particles even throughout an expanding fireball. But it was supposed to represent the early state of a Universe that is today decidedly uneven on every scale. Galaxies clump together in clusters and superclusters, which themselves form sheets and filaments around the edges of enormous, apparently empty voids (see page 385). It seemed impossible for a smooth early Universe to have developed into clumps of matter quickly enough to explain the presence of large-scale cosmic structures that lay billions of light years away and billions of years back in time.

In order to answer these questions, in 1989 NASA launched the Cosmic Background Explorer satellite (COBE). Equipped with a small but ultrasensitive microwave telescope, COBE was designed to make a microwave map of the entire sky from beyond the atmosphere over the course of several years.

When COBE's results were published in 1992, they made headlines around the world, answering some questions but raising new ones. In COBE's view, the CMBR was far from uniform. Instead, it was covered in ripples that indicated temperature variations or 'anisotropies' of just one part in 100,000 around the average temperature. Principal investigators George Smoot, of the University of California at Berkeley, and John Mather of NASA's Goddard Space Flight Center later won the Nobel Prize for the discovery of what Smoot memorably referred to as 'wrinkles in time'. Although minute, the variations were enough to indicate that the early Universe was far from uniform – warmer areas indicated concentrations of matter, and cooler ones relatively sparse regions. These were the seeds of today's superclusters, filaments and voids, embedded in the cosmos from its earliest epoch – but where had they come from? If the intense radiation of the newborn Universe was keeping normal matter widely dispersed, there was only one answer – the concentrations must be dark matter. This little-understood material does not interact with radiation, and could therefore begin to coalesce into uneven clumps while the cosmos was still in its infancy. Then once the fog cleared, normal matter could begin to coalesce around dark matter kernels that were already in place.

WMAP and beyond
In the years that followed COBE's success, several Earth-based telescopes and balloon-borne experiments investigated small areas of the CMBR in detail. Then in 2001, NASA launched a much more ambitious satellite, the Wilkinson Microwave Anisotropy Probe (WMAP). WMAP operated for more than seven years, and measured the ripples at far higher resolutions and with far greater sensitivity. Applying the results of the measurements to the currently accepted models of cosmic evolution (see pages 57 and 405), the WMAP team were able to put figures on a number of important properties of the early and present-day Universe.

'The glow from across the sky appeared featureless and uniform. But it was supposed to represent the early state of a Universe that is today decidedly uneven on every scale.'

The probe's data provided a good match for the measures of cosmic expansion made by the Hubble Space Telescope, putting the age of the Universe at some 13.75 billion years. It measured the energy composition of the modern Universe as 4.6 percent 'normal' matter, 22.8 percent dark matter (see page 397), and 72.6 percent dark energy (see page 401), while showing that at the time the CMBR was emitted, the breakdown was 22 percent normal matter (including 10 percent neutrinos – see page 89), 15 percent electromagnetic radiation, and 63 percent dark matter, with dark energy apparently negligible.

In 2009, the European Space Agency launched its Planck Telescope, which intended to map the CMBR to even greater precision. Cosmologists hope that its results over the next few years will allow them to further refine their understanding of the early Universe.

The Big Bang

13

DEFINITION THE THEORY THAT OFFERS OUR BEST MODEL OF THE ORIGIN OF THE UNIVERSE AND MATTER WITHIN IT.

DISCOVERY THE IDEA THAT THE UNIVERSE ORIGINATED IN A 'PRIMEVAL ATOM' WAS FIRST PROPOSED BY BELGIAN PRIEST AND COSMOLOGIST ABBÉ GEORGES LEMAÎTRE IN 1931.

KEY BREAKTHROUGH IN 1948, GEORGE GAMOW AND RALPH ALPHER DESCRIBED HOW LEMAÎTRE'S THEORY COULD PRODUCE THE OBSERVED MIX OF CHEMICAL ELEMENTS IN THE UNIVERSE.

IMPORTANCE THE THEORY GOVERNS LARGE-SCALE COSMIC PROPERTIES THAT AFFECT FAR SMALLER EVENTS AND PHENOMENA.

The idea that the Universe originated in a single fiery moment of creation, the 'Big Bang', is one of the most powerful scientific theories of the past century. Yet while the Big Bang has passed many scientific hurdles, there are still many outstanding questions around it.

The origin of the Big Bang theory is usually credited to Georges Lemaître, a Belgian Catholic priest and physicist who studied cosmology at Cambridge under Arthur Eddington, and at Harvard College Observatory under Harlow Shapley. In a 1927 paper based on his interpretation of general relativity (see page 45), Lemaître predicted that the Universe was expanding, but his theories, and the similar work of Russian cosmologist Alexander Friedmann, were rejected by Einstein and others until Edwin Hubble came up with the observational evidence for expansion in 1929 (see page 49).

Lemaître was also the first to consider the inevitable consequences of the expanding cosmos – specifically the fact that the Universe must have been far smaller and hotter in the distant past. This convinced him that the cosmos had originated in a single explosive event that he called the 'Primeval Atom'. At first the scientific establishment was sceptical of Lemaître's suggestion, with many suspecting it was influenced more by religious faith than scientific evidence. Other proposals aimed to explain cosmic expansion without abandoning the concept of an eternal, essentially unchanging, Universe. These included Friedmann's 'oscillatory Universe', which went through cycles of expansion and contraction, and the 'Steady State' theory, in which expansion was accompanied by continuous creation of new matter. Ironically, it was one of the Steady State's most ardent advocates, English astronomer Fred Hoyle, who in 1951 dismissed Lemaître's theory as a 'Big Bang'.

OPPOSITE Evidence that the Universe began life in the rapidly expanding fireball of the Big Bang is now overwhelming. The explosion is thought to have created not just matter and energy, but the fabric of spacetime itself.

The Big Bang vindicated

By this time, however, advances in nuclear physics were strengthening the case for Lemaître's theory. In a pivotal 1948 paper, physicists George Gamow and Ralph Alpher explained how the huge amounts of energy released in the Big Bang could have given rise to the lightest chemical elements, most importantly hydrogen and helium, in the proportions still found in unprocessed intergalactic material. They also predicted that the entire Universe should still be glowing with a very faint echo of the explosion – the cosmic microwave background (see page 53). Throughout the 1950s and 1960s, others continued to develop the Big Bang model, incorporating the latest ideas about atomic structure and fundamental forces (see page 33). Two of the most notable contributions came from American mathematical physicist Howard Robertson and British mathematician Geoffrey Walker.

'Lemaître was also the first to consider the fact that the Universe must have been far smaller and hotter in the distant past. This convinced him that the cosmos had originated in a single explosive event.'

The details of the Big Bang theory in its developed form are so complex they would take an entire book to describe, but in essence, they rely on the fact that mass and energy become increasingly interchangeable at high temperatures and energies. High temperatures also break matter into ever smaller component particles – so hydrogen molecules disintegrate into atoms, which then ionize, and eventually even protons and neutrons separate into their constituent quarks.

Replaying creation

In the first moments of the Big Bang, around 13.7 billion years ago, temperatures and energy levels were so high that matter was constantly being created and destroyed (in fact, both matter and antimatter were created, which raises interesting questions – see page 65). The four fundamental

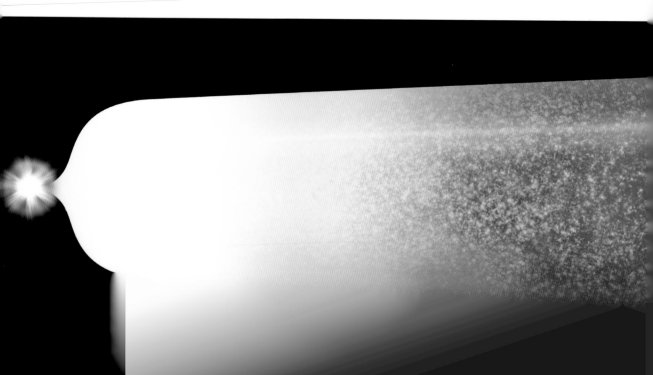

forces of physics – gravitation, the weak and strong nuclear forces, and electromagnetism, also manifested themselves as a single force, but rapidly separated from one another to influence particles in different ways.

As the Universe expanded and temperatures fell, it became less feasible to spontaneously create more massive particles such as the quarks that make up nucleons (protons and neutrons). As a result, the quark populations 'froze' after about a nanosecond, while much lighter lepton particles (such as electrons, positrons and neutrinos) were still able to wink in and out of existence. After about a microsecond, temperatures fell to a point where quarks were able to bond through the strong nuclear force and form nucleons. The vast majority were protons, but some neutrons were also created, and after the first second, these began to bind with protons in a nucleosynthesis phase that created nuclei of the heavy hydrogen isotopes deuterium and tritium, and the elements helium and lithium. The vast majority of protons, however, remained unattached as simple hydrogen nuclei.

After about three minutes, energy levels were no longer high enough to create electrons, so the population of these, too, froze. The Universe was now an expanding ball of matter and energy – atomic nuclei and electrons with high-energy photons bouncing between them, not unlike the radiative zone of a star like the Sun. This expansion continued for some 380,000 years before cosmic temperatures dropped below about 2,700°C (4,900°F). At this point, the atomic nuclei and electrons were able to combine to form the first atoms. The sudden drop in particle density turned the Universe transparent, and photons of light from the last scattering surface raced off into empty space. It is these photons, now redshifted into low-energy microwaves, that form the cosmic microwave background radiation (see page 53).

BELOW The Big Bang began with a spontaneous burst of energy that created space, time and all the energy in the Universe simultaneously. After a sudden period of expansion called inflation (see page 61), the Universe continued to grow at a steadier pace, with energy converted mostly into matter. Following a cosmic 'Dark Age', coalescing matter grew dense enough to trigger nuclear fusion, forming the first stars that reilluminated the Universe.

14 Before the Big Bang

DEFINITION A NUMBER OF RECENT THEORIES OFFER POSSIBLE CAUSES FOR THE BIG BANG, OR PUT IT IN A WIDER CONTEXT.

DISCOVERY THE IDEA OF CHAOTIC INFLATION WAS PROPOSED BY ANDREI LINDE IN 1986.

KEY BREAKTHROUGH THE EUROPEAN SPACE AGENCY'S PLANCK TELESCOPE SHOULD COLLECT DATA THAT CAN PROVE OR DISPROVE SEVERAL OF THESE THEORIES.

IMPORTANCE UNDERSTANDING CONDITIONS PRIOR TO THE BIG BANG COULD HELP TO RESOLVE SOME OUTSTANDING PROBLEMS WITH THE THEORY.

Questions about the cause of the Big Bang can be easily dismissed: the event created space and time themselves, so asking about what came before is seen by some as meaningless. However, that has not stopped cosmologists from speculating, and at least some of their theories may be testable after all.

Quantum physics sets an ultimate limit on how far even the most complex models of the Big Bang can look back. Before 10^{-43} seconds after the origin of the Universe, the primordial fireball was a singularity – so tiny and dense that it was smaller than the Planck Length, a fundamental constant of nature below which the predictable laws of classical physics break down.

For this reason, the Big Bang theory has always carried a large disclaimer about the impossibility of knowing the conditions in that first singularity, let alone anything that happened 'before'. The usual scientific explanation of the Big Bang has been that it erupted spontaneously in a primordial vacuum devoid of concepts such as space and time, most likely as the result of a quantum fluctuation (see page 39). Since the 1980s, however, three rival theories have been developed to dodge the singularity issue, creating a hot, dense and rapidly expanding infant Universe from a conventional, though complex, trigger event occurring before the Big Bang.

Inflating the Universe

The first of these ideas arises naturally from the idea of inflation – the theory that a small portion of the primordial Universe underwent an immense growth spurt, perhaps powered by the separation of the fundamental forces, very shortly after the Big Bang, expanding to such an extent that the entire Universe we observe today comprises just a tiny fraction of the original.

OPPOSITE According to the 'chaotic Inflation' theory of cosmic origins, our Universe is just one among an infinity of 'bubbles' that have emerged from an ongoing inflationary process triggered in the early Universes.

Inflation was first proposed by Alan Guth of the Massachusetts Institute of Technology in 1981 as a way to explain the relatively smooth distribution of matter in the Universe today: by magnifying a small region of the turbulent pre-inflationary cosmos, the Universe was smoothed out. The minute fluctuations found in the cosmic microwave background radiation (CMBR – see page 53) are the magnified echoes of quantum-scale variations in the Universe during inflation.

While inflation helps predict many of the Universe's observed large-scale properties, and has been generally accepted as part of the standard Big Bang narrative, it generates some significant problems, the most serious of which was pointed out by Russian-American physicist Andrei Linde as early as 1986. Because the point at which inflation ends can itself be affected by quantum-level fluctuations, some part of the originally inflated region would inevitably have continued to expand beyond the rest, rapidly outgrowing the remainder of the original inflated Universe. Within the region experiencing extended inflation, some areas would again continue to inflate while the rest came to a halt, and so on. The result is what Linde called 'chaotic inflation' – the creation of an infinite series of 'bubble Universes', each with its own structure and laws of physics.

'The cyclic Universe theory suggests that new Big Bangs are triggered at trillion-year intervals by collisions between these branes.'

One side-effect of chaotic inflation is that many of the bubble Universes will die in infancy thanks to the wrong mix of fundamental constants governing their laws of physics – our Universe only took root and flourished thanks to just the right mix, so the number of other bubbles out there may be more limited than it seems at first. Nevertheless, for some cosmologists, chaotic inflation throws significant doubt on the validity of inflation as a scientific theory – if it generates an infinite number of varied outcomes, then the fact that it offers a way to produce the conditions of our own Universe becomes rather less impressive.

However, some cosmologists have adopted the idea of chaotic inflation wholeheartedly, since if our Universe emerged from such an origin, it sidesteps the need to trace its origins directly to a singularity and allows the old idea of an eternal cosmos to be reinstated. Weighed against this is the fact that others have serious doubts about the validity of inflation at all – aside from philosophical issues, it may be that inflation requires such a specific set of conditions to begin that, in comparison, our Universe is far more likely to have developed its current properties by coincidence.

The oscillatory theory
Another idea harks back to the work of Soviet cosmologist Alexander Friedmann (who predicted cosmic expansion before its discovery in the 1920s – see page 49). Friedmann argued for an 'oscillating Universe', in which the Big Bang emerged from the collapse of a previous Universe, a so-

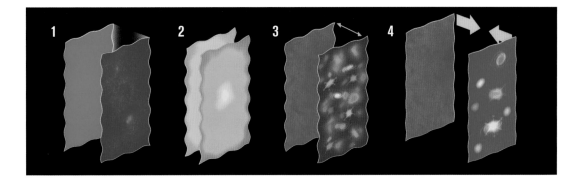

called 'Big Crunch' (see page 405). Now a broadly similar theory, known as loop quantum cosmology (LQC), has emerged from loop quantum gravity, one of several attempts to unite gravity with the other fundamental forces of the Universe (see page 34).

In the LQC model, spacetime itself is quantized – made up of tiny, one-dimensional units that form a 'substructure' through which other objects move. This would allow a Universe to grow through expansion of the substructure, and then contract through shrinkage of these same spacetime units, regardless of the matter content of the Universe (the traditional restriction on models of the fate of the Universe – see page 405). When the concentration of matter in each quantum unit reached a critical density, spacetime would rebound, and a new oscillation would begin.

When branes collide

Since the 1990s another theory, known as the 'cyclic Universe', has also risen to prominence, developing from string theory, a 'Theory of Everything' that requires the Universe to have several extra unseen dimensions. According to cosmologists such as Neil Turok of Canada's Perimeter Institute and Princeton's Paul Steinhardt, our Universe could be a single four-dimensional 'brane' of spacetime (see page 45), separated from other similar branes by a minute but uncrossable gap in another dimension. The cyclic Universe theory suggests that Big Bangs are triggered at trillion-year intervals by collisions between these branes. It also offers a natural way to smooth the preceding empty Universe, thus avoiding the need for inflation.

Amazing though it might seem, some of these theories should be testable through accurate measurement of the CMBR. The chaotic inflation theory might generate the telltale signs of other bubble Universes intruding on our own, while both traditional inflation and the cyclic theory predict the creation of powerful gravitational waves during the flattening phase, which would leave their own imprint on the background radiation. Cosmologists hope that ongoing and planned future missions to map the CMBR, such as the European Space Agency's Planck Surveyor, launched in 2009, should be able to settle the question, or at least rule out some of the options.

ABOVE According to a branch of theoretical physics called 'M theory', our Universe may exist on a single four-dimensional 'brane' separated from others in multi-dimensional space (1). The Big Bang may have been triggered by a collision between branes (2), which then move apart, flattening out the ripples in our Universe (3). Eventually, the branes come together again (4) and the cycle repeats itself.

15 Matter and antimatter

DEFINITION THE EXISTENCE OF PARTICLES WITH SIMILAR PROPERTIES TO NORMAL MATTER, EXCEPT FOR AN OPPOSITE ELECTRIC CHARGE.

DISCOVERY ANTIMATTER WAS POSTULATED BY PAUL DIRAC IN 1928, AND IT WAS FIRST DETECTED IN 1932.

KEY BREAKTHROUGH IN 1967, ANDREI SAKHAROV OUTLINED THE CONDITIONS NECESSARY TO PRODUCE OUR PRESENT MATTER-DOMINATED UNIVERSE.

IMPORTANCE QUESTIONS AROUND THE DISAPPEARANCE OF ANTIMATTER HAVE MAJOR IMPLICATIONS FOR BOTH COSMOLOGY AND PARTICLE PHYSICS.

According to current understanding, the Big Bang should have created just as much antimatter as it did normal matter – yet today, antimatter is rare and the Universe seems to be dominated by normal matter. So where did all the antimatter go?

Antimatter is simply matter composed of fundamental particles with the opposite electric charge to normal matter. The existence of such particles was first seriously proposed by British theoretician Paul Dirac in 1928 – he realized that the quantum description of the electron (see page 38) predicted the existence of an 'antielectron' with the same properties but a positive, rather than negative, charge. American physicist Carl Anderson succeeded in producing and detecting these particles (known as positrons) at Caltech in 1932, and today we know that they are produced naturally by certain forms of radioactive decay. Larger antiparticles are unknown in nature, but in 1955, Emilio Segré and Owen Chamberlain were able to create antiprotons, themselves composed of antiquarks. There is also an antineutron, an uncharged particle that is itself composed of reverse-charged antiquarks.

In theory, antiparticles can combine to form antiatoms and antimolecules, but it was not until 1995 that a handful of antihydrogen atoms, each consisting of a positron in orbit around an antiproton, were created using the Low-Energy Antiproton Ring particle accelerator at CERN in Switzerland.

Gone in a flash

The best-known property of antimatter particles is their tendency to 'annihilate' when they encounter their normal-matter counterparts. During these events, the mass of both particles is converted directly into energy,

OPPOSITE Neutrons stars such as the pulsar at the heart of the Crab Nebula generate large quantities of electrons and positrons in beams of particles that emerge from their magnetic poles at around half the speed of light, forming the jets visible in this multi-wavelength image.

disappearing in a burst of high-powered gamma rays in accordance with Dirac's equations and Einstein's famous $E = mc^2$. This property of antimatter understandably makes it difficult to study, and it can only be protected from immediate annihilation with normal matter using powerful magnetic fields.

While the properties of antimatter fascinate theoretical physicists, they present a distinct problem for cosmologists. In extreme conditions such as those of the Big Bang itself, matter and energy were essentially interchangeable, and as energy was transformed into matter, it should have produced balanced particle–antiparticle pairs that would have annihilated each other, releasing the energy bound up in their mass. Eventually the Universe would have cooled to a point where particles were no longer spontaneously created, but at this point, there should still have been a balance of closely packed particles and antiparticles to annihilate one another.

The unbalanced Universe

In which case, why does our present-day Universe appear to be dominated by matter? One possibility is that this is an illusion, and that many of the distant stars and galaxies we see are in fact made of antimatter – a small body of antimatter has even been suggested as a cause for the Tunguska explosion of 1908 (see page 150). Antimatter objects in isolation would essentially be indistinguishable from normal ones, but the space between stars and even galaxies is not as empty as it appears, and we would expect to see tell-tale signs of annihilation in regions where matter and antimatter encounter each other. Since these are nowhere to be seen, most astronomers believe that the Universe (or at least the observable Universe, which is not necessarily the same thing – see page 61), is essentially matter-dominated.

Clearly there must have been an imbalance between matter and antimatter in the Big Bang itself – most significantly an excess of matter quarks that is known as the baryon asymmetry. According to theoretical models, this imbalance came into existence within the first billionth of a second, and produced 1,000,000,001 normal quarks for every 1,000,000,000 antimatter quarks. In 1967, Soviet physicist and dissident Andrei Sakharov proposed three conditions that must have been met in order to produce an early baryon asymmetry.

Explaining asymmetry

The most significant of these Sakharov conditions is known as CP violation – a divergence from the CP symmetry postulate of fundamental physics under high-energy conditions. Simply put, CP symmetry states that the laws of physics should be the same if a particle is swapped for its antiparticle (charge conjugation or C symmetry), or for its mirror image (parity or P symmetry). A wealth of evidence suggests that CP symmetry holds for interactions involving electromagnetism, gravitation and the strong force (see page 34), but CP violation is known to occur during weak-force interactions involved in radioactive decay. However, the weak-force CP violations as they are currently known are far too small to create the baryon asymmetry in the early Universe. As a result, it seems that there is either a significant gap in the standard model of particle physics involving an overlooked source of further CP violations, or that the missing antimatter is out there in remote parts of the Universe, but is somehow hidden from our observations.

'Eventually the Universe would have cooled to a point where particles were no longer spontaneously created, but at this point there should still have been a balance of particles and antiparticles to annihilate one another.'

Meanwhile, antimatter is still being generated on a moderate scale in the present-day Universe, where it can be detected from the energy produced during its annihilation. Positrons are created in the extreme conditions around supernova remnants such as neutron stars and black holes (see page 338), and in 1997, NASA's Compton Gamma-Ray Observatory discovered a huge cloud of gamma rays coming from annihilation above the centre of the Milky Way. At first, this was thought to be a sign that the supermassive black hole in the galactic centre had been actively spewing out jets of antimatter in the relatively recent past. However in 2010, further observations from the European Space Agency's Integral satellite linked the cloud's lopsided shape to the distribution of the many smaller supernova remnants surrounding the centre of the Milky Way.

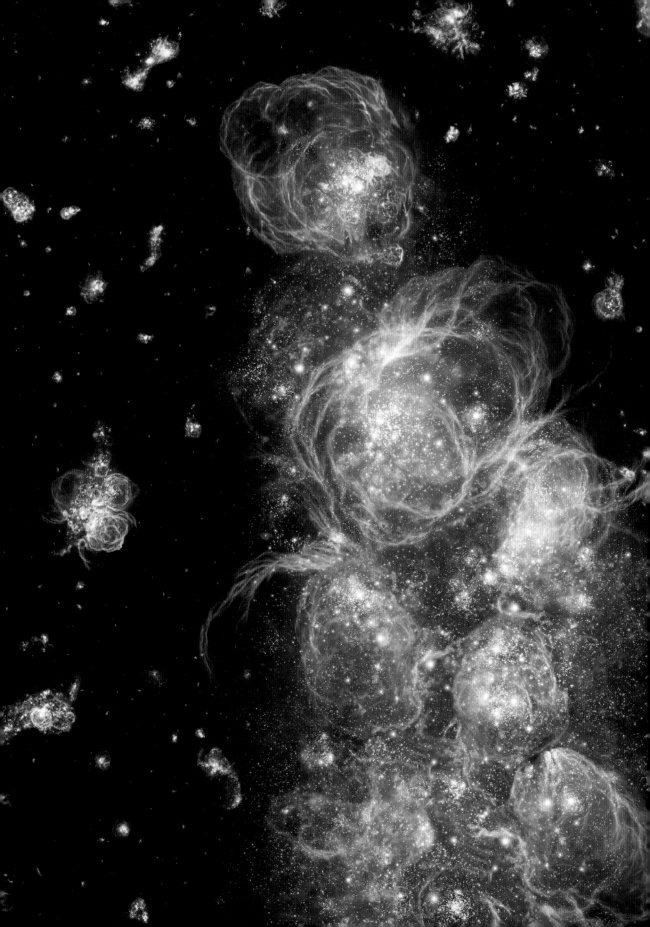

16

The first stars

DEFINITION AN INITIAL GENERATION OF ENORMOUS STARS THAT CREATED THE FIRST HEAVY ELEMENTS IN THE UNIVERSE AND LEFT BEHIND THE SEEDS OF TODAY'S GALAXIES.

DISCOVERY THE NEED FOR AN EARLIER GENERATION OF STARS WAS FIRST RECOGNIZED IN THE 1970s.

KEY BREAKTHROUGH IN 2002, SCIENTISTS SHOWED HOW THE FIRST STARS COULD HAVE COALESCED AROUND KNOTS OF DARK MATTER.

IMPORTANCE THE FIRST STARS PLAYED A VITAL ROLE IN CREATING THE UNIVERSE WE KNOW TODAY.

Following the decoupling of matter and energy around 400,000 years after the Big Bang, the cosmos was plunged into a Dark Age. From this, the first generation of stars emerged – monsters far bigger than anything known today, which played a vital role in the evolution of the Universe.

As the high-temperature fog that filled the early Universe cleared (see page 59), the cosmos was plunged into a lightless era known as the Dark Age. One consequence of this was to suddenly remove the radiation pressure that had previously prevented normal matter from clumping together under the pull of gravity. Dominated by hydrogen and helium, and with only tiny traces of the heavier elements lithium and beryllium, this matter now began to coalesce around the knots of dark matter that had already begun to form from the very earliest times. But rather than initially creating complex structures such as galaxies, computer models and observational evidence suggest that it first formed an early generation of truly massive stars.

Era of the megasuns

These early giants are needed in part because even the oldest stars we can see today – the ancient Population II stars of globular clusters and galactic cores – contain larger amounts of heavier elements than can be explained if they formed directly from the raw material of the Universe. Instead, it seems there must have been a preceding generation of early but short-lived stars that seeded heavier elements into the raw material for the first galaxies – the so-called Population III.

The need for a Population III of some sort was first recognized in the late 1970s, but it was not until the 1990s that deep-field views looking back to

OPPOSITE An artist's impression depicts a blaze of starbirth lighting up the early Universe. Already the most massive of these stars have exploded, creating supernovae whose expanding shock waves distribute the first heavy elements across the cosmos.

the time of the earliest galaxies revealed that they were already enriched with heavy elements, and therefore emphasized the case for Population III as a separate phase of cosmic evolution.

In 2002, Volker Bromm, Paolo S. Coppi and Richard B. Larson of Yale University published a detailed analysis of the conditions in which these stars were formed, around 150 million years after the Big Bang. Because conditions were relatively warm, the gases that created them would have been fast-moving and difficult to capture into stars, but they showed that knots of gas around dark matter nuclei could be cooled through the combination of individual hydrogen atoms into molecules. These slower-moving molecules could then coalesce into protostars with enough gravity to pull in more gas from their surroundings, before splitting up again as the protostar became hotter. Eventually, nuclear fusion would begin to transform hydrogen into helium (see page 82), but the lack of heavy elements within the newborn star would allow it to grow to enormous size while restraining the ferocity of its nuclear furnace. Such a star could reach a mass of several hundred Suns – far greater than any present-day star – without blowing apart. Nevertheless, such enormous stars would still consume their fuel at a prodigious rate, and as they aged and died, they would begin to transform helium into heavier elements (see page 318).

'Early stars might have been powered by annihilation between hypothetical dark matter particles called neutralinos. These would have transformed dark matter into normal matter.'

The first supernovae

Within a few million years of their birth, these early giants would have exhausted the supply of fuel in their core. Robbed of the outward pressure of radiation to support them from within, they collapsed, triggering supernova explosions more powerful than any known today (see page 333). The precise outcome of such extreme supernovae is still open to debate: some models suggest they would have destroyed the stars so completely that not even a black hole was left behind, while others suggest they would have left black holes with the mass of tens of Suns in their wake. In 2002, Piero Madau of the University of California at Santa Cruz and Martin Rees of the University of Cambridge pointed out that such black hole remnants, perhaps coalescing and merging together, would have made ideal beginnings for the supermassive black holes at the heart of many modern galaxies. Whatever the process involved, the destruction of these enormous stars would have seeded space with the heavy elements seen in the earliest galaxies.

Another key role played by the Population III stars would have been to re-ionize the intergalactic medium. While the formation of hydrogen atoms was key to the decoupling that plunged the Universe into its Dark Age, the gas clouds between today's galaxies are dominated by electrically charged hydrogen *ions* – in other words, the atoms within them have been broken apart again. Such ionization usually involves a fierce source of ultraviolet radiation, and the earliest stars could have provided just such a source.

Problems and solutions

But while this model of giant Population III stars solves many problems for cosmologists, it is not yet entirely settled. Doubts still surround the precise mechanism by which gas clouds could have collapsed into stars in such a warm environment, and not everyone thinks that cooling by molecule formation provides all the answers. In 2008, a team of astronomers led by Douglas Spolyer of the University of California at Santa Cruz put forward an intriguing theory that the early stars might have been powered by annihilation between hypothetical dark matter particles called neutralinos. These would have transformed dark matter into normal matter, helping to build the density of the star's core until fusion reactions could take over.

Another possibility is that the first stars did not quite reach the monstrous proportions that have been widely assumed. In 2011 a team led by Takashi Hosokawa of NASA's Jet Propulsion Laboratory published the results of new simulations that showed how any giant stars attempting to form in the early Universe would have generated enormous outflows (see page 273) that cut off the supply of infalling material and prevent the star growing above about 35 solar masses. Such stars would still be capable of fulfilling most of the roles required of Population III, and are more likely to produce the fairly routine supernovae that create black holes.

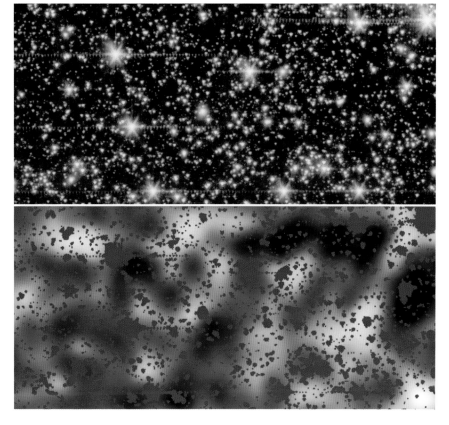

LEFT In 2005, scientists used NASA's Spitzer Space Telescope in an attempt to measure the Universe's 'infrared background radiation' – faint heat from objects that are invisible to even the most powerful telescopes. When infrared light from these sources (top) was subtracted from the overall image of the sky, faint infrared signals remained (below). This radiation is likely to be light from the first generation of stars, redshifted into invisibility.

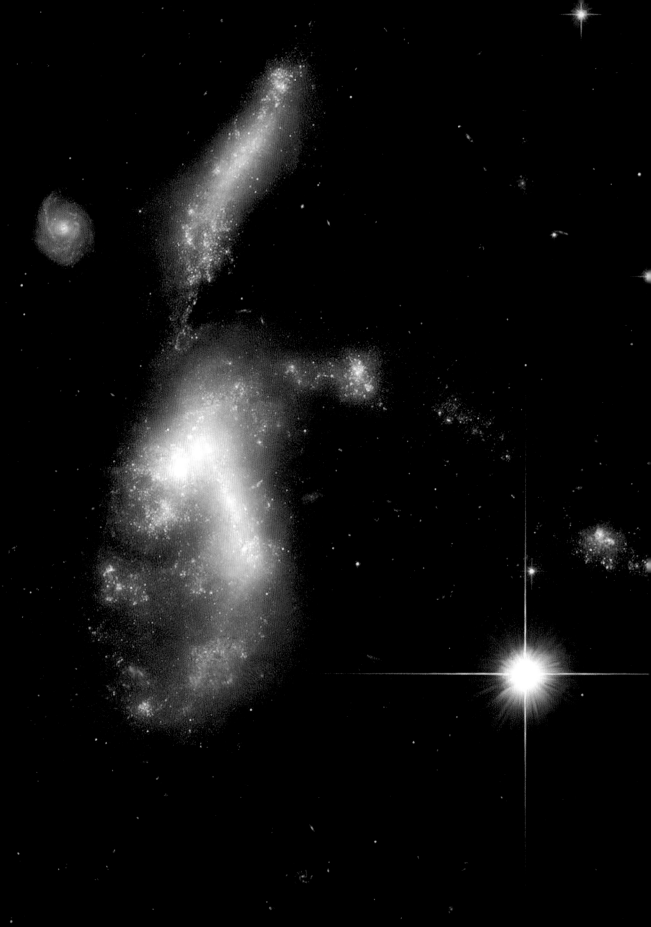

Primeval galaxies

17

DEFINITION THE FIRST GALAXIES TO FORM AFTER THE BIG BANG, AT THE LIMITS OF OUR CURRENT OBSERVING TECHNOLOGY.

DISCOVERY THE FIRST ANCIENT GALAXIES WERE OBSERVED IN THE HUBBLE DEEP FIELD IMAGE CAPTURED IN 1996.

KEY BREAKTHROUGH IN JANUARY 2011, ASTRONOMERS DETECTED A GALAXY FROM JUST HALF A BILLION YEARS AFTER THE BIG BANG.

IMPORTANCE EARLY IRREGULAR GALAXIES FORMED THE BUILDING BLOCKS OF LATER, MORE COMPLEX SYSTEMS LIKE OUR OWN.

'Deep field' images from the Hubble Space Telescope allow astronomers to track down the earliest generation of galaxies in the Universe. These infant star systems are very different from those we know today, and important questions still surround their formation and evolution.

In 1996, astronomers from the Space Telescope Science Institute in Baltimore aimed the orbiting Hubble Space Telescope (HST) at a single small patch of apparently empty sky in the northern constellation of Ursa Major, allowing photons of light from the depths of the Universe to sink into the sensitive detectors of its Wide Field and Planetary Camera (WF/PC2) instrument for a total of ten days across 342 separate exposures that could then be electronically stacked to produce the deepest view of the Universe obtained up to that time.

Deeper and deeper

With no stars or bright nearby galaxies in the way, the resulting iconic image, known as the Hubble Deep Field, revealed a sky crowded with some 3,000 remote galaxies stretching all the way to the limits of visibility, including the most distant and therefore oldest galaxies yet identified. The experiment was deemed so successful that it was repeated several times, producing the Hubble Deep Field South (an area of the constellation Tucana) in 1998, and the Hubble Ultra-Deep Field – a million-second study of an area within the constellation Fornax, in 2004. More recently, the HST has been used in conjunction with NASA's Chandra X-Ray Observatory and Spitzer Space Telescope, and the European Space Agency's XMM-Newton and Herschel Space Observatory to produce multi-wavelength images in a project called the Great Observatories Origins Deep Survey (GOODS).

OPPOSITE Hickson Compact Group 31 is an unusual example of 'arrested development' – a group of primitive irregular galaxies that have somehow resisted merging into larger, more highly evolved systems until the present epoch.

Ancient irregulars

Using these spectacular images, and rare occasions where gravitational lenses (see page 393) have focused and amplified the light from even more distant galaxies, astronomers can now look back across some 13.2 billion light years of space and time, to the period when the first galaxies were forming.

As light from the most distant galaxies has travelled towards Earth over billions of years, it has experienced strong Doppler shifting due to the expansion of the Universe (see page 49). Because of this, distant galaxies always appear far redder than they would from their immediate neighbourhood. In fact, when this is taken into account, early galaxies turn out to have a strong bias towards blue and white stars, known as the 'blue excess'. What's more, even based on images a few pixels across, its clear that the vast majority of these galaxies lack the more organized structure displayed by spiral and elliptical galaxies (see page 365) in the modern, local Universe. In the foreground of the images, astronomers have found multiple examples of these small galaxies merging together to form larger and more structured systems that begin to show signs of spiral features. Patterns such as these offer important clues to the way in which galaxies evolve over time (see page 389).

Primitive neighbours

In 2010, the HST team released a stunning image that showed ancient primeval galaxies not in the far-off depths of the Universe, but on our cosmic doorstep some 166 million light years away. Hickson Compact Group 31 is a cluster of four dwarf galaxies that have survived unchanged from ancient times, and are only now coming together to form a larger and more complex structure. Collisions between the galaxies have triggered a wave of star formation, creating brilliant young star clusters that are no more

BELOW In 2011, the Hubble Space Telescope identified a new population of tiny, distant galaxies more than 9 billion light years from Earth. Shining like beacons in the early Universe, these irregular galaxies are bursting with starbirth, most likely triggered as they rapidly accumulate mass through mergers and attraction of material from the surrounding intergalactic space.

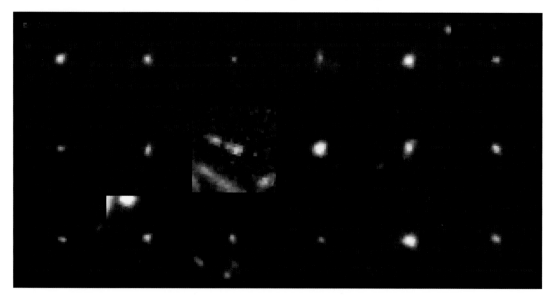

than 10 million years old. Finding such primitive galaxies coalescing in our neighbourhood is the equivalent of finding a 'living fossil'.

Into the infrared

The Doppler shifting of light from distant galaxies also creates another problem – the most remote and fastest-receding galaxies are redshifted to such an extent that much of their light becomes invisible, and can only be detected at infrared wavelengths. In 2009, during the final Hubble servicing mission, astronauts aboard the Space Shuttle Atlantis fitted the HST with a new instrument, the Wide-Field Camera 3. One of the camera's first tasks was to revisit the Hubble Ultra-Deep Field region, using its enhanced infrared abilities to create an improved image.

'In the foreground of the images, astronomers have found multiple examples of these small galaxies merging together to form larger and more structured systems that begin to show signs of spiral features.'

By analysing the new improved HUDF09, astronomers have been able to discover a new wave of ancient galaxies, pushing ever further back towards the beginnings of the Universe. In October 2010 a University of Paris team announced their discovery of a galaxy whose redshift puts it at 13.1 billion years old, confirmed with further observations from the European Southern Observatory's Very Large Telescope in Chile. Three months later, Dutch astronomer Rychard Bouwens of the University of Leiden and Garth Illingworth of the University of California at Santa Cruz published evidence of a candidate galaxy some 100 million years older, shining just 500 million years after the Big Bang itself.

Such galaxies are too small and distant to reveal any structure, but the evidence of their spectra suggests they are densely packed with stars that formed perhaps 200 million years previously. As we might expect from galaxies that formed mostly out of the raw materials created in the Big Bang, they appear to contain very little dust. What's more, according to studies using the National Observatory of Japan's giant Subaru telescope, these galaxies are emitting an excess of ultraviolet radiation. This is important because it indicates that early galaxies, as well as the initial wave of giant Population III stars (see page 69), may have played an important role in the reionization of intergalactic gas.

Despite improvements, even Hubble ultimately has its limits, and most astronomers agree that these recent discoveries are about as far as the HST can ever hope to see. More remote galaxies will have such high redshifts that their light will shine at infrared wavelengths too long for Hubble, yet too short for the current generation of dedicated infrared telescopes. Capturing the light of the very first galaxies and the Population III stars beyond them will be one of the key goals of Hubble's successor, the James Webb Space Telescope. With a 6.5-metre (21.3-ft), cryogenically cooled mirror, this giant infrared observatory is scheduled for launch in the latter half of this decade.

The birth of the Sun

18

DEFINITION THE SUN ORIGINATED FROM THE COLLAPSE OF AN INTERSTELLAR GAS CLOUD AROUND 4.5 BILLION YEARS AGO.

DISCOVERY THE SUN'S ORIGIN AS A COLLAPSING NEBULA WAS FIRST PROPOSED BY EMANUEL SWEDENBORG IN 1734.

KEY BREAKTHROUGH RECENT STUDIES OF THE INTERNAL CHEMISTRY OF METEORITES HAVE BEGUN TO REVEAL INFORMATION ABOUT THE PROTOSTELLAR ENVIRONMENT.

IMPORTANCE AN ACCURATE MODEL OF CONDITIONS IN WHICH THE SOLAR SYSTEM FORMED IS CRUCIAL TO UNDERSTANDING THE CHANGES IT HAS UNDERGONE THROUGH THE REST OF ITS HISTORY.

A variety of evidence suggests that Earth and the other planets originated around 4.56 billion years ago, in orbit around a central Sun that had only recently begun to shine. But what triggered the formation of the solar system in the first place?

In an ironic twist of fate, the very first scientific theory put forward to explain the origins of the Sun and planets has ultimately proved to be correct, despite being neglected for the best part of two centuries in favour of ideas that sound outlandish to modern astronomers.

The so-called nebular hypothesis, in which the Sun and the rest of the solar system formed through the collapse of an enormous cloud of gas and dust, was first proposed by the Swedish scientist and mystic Emanuel Swedenborg in 1734. It was further refined later in the 18th century by two giants of the European Enlightenment – German philosopher Immanuel Kant and French mathematician Pierre-Simon Laplace. The Laplacian version of the theory described how collisions within the cloud caused it to flatten into a spinning disc with a bulge at its centre – the ideal scenario for creating a central Sun and surrounding planets.

A momentous problem

However, in the following century, the nebular hypothesis was temporarily abandoned because of what appeared to be a fundamental flaw. As the cloud collapsed and its mass became more concentrated, it should have spun more rapidly as its mass became more concentrated. However, the Sun in fact rotates very slowly (in around 25 days) and so accounts for just 1 percent of the solar system's angular momentum, despite having 99 percent of its

OPPOSITE Stars like the Sun are formed in large star-forming nebulae such as Sharpless 2-106, several light years across and 2,000 light years from Earth. The wing-like structures in this particular nebula are lobes of gas inflated by stellar winds from a hot newborn star (undetectable in visible light) embedded in the central dust lane.

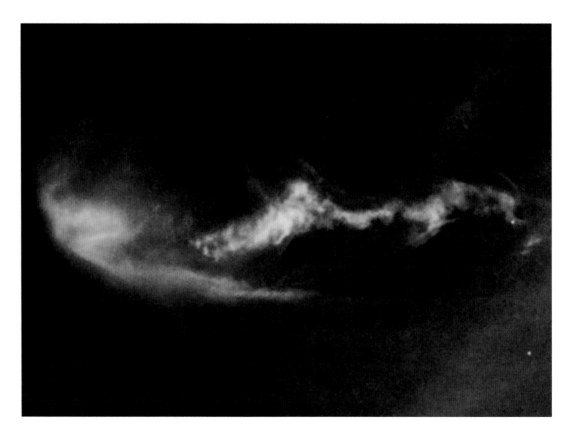

ABOVE Herbig-Haro objects such as HH 47 in Vela are created as matter escapes in jets from unstable young stars. This Hubble Space Telescope image, released in 2011, is the clearest view yet of these strange nebulae.

mass. With no obvious answer to this dilemma, astronomers suggested a number of alternative models for the origin of the planets from a pre-existing Sun – one idea was that a trail of planet-forming material could have been ripped out of the Sun by tides from another star passing nearby.

Another suggestion was that material was ejected when a comet smashed into the Sun (at the time the true nature of comets was not known). However, these theories were soon disproved, and briefly replaced with models in which the planets originated separately from the Sun (either independently or in orbit around another star) and were captured into its orbit.

It was only in the late 1970s that astronomer Andrew Prentice of Monash University in Melbourne, Australia, put forward a workable mechanism for slowing the Sun's rotation to its present pace – drag caused by dust grains close to the centre of the original disc. At around the same time, an exhaustive study of the nebular hypothesis by Russian scientist Victor Safronov began to gain popularity outside the Soviet Union. Together, these breakthroughs ensured that a modern version of the solar nebular hypothesis rose to prominence in the 1980s. Coincidentally, breakthroughs in observing techniques linked to the launch of the first infrared space telescopes produced conclusive evidence to support it. IRAS (the Infrared Astronomical Satellite) revealed that many young stars emit an excess of infrared radiation that indicates they are surrounded by large amounts of relatively cool dust. It also produced photographic evidence for discs of dusty material around stars such as Beta Pictoris, some 64 light years from Earth.

Thanks to the theoretical breakthroughs of Safronov and the observations of IRAS and its successors, the nebular hypothesis is today largely unchallenged, although there are still some significant unanswered questions surrounding the formation of planets within the leftover material (see page 97). Hubble Space Telescope photographs have revealed the process of star formation in unprecedented detail, revealing young stars emerging from dense, dark knots of material called Bok globules, within extensive star-forming nebulae. The HST has even photographed discs of planet-forming material around young stars in the Orion Nebula.

Dating solar origins

It seems clear that our Sun was born in a similar process – the initially slow collapse of a cloud of gas and dust within a broader star-forming nebula region. But how much more can we learn about its origins? Recent research has helped to pin down the exact date of the solar system's origins, and also pointed to the events that triggered the original collapse.

In 2010, chemists Audrey Bouvier and Meenakshi Wadhwa of Arizona State University published their analysis of mineral inclusions within an ancient chondritic meteorite found in northwest Africa in 2004. Chondrite meteorites are widely regarded as the most primitive objects in the solar system (see page 109). They are composed of dust grains that simply clumped together in the solar nebula, melted enough to stick together and have undergone little chemical processing in the billions of years that have since passed.

'Collisions within the cloud caused it to flatten into a spinning disc with a bulge at its centre – the ideal scenario for creating a central Sun and surrounding planets.'

Within the meteorite, Bouvier and Wadhwa focused on white specks known as calcium-aluminium-rich inclusions (CAIs). These are typically a few millimetres across at most, and are thought to be the first solid materials to have formed in the solar nebula – they have high melting points, so they would have condensed into solid form while most of the other material within chondrites was still molten or gaseous. What's more, their high melting points have made them resistant to melting and reprocessing since their formation.

The condensation of CAIs marks the starting point for several radiometric clock systems, including one that involves the lead isotopes Pb-207 and Pb-206. By studying the precise ratio of these two isotopes within the CAIs, Bouvier and Wadhwa concluded that they formed 4,568.2 million years ago – putting a very precise date on the early days of the solar system that is around a million years earlier than previous estimates.

19 Powering the Sun

DEFINITION THE NUCLEAR FUSION PROCESSES THAT ENABLE STARS LIKE THE SUN TO SHINE FOR BILLIONS OF YEARS.

DISCOVERY ARTHUR STANLEY EDDINGTON FIRST PROPOSED THAT THE SUN SHINES THROUGH NUCLEAR FUSION IN 1926.

KEY BREAKTHROUGH IN 1939, HANS BETHE OUTLINED THE CHAIN REACTIONS THAT ENABLE FUSION TO TAKE PLACE.

IMPORTANCE NUCLEAR FUSION IS THE PROCESS THAT POWERS EVERY STAR. IT IS RESPONSIBLE FOR ALL THE HEAVY ELEMENTS IN THE UNIVERSE, INCLUDING THOSE THAT MAKE UP EARTH.

The discovery of the fuel source that allows stars to shine so brightly for billions of years resulted from a combination of astrophysical theory and laboratory work on the internal structure of the atom in the first half of the 20th century.

Until the 19th century, the question of how the Sun and other stars shine was generally ignored, or at least taken for granted – the Sun was considered to be a huge ball of flammable material shining through the familiar chemical processes of combustion. It was only with breakthroughs in the geological sciences, and, specifically, the rise of gradualism – the theory that the modern Earth has, on the whole, been shaped not by sudden cataclysmic events, but by the same slow but inexorable processes we see around us today, acting over unimaginable spans of time – that the nature of the Sun and its fuel source came under close scrutiny.

Specifically, if Earth was at least tens of millions of years old rather than the few thousand promulgated in the Bible, then simple calculations showed that even a massive body like the Sun, shining through chemical combustion, would have become a burnt-out cinder long ago. In the mid-1800s, Scottish physicist John James Waterston put the age limit for a chemically powered Sun at 20,000 years, and proposed that the Sun must be powered by some form of gravitational energy instead. However, even Waterston recognized that the only plausible mechanism he could suggest – the impact of huge numbers of meteorites on the Sun's surface – fell woefully short.

German physicist Hermann Helmholtz proposed a better solution in 1854, in which the Sun's energy was provided by its own compression under gravity.

OPPOSITE This image from NASA's Solar and Heliospheric Observatory (SOHO) satellite combines an extreme ultraviolet view of the Sun's disc with a second simultaneous view of its faint outer atmosphere or corona. It reveals an enormous eruption from the surface, known as a coronal mass ejection or CME.

However, Helmholtz's theory could only produce an initial burst of energy during the Sun's formation, and it was the modifications proposed by British physicist William Thomson (otherwise known as Lord Kelvin), that turned it into a viable long-term power source. Kelvin's crucial suggestion that the Sun had been born from a collapsing cloud of gas rather than colliding solid objects foresaw modern theories of star formation, and provided a mechanism by which the Sun could shine for around 100 million years.

Atomic energy

Despite this, geological discoveries continued to outpace astronomical theories, and by the early 20th century many geologists were sure that Earth was well over a billion years old. Fortunately by the time this evidence became overwhelming, astrophysicists had a new power source available to take the place of chemical reactions and gravitational contraction. The turn of the century saw the discovery of subatomic particles, and the realization that every atom contained energy within it. Then in 1905, Einstein explained the source of this energy with his special theory of relativity and the famous equation linking energy, mass and the speed of light c: $E = mc^2$.

Nevertheless, it took until 1926 for Cambridge astrophysicist Arthur Stanley Eddington (whose earlier observations had been crucial in proving Einstein's theories correct – see page 47) to propose a detailed mechanism by which the Sun could shine for billions of years. Eddington outlined a process of transmutation of the elements in which, in the high temperatures and pressures of the Sun's core, four subatomic particles called protons (the stripped-down nuclei of the simplest and most abundant element, hydrogen), were forced together to form a single nucleus of helium, the next lightest element. (Helium itself had only been discovered by French astronomer Jules Janssen and English astronomer Norman Lockyer through studies of the Sun's atmospheric spectrum during an eclipse of 1868.)

'The Gamow factor soon showed that the chance of four protons coming together to form a helium nucleus in a single event were vanishingly small.'

In the process of binding together, Eddington suggested, two of the original protons were transformed into neutrons, another type of subatomic particle. Crucially, the resulting nucleus would end up with only 99.3 percent of the mass of its component protons. The missing mass would be transformed directly into a small amount of energy that, when multiplied by countless trillions of reactions occurring at the same time, would be enough to account for the Sun's enormous energy output for billions of years. Today, the process suggested by Eddington is better known as nuclear fusion.

Working out the details

But although Eddington's proposal proved to be essentially correct as a description of the process by which main-sequence stars like the Sun shine, there were many unanswered questions. In particular, the Gamow factor, a

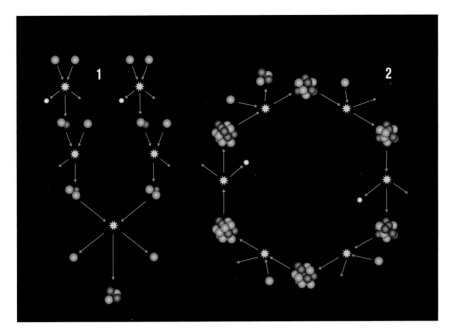

formula derived in 1928 by Russian physicist George Gamow to describe the frequency of fusion reactions under different temperatures and pressures, soon showed that the chance of four protons coming together to form a helium nucleus in a single event were minute. As a result, intermediate stages were clearly needed, and in 1939, German physicist Hans Bethe, working at Cornell University in New York, showed the most likely processes involved.

Bethe's Nobel-prizewinning work pinpointed two chain reactions: the proton–proton (p–p) chain that dominates in low-mass stars with relatively cool cores such as our own Sun, and the carbon–nitrogen–oxygen (CNO) cycle that rapidly overwhelms the p–p chain in higher-mass, hotter stars. Each process has the same end result, but the p–p chain, which involves a steady addition of protons to build up larger nuclei, runs at a far slower rate than the CNO cycle (which involves addition of protons to a carbon nucleus, building up nitrogen and oxygen nuclei before eventually breaking apart to release the original carbon and a helium nucleus).

One other important question remained – how exactly did the heavier elements revealed by stellar spectra get there? The likely pathways for the formation of nuclei up to and including iron were worked out by English astronomer Fred Hoyle and others between 1946 and 1957. They rely on fusion of helium and other nuclei to make successively heavier elements – processes that are not significant in middle-aged stars like the Sun, but become important during the last stages of a star's life (see page 318). The formation of elements heavier than iron, meanwhile, has proved to be the exclusive preserve of stars far heavier than the Sun (see page 335).

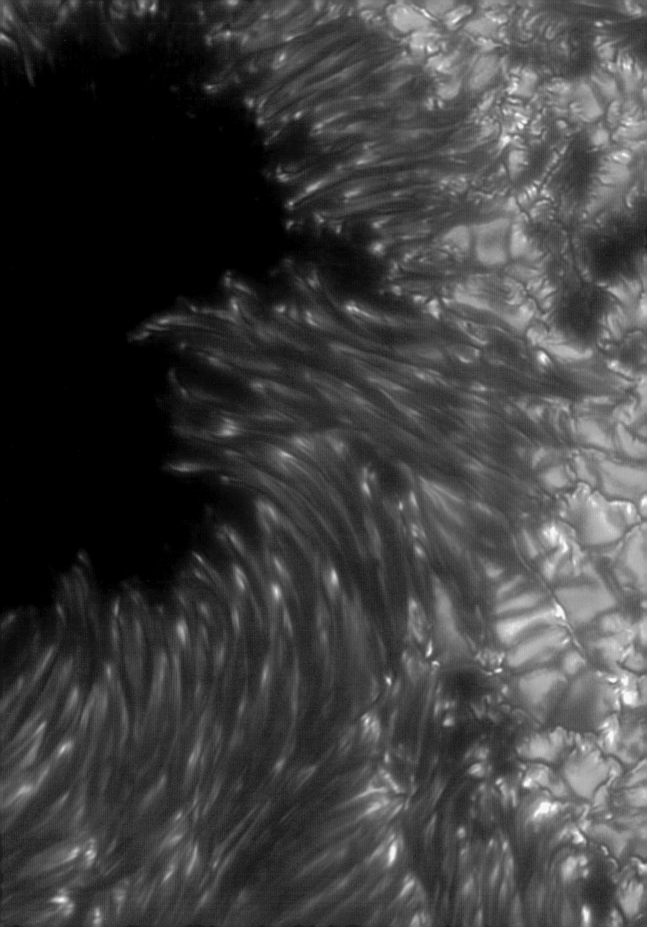

20 Helioseismology

DEFINITION A TECHNIQUE FOR INVESTIGATING THE SUN'S INTERIOR BY MEASURING THE WAVES AFFECTING ITS SURFACE.

DISCOVERY THE PRINCIPLES GOVERNING THE INTERNAL STRUCTURE OF STARS WERE FIRST OUTLINED BY ARTHUR EDDINGTON IN 1926.

KEY BREAKTHROUGH OSCILLATIONS ON THE SURFACE OF THE SUN WERE FIRST OBSERVED IN 1962, BUT THEIR ORIGINS WERE ONLY EXPLAINED BY ROGER ULRICH IN 1970.

IMPORTANCE THE TECHNIQUES OF HELIOSEISMOLOGY ARE THE ONLY WAY OF LOOKING BENEATH THE SUN'S FIERY SURFACE.

While astronomers have understood for several centuries that the Sun is a huge ball of gas, models of its internal structure have had to rely on theoretical calculations. However, this has begun to change thanks to recent studies of oscillations in the Sun's upper layers.

Our Sun is an extraordinarily complex object, and the testbed for many of our theories about the properties of stars in general. As an enormous spinning ball of gas with a powerful energy source at its centre, it often behaves in ways that are counterintuitive. For instance, the equatorial regions rotate much faster than the polar regions, and the consequences of this (in particular the tangling of the magnetic field generated in the Sun's upper layers) help to generate an 11-year cycle of solar activity. Even in the modern era of computerization, modelling the behaviour of the Sun's interior presents a huge challenge.

Inner balance

Our modern view of the Sun's inner structure has changed little from the ideas put forward by English astrophysicist Arthur Stanley Eddington in his 1926 book *The Internal Constitution of Stars*. Eddington viewed the interior of a star as a series of arbitrary layers, any one of which must be kept in a fine balance between the inward pull of gravity and the outward pressure of radiation. While material within the star could move up or down through these layers, the layers themselves must always remain in this balance, known as hydrostatic equilibrium. Changes to the amount of energy generated within the star would affect the balance and cause the star to expand or contract until a new equilibrium was achieved – a crucial concept for theories of stellar evolution (see page 265).

OPPOSITE A close-up image from the Swedish Solar Telescope reveals the turbulent structure of the Sun's surface around a major sunspot group. Dark, relatively cool regions of enhanced magnetic field are surrounded by flame-like 'spicules' many thousands of kilometres long.

Based on laboratory investigations into the behaviour of gases, Eddington went on to show that the majority of energy transported in the pressurized interior of a star would be moved by radiative transfer – the emission and absorption of high-energy electromagnetic waves (gamma rays and X-rays). Only in the star's outer layers would the bulk motion of gases (with hotter material rising up and cooler material sinking down in convection cells) take over to transfer energy up to the star's visible surface or photosphere. The internal layers of a Sun-like star can therefore be split into an energy-producing core (now known to be powered by nuclear fusion), an intermediate radiative zone, and an outer convection zone. Since Eddington's time, astronomers have learned more about the behaviour of other stars and discovered that the internal structures of low- and high-mass stars are somewhat different from the Sun, but this model is still essentially correct for the Sun itself.

Sounding out the Sun

But how can astronomers investigate the Sun's internal structure? Perhaps surprisingly, the answer is often by listening to it – the Sun's surface oscillates in a variety of ways that are analogous to sound waves, and the properties of these waves, rippling around the photosphere and passing through the interior, can reveal properties of the material through which they travel.

'The internal layers of a Sun-like star can be split into an energy-producing core, an intermediate radiative zone, and an outer convection zone.'

These oscillations were first recognized in 1962, when solar physicists including Robert Leighton of California Institute of Technology investigated the red- and blueshifts in light (see page 51) coming from different parts of the Sun. They discovered that patches on the surface of the Sun were oscillating, moving towards and then away from Earth in cycles that averaged five minutes. At first, these patterns were assumed to be a surface effect, but they defied explanation until 1970, when Roger Ulrich of the University of California at Los Angeles outlined a theory in which the movement of pressure waves (equivalent to sound waves) deep within the Sun created bump-like standing wave disturbances at the surface. As the wave patterns move slowly in different directions around the Sun, they interfere with one another to create the oscillating patterns.

Observations confirmed the accuracy of Ulrich's 'p-wave' model in 1975, and a year later, Douglas Gough of the University of Cambridge published a paper describing how analysis of solar pressure waves could provide a new tool for investigating the Sun. The principles involved are similar to techniques used to study Earth's interior through the distribution of earthquake waves, and the field soon became known as helioseismology.

Seismic discoveries

Perhaps the most intuitive use of this technique is for identifying transitions within the Sun's interior. These boundaries usually involve physical changes to the material inside the Sun, which in turn alter the speed or direction of the p-waves, leaving traces on the surface. In 1991, Gough and others used this principle to identify the base of the Sun's convection zone, roughly one third of the way from the photosphere to the core, and in 1995–7, using observations from Earthbound telescopes and the orbiting Solar and Heliospheric Observatory (SOHO) satellite, several teams showed that, beneath the convection zone, the Sun rotates uniformly down to four fifths of its total depth, independently from the convection zone. This property defines the radiative zone, and therefore the size of the core beneath it.

Other applications of helioseismology are more localized – for instance in 2002, studies of the convection zone revealed jet streams of fast-moving superhot plasma far beneath the photosphere. Surface features such as sunspots, meanwhile, tend to absorb seismic waves – an effect that can be used to track the development of sunspot groups on the far side of the Sun. This can be useful for forecasting space weather – solar flares and other sunspot-related outbursts – and as a result SOHO and other satellites have continuously monitored solar seismic activity since 2001.

However, helioseismology is still a young science, and there are many unanswered questions. For example the Sun's oscillations are now thought to come in three varieties or 'modes' – the pressure-driven p-mode waves identified by Ulrich, f-mode waves that move across the solar surface, and deep g-mode waves that only occur beneath the convection zone. Tracking down the g-mode waves is a considerable challenge, and so far various claims of detection have not been confirmed, but if they can be found, they have the potential to unlock the hidden structure of the Sun's core itself.

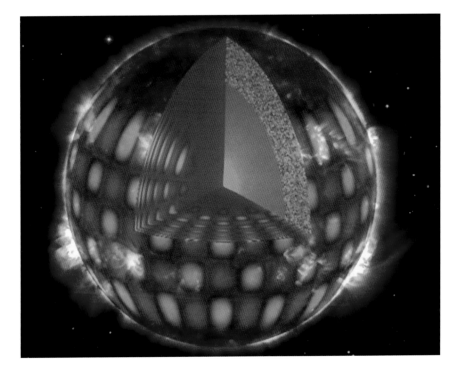

LEFT A composite image reveals patterns of oscillation on the surface of the Sun, which allow the structure of its interior to be mapped with increasing detail.

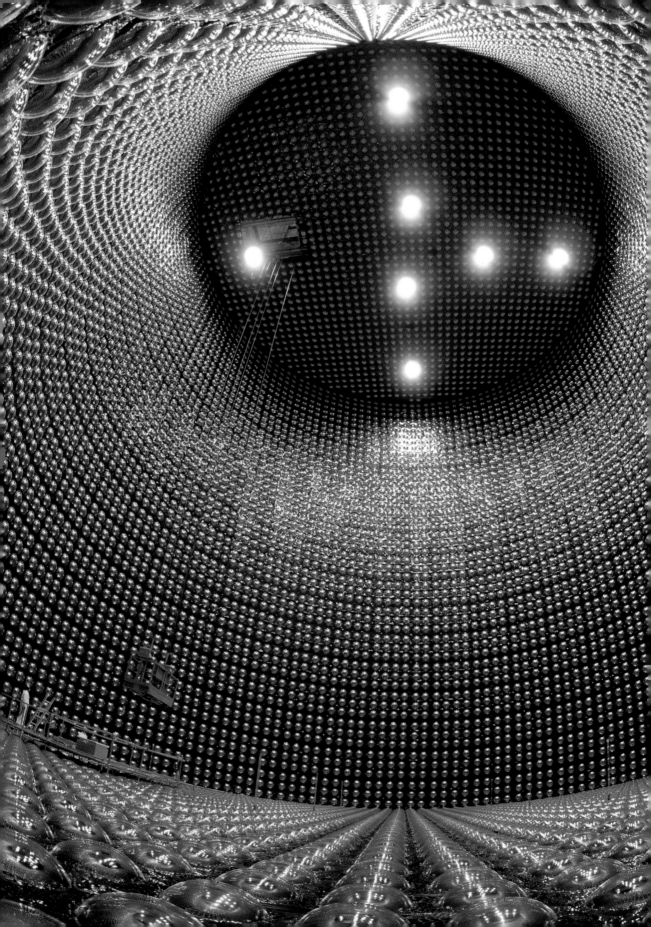

Neutrinos

DEFINITION ELUSIVE PARTICLES PRODUCED BY NUCLEAR FUSION, WHOSE PROPERTIES HAVE CAUSED ONGOING PROBLEMS.

DISCOVERY A DRAMATIC SHORTFALL IN NEUTRINOS FROM THE SUN WAS DISCOVERED AT HOMESTAKE MINE IN THE LATE 1960s.

KEY BREAKTHROUGH NEUTRINO OSCILLATIONS DETECTED AT JAPAN'S SUPER-KAMIOKANDE OBSERVATORY IN 1998 SHOWED THAT NEUTRINOS HAVE MASS, AND OSCILLATE BETWEEN THREE FORMS.

IMPORTANCE NEUTRINOS OFFER A DIRECT PROBE OF PROCESSES UNDERWAY IN STELLAR INTERIORS.

By the middle of the 20th century, astronomers had at least a basic understanding of the Sun's internal structure, power source and major types of surface activity. But in the late 1960s, an attempt to probe the Sun's nuclear core produced puzzling results.

Representing an apparent fundamental mismatch between the measured behaviour of the Sun and the predictions of nuclear physics, the solar neutrino problem came to light after American astrophysicists Raymond Davis and John N. Bahcall built perhaps the world's strangest telescope 1.5 kilometres (0.9 miles) below ground in a South Dakota gold mine.

The Homestake Mine experiment used a huge tank of perchloroethylene (commonly used as dry-cleaning fluid) to detect the passage of tiny and apparently massless subatomic particles called neutrinos that are continuously emitted by nuclear fusion processes in the core of the Sun. Neutrinos pass through most matter as if it wasn't there, and they provide a direct measure of the rate at which fusion is happening in the Sun's core. However detection is notoriously tricky, since neutrinos also pass straight through both rock and scientific instruments. the experiment relied on rare capture events, in which a direct hit by a neutrino on a chlorine atom in the fluid would transform the atom into a radioactive isotope of argon. The tank was located deep underground to block out the influence of other particles.

Missing neutrinos

Based on the Sun's energy output, Bahcall calculated the predicted rate at which neutrinos would be captured in the telescope, but Davis found that the experiment was only detecting about one third of the events

OPPOSITE The cavernous interior of Japan's Super-Kamiokande neutrino telescope consists of a tank filled with 50,000 tonnes of water and lined with more than 10,000 light-sensitive detectors. These sensors trace the glow of Cerenkov radiation (see page 42) emitted by neutrinos passing through the tank at close to the speed of light.

that they expected. At first, the results were met with incredulity by the scientific community, but as other neutrino observatories around the world reported similar results through the 1970s, it became clear that something was seriously amiss. Since Bahcall's predictions of the rate of fusion in the core relied on measurements of the energy currently being released at the surface after a 100,000-year journey from the core, one alarming possibility was that the Sun's internal power plant really was faltering for some reason. Fortunately, developments in helioseismology (see page 86) soon ruled this out, and another, less dramatic, explanation came to the fore.

Oscillate wildly

As early as 1962, physicists had realized there were, in fact, three different types of neutrino that can be produced in different ways. Those generated by hydrogen fusion, and detectable by the Homestake Mine and other early experiments, are known as electron neutrinos, while the other forms are called muons and tau neutrinos. In 1968, Italian-Russian physicist Bruno Pontecorvo showed that if the seemingly massless neutrinos actually did have mass, however small, then they could oscillate between different types. For instance, large numbers of electron neutrinos could transform into muons and tau neutrinos during the journey from the Sun to Earth.

In 1987, astronomers got a rare chance to observe neutrinos from a non-solar source thanks to Supernova 1987A. Particles from this stellar explosion (see page 357) were detected before the explosion's visible light by neutrino experiments around the world. By this time, Homestake Mine had been

RIGHT Bubble chambers such as the one at Brookhaven National Laboratory track the motion of particles such as neutrinos from the condensation trails they create as they pass through an area supersaturated with water vapour.

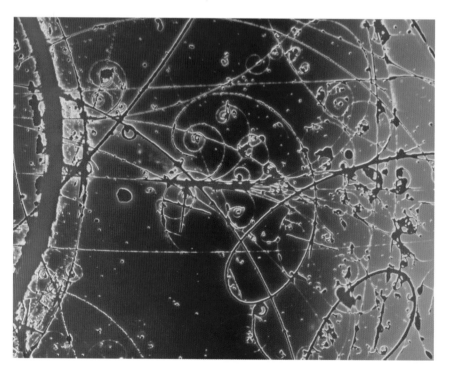

succeeded by more sophisticated detectors, some of which could track the direction of incoming neutrinos and capture their passage in real time. Intriguingly, it seemed that Japan's Kamiokande observatory and the Irvine–Michigan–Brookhaven experiment in the United States had measured the burst at slightly different times, suggesting the neutrinos were travelling at slightly less than the speed of light, and therefore might indeed have mass.

In 1998, scientists used the revamped Super-Kamiokande detector to find further evidence for mass, in the form of oscillations among muon neutrinos. These higher-energy particles are created when cosmic rays (see page 373) collide with air molecules in the upper atmosphere. The Japanese team found that more muon neutrinos entered the detector from overhead rather than from beneath, and explained this variation as a result of the muons from below having more time, on their journey through our planet, to transform into undetectable tau neutrinos. The speed of oscillation even allowed the team to estimate the neutrino's mass as about one ten-millionth that of an electron.

'Neutrinos were being detected at Gran Sasso around 60 nanoseconds sooner than expected – a result that implied they were actually moving faster than light.'

Finally in 2001, experiments at Canada's Sudbury Neutrino Observatory detected all three neutrino types for the first time, and confirmed that the overall number of neutrinos reaching Earth matches closely with the predictions of Bahcall and others.

A solution – and a new puzzle

The solution to the neutrino problem was welcomed not just by solar physicists, but also by cosmologists searching for possible cosmic dark matter (see page 397). However, these elusive particles have recently thrown up yet another mystery, threatening to overturn long-cherished laws of physics.

Since 2006, physicists at the CERN particle physics complex on the Franco-Swiss border have routinely generated a beam of muons, directed towards the subterranean OPERA and ICARUS detectors at Gran Sasso National Laboratory in Italy, some 730 km (453 miles) away. In 2010, the OPERA experiment detected tau neutrinos within the muon stream for the first time, confirming the existence of neutrino oscillation. However, in September 2011, a team of OPERA scientists sheepishly reported a problem: neutrinos were being detected at Gran Sasso around 60 nanoseconds (billionths of a second) sooner than expected. And since the calculations assumed the neutrinos were travelling at the speed of light, this result implied they are actually moving faster than light. Understandably, most scientists are highly sceptical: the fixed and ultimate nature of the speed of light is a fundamental pillar of modern physics (see page 41). However, most experimental errors have been ruled out and the problematic results have since been replicated at Gran Sasso with higher precision. Laboratories around the world are now planning experiments that will hopefully settle the controversy.

22 The solar cycle

DEFINITION AN 11.1-YEAR CYCLE IN THE APPEARANCE OF SUNSPOTS AND OTHER ASPECTS OF SOLAR ACTIVITY.

DISCOVERY THE CYCLE WAS FIRST IDENTIFIED BY HEINRICH SCHWABE IN 1843.

KEY BREAKTHROUGH IN 1908, GEORGE ELLERY HALE DISCOVERED THE MAGNETIC PROPERTIES OF SUNSPOTS.

IMPORTANCE THE SOLAR CYCLE MAY PLAY AN IMPORTANT ROLE IN GOVERNING EARTH'S CLIMATE.

Fortunately for all life on Earth, the Sun is relatively stable, shining steadily and predictably compared with many stars. But despite this, it still displays an 11-year cycle of activity, and there are suggestions that longer-term changes are enough to affect our planet's climate.

The solar cycle was discovered by German amateur astronomer Heinrich Schwabe in the mid-19th century. From 1826, he began a systematic hunt for Vulcan, a planet that was hypothesized to orbit closer to the Sun than Mercury. The best way of locating this small, fast-moving planet would be to spot it when it passed across the face of the Sun, and so, to avoid confusing Vulcan with the dark sunspots that also appeared on the Sun, Schwabe began to keep records of their location and appearance. By 1843, he had no new planet to show for his efforts, but was convinced he had found a ten-year cycle in the number and distribution of sunspots. Swiss astronomer Rudolf Wolf, of the Berlin observatory, soon refined this to 11.1 years.

Individual sunspots come and go over the course of a few weeks. However, their numbers and distribution show a distinctive pattern. Around the start of each solar cycle, the first few spots appear far from the equator at high latitudes. Slowly, they increase in number, and also move towards the equator, until after about four years they reach their peak numbers, centred on latitudes of around 15° north and south of the equator. This phase is known today as the solar maximum, and from here on, the sunspots continue to move towards the equator, but fall away in number. After another seven years, the sunspot numbers fall to solar minimum, marking the end of the cycle. The latitude and number of sunspots appearing over time can be plotted onto a graph to produce an elegant butterfly-like pattern.

OPPOSITE The breakup of Antarctica's huge Larsen-B ice shelf in 2002 was a potent sign of the global climate change our planet is currently experiencing. But could these changes be linked to long-term fluctuations in solar activity?

Mapping the Sun's magnetism

From 1859 onwards, when a giant cloud of charged particles ejected by the Sun engulfed Earth shortly after bright spots were noticed on its surface, astronomers have realized that solar flares and other outbursts also come and go in patterns linked to the sunspot cycle. However the origin of the cycle itself did not start to become clear until 1908, when American astronomer George Ellery Hale used the newly discovered Zeeman effect (a modification to the appearance of spectral lines passing through a magnetic field) to map the Sun's own magnetism. Hale realized that the sunspots were regions with strong magnetism, and that spots came in pairs of opposing magnetic polarities, with distinctive leading and trailing spots. Throughout a given solar cycle, all the leading spots would be closer to the pole, but in the next cycle the situation would be reversed and the leading spots would be closer to the equator. So it takes a little over 22 years (a 'Hale cycle') for the Sun to return to its original situation.

Hale's discovery allowed astronomers to develop a model of the cycle that describes many of its features in relation to the solar magnetic field. In this model, the outward manifestation of the Sun's magnetism is controlled by the churning currents of its convection zone (see page 86), a layer that moves faster at the equator than at the poles. At the beginning of a Hale cycle, the Sun's general magnetic field runs between the north and south poles, with parallel field lines running through the convection zone rather like lines of longitude on a map of Earth. As the Sun rotates, field lines become tilted and then stretched out as the equator races ahead of the poles. Eventually, magnetic loops are forced out through the photosphere, creating sunspots at their exit and re-entry points with opposite polarities, and occasionally triggering solar flares and other activity. These loops grow in number up to the solar maximum, but as they converge on the equator, they start to interfere with one another, cancelling out and eventually breaking down the entire solar magnetic field at solar minimum. The field soon regenerates itself in the opposite polarity to the previous one, and the second half of the cycle begins.

'Around the start of each solar cycle, the first few spots appear far from the equator at high latitudes. Slowly, they increase in number, and also move towards the equator, until after about four years they reach their peak.'

Solar influences

Throughout a typical solar cycle, the Sun's total brightness varies by an average 0.1 percent. However, there is little doubt that the cycle can sometimes affect Earth's climate. As soon as the pattern was identified, astronomers looked for confirmation in sunspot records from earlier times, and English astronomer Edward Maunder identified a clear pause in the cycle between around 1645 and 1715 – a period that coincided with a widespread cold snap known as the Little Ice Age, during which the northern hemisphere suffered particularly harsh winters. The admittedly patchy records of sunspots seen in the pre-telescopic era suggest that numbers may have been higher during the late Middle Ages, coinciding with a warmer climate.

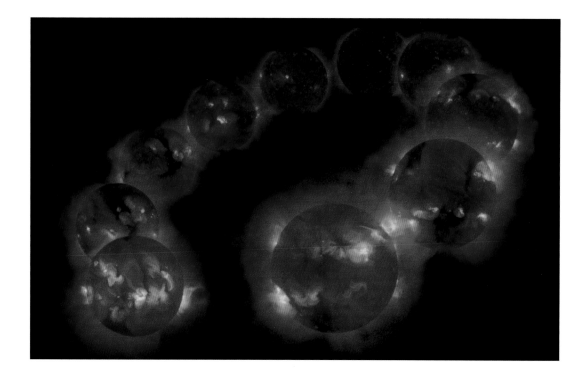

On the basis of this evidence, and theoretical models, some scientists have proposed various 'supercycles' – ranging in length from 87 years to several thousand – that could govern the strength of individual solar cycles. The question of whether and how the cycle affects Earth's climate, however, is still unresolved, and it has become increasingly important since some climate-change sceptics have argued that our planet's present-day global warming is linked to solar effects rather than human greenhouse gas emissions.

In 2011, a group of scientists from CERN announced intriguing evidence for such a link, showing that cosmic ray particles (which enter Earth's atmosphere in greater numbers when solar magnetism is at its weakest – see page 373) can act as seeds for the condensation of water vapour into clouds. However, since the effect of clouds themselves on Earth's climate remains complex and unclear, and different cloud types can produce either warming or cooling, the overall influence of cosmic rays remains unclear.

Depending on the exact web of influences and interactions at work, of course, it is also possible that the unusually spotless and subdued nature of the current Solar Cycle 24, which officially began in January 2008, could in fact be helping to mask the influence of anthropogenic (human-originated) global warming. Despite the lack of spots, however, August 2010 saw the violent release of a series of four huge coronal mass ejections from the solar atmosphere, and 2011 saw the release of several extremely powerful X-class flares. While the Sun's activity may follow broad patterns it seems that, from cycle to cycle, it is still far from predictable.

ABOVE A sequence of images of the Sun's X-ray corona, captured by the Japanese Yohkoh satellite between 1991 and 2001, captures changing activity levels throughout a complete solar cycle.

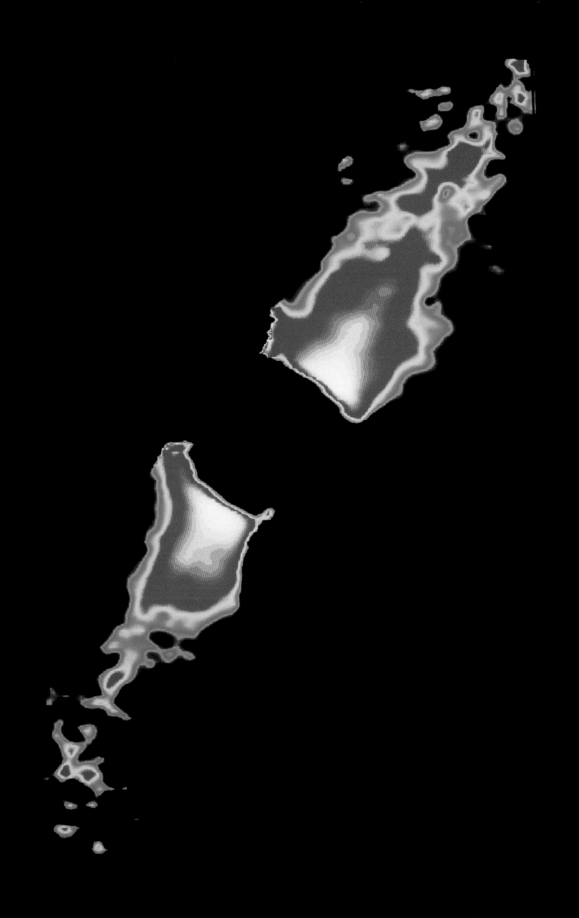

23 Formation of the planets

DEFINITION THE PROCESS BY WHICH THE PLANETS GREW OUT OF THE PROTOPLANETARY NEBULA AROUND THE YOUNG SUN.

DISCOVERY MODERN THEORIES OF PLANETARY FORMATION DEVELOPED FROM THE WORK OF VICTOR SAFRONOV IN THE 1970s.

KEY BREAKTHROUGH THE 'NICE MODEL', FIRST PROPOSED IN 2005, OFFERS AN EXPLANATION FOR THE RATE AT WHICH THE GIANT PLANETS FORMED, AS WELL AS THEIR CHEMICAL COMPOSITION.

IMPORTANCE UNDERSTANDING THE ORIGIN OF THE PLANETS IS A FIRST STEP TO MODELLING THE HISTORY OF OUR SOLAR SYSTEM.

As the Sun ignited at the heart of the ancient solar nebula, a disc-like cloud of material was left in orbit around it. Ultimately, material in this disc coalesced to form the planets and other bodies of the solar system, but scientists are still discovering the exact processes involved.

According to the latest measurements of material from the primitive solar nebula, the Sun began to form around 4.568 billion years ago (see page 77), and would have begun to shine by nuclear fusion within around 100,000 years. At this stage, the Sun would have been an unstable adolescent star (see page 273), prone to violent outbursts as it continued to draw in matter from the inner regions of the surrounding nebula, but increasingly bright and hot. Meanwhile the planets would have begun to form within this nebula, through the process that astronomers call accretion.

Separating the solar system

Competition between the inward pull of gravity and the outward pressure of the fierce solar wind now saw the remaining nebula settle into equilibrium as a bulging disc, stretching from the Sun out to around 200 astronomical units (well beyond the edge of the Kuiper Belt – see page 253). The effect of the Sun's heat on the inner edge of this protoplanetary nebula caused volatile materials with low melting points ('ices' in chemical terms) to evaporate into gas that blew away from the Sun, leaving only relatively sparse dust grains behind. Between the present orbits of Mars and Jupiter lay the frost line, where the temperature of the nebula became cool enough for icy materials to survive. In this region, too, the solar wind was too weak to blow away the nebula's gaseous component, so a great deal more material accumulated here, dominated by large amounts of hydrogen and helium.

OPPOSITE An infrared image shows the protoplanetary disc around the nearby star Beta Pictoris. Radiation from the central star has been blocked to prevent overexposure, revealing turbulent structures in the outer reaches of the disc that may be linked to the formation of new planets. Billions of years ago, our own solar system passed through a similar phase.

According to the latest models, the four giant planets formed within the first ten million years of the solar system's history, more or less in order. Jupiter formed first, thanks to a large accumulation of water-rich material that piled up just beyond the frost line as infalling icy bodies evaporated. Eddies within this region allowed the gas and ice to coalesce into a protoplanet with the mass of about 10 Earths, which then snowballed, rapidly pulling in material from its surroundings and growing towards Jupiter's present mass of 318 Earths in just a few thousand years. Saturn went through a similar process a little further out in the solar system and a few million years later, by which time there was less gas around for it to accumulate.

Of course the initial collapse of these gas giants was not the end of their story. Their coalescence generated considerable heat, and under high pressure certain gases (especially hydrogen) were liquefied. Meanwhile the planets themselves became increasingly compressed, and dust particles pulled into the newborn planet began to filter down to the centre of the planets, creating the internal power plants that still allow these planets to generate more energy than they receive from the Sun (see page 241). Meanwhile, ice-rich material left in orbit around the planets began to coalesce to form large families of satellites.

'Over millions of years, chance collisions between the sparsely scattered dust fragments caused them to stick together, eventually growing into asteroid-sized rocks with sufficient gravity to pull in more material from their surroundings.'

Problematic ice giants

Unfortunately, the outer giants, Uranus and Neptune, present a problem for this neat model of the solar system's formation. They are composed almost entirely of volatile ices, and contain very little hydrogen and helium. This suggests that they formed some time after Jupiter and Saturn, by which time the strengthening solar wind had almost cleared out the lighter gases from the protoplanetary nebula. However, accumulating so much ice at their current distances from the Sun would require an unfeasibly long timescale of perhaps a hundred million years. As a result, many astronomers believe that the 'ice giants' formed much closer to the Sun, in the same region as Jupiter and Saturn, from icy materials that had survived the formation of the larger planets. Subsequently, they migrated out to their present orbits, in an event that had a cataclysmic influence on the solar system (see page 101).

Meanwhile, events in the inner solar system were progressing somewhat more slowly. Over millions of years, chance collisions between the sparsely scattered dust fragments in this region caused them to stick together, eventually growing into asteroid-sized rocks with sufficient gravity to pull in more material from their surroundings. Within about 10 million years, most of the material in the inner solar system was concentrated in several dozen bodies called planetesimals, each roughly the size of our Moon. According to a study by University of Tokyo scientists, these objects would have followed more-or-less circular orbits thanks to the braking effects of the nebula remnants in which they had formed. Over the next hundred million

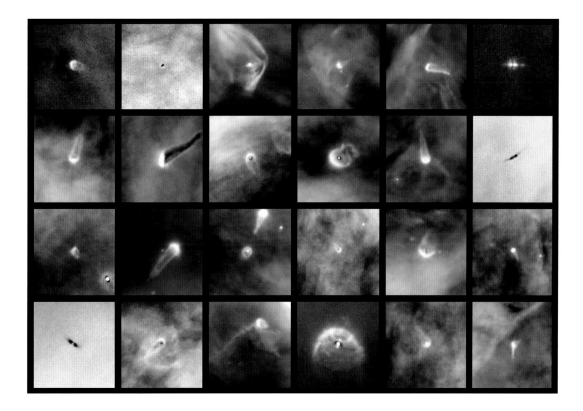

years or so, gravitational interactions with the more distant but massive giant planets disrupted the planetesimal orbits, pushing some onto paths that collided with each other, sending others plummeting to their doom in the Sun itself and ejecting yet more into the cold depths of interstellar space. The planetesimals that collided and coalesced ultimately became the terrestrial planets we know today.

Outstanding questions

Of course, this model does not answer all the outstanding questions about planetary formation. Most significantly, it does not explain the remarkable fact that the inner terrestrial planets settled into such neat, near-circular (low-eccentricity) orbits. At one time this was seen as an inevitable part of the process, but the discovery of a host of extrasolar planets in far stranger orbits (see page 289) has shown that this is certainly not the case. One possible explanation links the circularity of orbits in the inner solar system to the processes of planetary migration that took place further out.

Another intriguing question involves the orbital features of the planets. Aside from the issue of orbital eccentricity, the accretion model should produce very uniform features – the planets should orbit precisely in the plane extending out from the Sun's equator, and their axes of rotation should be straight up, rather than tilted. Instead, almost every planet's orbit and axis are tilted, sometimes radically, from the ideal.

ABOVE In 2009, astronomers used the Hubble Space Telescope's Advanced Camera for Surveys to study the famous Orion Nebula star-forming region in unprecedented detail. Its images revealed traces of protoplanetary discs known as proplyds around 42 of the nebula's new-born stars.

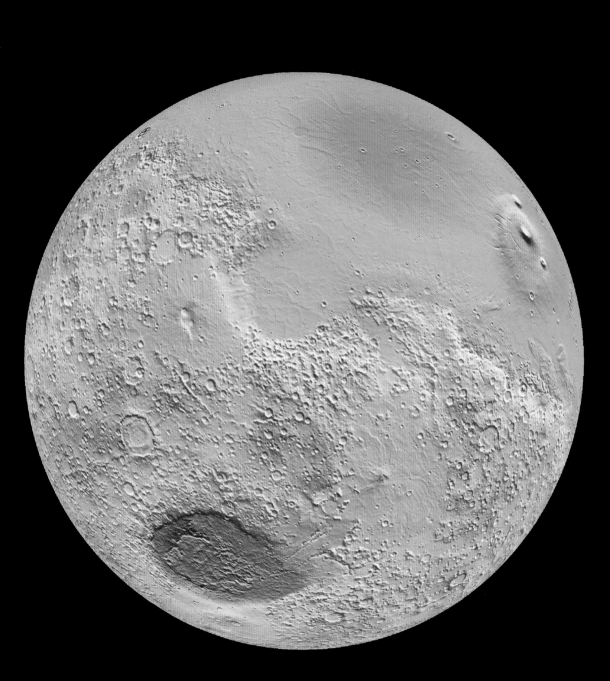

24 Planetary migration

DEFINITION LARGE-SCALE CHANGES TO THE ORBITS OF THE PLANETS SHORTLY AFTER THE SOLAR SYSTEM'S FORMATION.

DISCOVERY THE 'NICE MODEL' OF PLANETARY MIGRATION WAS FIRST PUBLISHED IN 2005.

KEY BREAKTHROUGH A 2006 DEVELOPMENT OF THE NICE MODEL OFFERS A METHOD FOR EXPLAINING THE TILTED AXES OF THE OUTER GIANT PLANETS.

IMPORTANCE PLANETARY MIGRATIONS IN THE EARLY SOLAR SYSTEM MAY HAVE PLAYED A KEY ROLE IN SHAPING OUR OWN WORLD.

According to the latest research, the planets did not always occupy their present orderly orbits. Instead, the early days of the solar system saw significant migrations that had a dramatic influence on the distribution of smaller bodies in interplanetary space.

According to the widely accepted model known as collisional accretion (see page 97), the planets formed from a protoplanetary nebula left in orbit after the Sun ignited around 4.65 billion years ago. This model accurately describes the broad properties of the planets, with rocky worlds closer to the Sun, and gas giants and icy moons beyond the frost line where volatile chemicals could remain frozen until they were incorporated into planets and their moons. However, it produces some intriguing mismatches with the solar system as we see it today.

The biggest problem is that none of the giant planets has an orbit that quite fits the model. This is particularly pronounced in the case of Uranus and Neptune, which today orbit in regions of the solar system where the protoplanetary nebula should have been relatively sparse. Another significant problem lies with the origins of the ice dwarf worlds and the comets – today the solar system is surrounded by the relatively close inner Kuiper Belt and related Scattered Disc of ice dwarfs (see page 253), and the far more distant, spherical Oort Cloud of deep-frozen cometary nuclei. Yet with the possible exception of the inner Kuiper Belt, none of these icy fragments could have originated at the distances from the Sun where they currently orbit.

In the early 2000s, an international team of astronomers based around the Nice Observatory in France developed a variety of computer models for

OPPOSITE A false-colour view of the complex geography of Mars reveals a marked difference between its northern and southern hemispheres. Huge impact basins that today form the northern plains (see page 158) are thought to have been produced by devastating impacts during the period of planetary migration.

various scenarios in the early solar system. These indicated that certain initial conditions were highly likely to lead to the arrangement of planets and small bodies we know today, while remaining consistent with what we know of conditions in the original protoplanetary nebula. In 2005, R. Gomes, Hal Levison, Alessandro Morbidelli and Kleomenis Tsiganis published their findings as a trio of papers in the prestigious journal *Nature*. Although not without its problems, their scenario for the early evolution of the solar system, often called the Nice model, has been widely accepted.

The Nice model

The key feature of the 2005 proposal is that the four giant planets were initially far more closely spaced, with orbits between 5.5 and 17 astronomical units (AU) from the Sun (well within the present orbit of Uranus). Beyond them lay a broad disc of ice-dwarf planetesimals, stretching to around 35 AU and containing the mass of 30–40 Earths.

'As Saturn bore down on the smaller ice-giant planets, it in turn pushed them into highly elliptical orbits, which ploughed straight through the planetesimal belt.'

Occasional encounters between the innermost of these small worlds and the outermost giant (which may have been either Uranus or Neptune at the time – see below) tended to result in an exchange of momentum that saw the small body catapulted towards the inner solar system, and the giant planet moving slightly outwards. As inward-scattered worlds occasionally encountered the next giant in, the process repeated, and so the planets gradually drifted outwards while the primordial belt of ice dwarfs was depleted. However, the process reversed when the planetesimals encountered Jupiter – the giant planet's overwhelming gravity tended to fling them back into the depths of the outer solar system, or even eject them completely, while at the same time these encounters moved Jupiter slowly inwards.

The outer planets evolved steadily in this way for several hundred million years, until around 3.9 billion years ago when the process kicked into a much higher gear. The trigger for this change involved the inward-spiralling Jupiter and outward-drifting Saturn reaching a 1:2 resonance, with Jupiter orbiting the Sun twice for each Saturnian orbit. This effect led to frequent alignments between the two planets, boosting Jupiter's gravitational effect on Saturn and sending it on a rapid spiral out to its present position. As Saturn bore down on the smaller ice-giant planets, it in turn pushed them into highly elliptical orbits, which ploughed straight through the planetesimal belt. The smaller worlds were flung in all directions – some were flung into the Scattered Disc or beyond, while many were sent plunging towards the Sun and the inner planets. The result was the Late Heavy Bombardment, an event that has left its scars across the solar system (see page 105). Finally, the scattering effects reduced the eccentricity of the ice giants' orbits, pushing them into their current, more or less circular, paths around the Sun. Only the outer edge of the original planetesimal disc, stripped of most of its mass, survived to form the modern Kuiper Belt.

Variations on a theme

The success of the Nice model in explaining puzzling features of the modern solar system, alongside the discovery of extrasolar planetary systems that are markedly different to our own (see page 289), has led to a renaissance in the study of planetary dynamics. No longer is our neatly ordered solar system seen as a pattern set in stone from the earliest time – instead, it seems to be the chance result of a complicated evolutionary process that may not yet be complete. Not surprisingly, astronomers have developed dynamical theories to explain any number of other solar system mysteries.

For example, in around half of the simulations modelled by the Nice team, the ice giants switch places after about a billion years. This swap has little effect on the general development of the solar system, since the two planets have roughly the same mass, but it would have been a traumatic time for the planets themselves. Argentinian astronomer Adrian Brunini has proposed that this might explain the otherwise puzzling axial tilts of Saturn, Neptune and, above all, Uranus. In 2006, Brunini suggested that the period of the crossover would have seen frequent close encounters between all three outer planets, which could have tugged at their bulging equators and gradually tipped them onto their present axes. One significant advantage of this theory is that the disruption would have happened on a relatively long timescale, giving time for rings and moons orbiting in the planets' equatorial planes to adjust to the shifting orientation. The alternative 'giant impact' explanation not only requires several unusually large collisions, but also needs them to have happened very early in the solar system's history, so that the rings and moons could form above the planets' present equators.

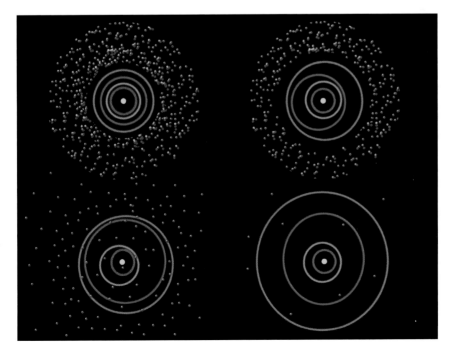

LEFT During the first billion years of the solar system's history, the orbits of the giant planets (shown as coloured ellipses) drifted in different directions to become more widely spaced. In the process, countless small bodies (shown in brown) were scattered out of the region where the giants now orbit.

The Late Heavy Bombardment

DEFINITION A PROBABLE PERIOD OF INTENSE IMPACT CRATERING ACROSS THE SOLAR SYSTEM AROUND 3.9 BILLION YEARS AGO.

DISCOVERY EVIDENCE FOR THE BOMBARDMENT EMERGED FROM ANALYSIS OF LUNAR IMPACT MELTS IN 1974.

KEY BREAKTHROUGH THE NICE MODEL OF PLANETARY MIGRATION, PROPOSED IN 2005, OFFERS THE MOST PLAUSIBLE CAUSE YET FOR AN INTENSE SPIKE IN BOMBARDMENT.

IMPORTANCE THE LATE HEAVY BOMBARDMENT IS KEY TO DATING PLANETARY SURFACES ACROSS THE SOLAR SYSTEM.

Around 3.9 billion years ago, the planets of the inner solar system experienced a cataclysmic bombardment at the hands of material from the outer solar system. That, at least, is the consensus view among planetary scientists – but did this Late Heavy Bombardment really happen?

Impact craters, large and small, are found on the surface of every solid body in the solar system, and stand as testament to the fact that the planets are constantly bombarded by debris from space. These days, the bombardment happens at a relatively slow but steady pace, and impacts large enough to form craters are mercifully rare – but in the past, impacts were far more common.

What's more, the cratering record offers a crucial tool for dating planetary surfaces – since the rate of impacts is either steady or slowly declining, and the location of impact events are effectively random, scientists can use the number of craters in a region as an indicator of the time since it was last wiped clean or resurfaced, and therefore of its relative age or youth. Another key technique is the identification of ejecta – sheets and rays of material vaporized during an impact and spread across the surrounding landscape. Clearly, any feature that is overlain by ejecta must be earlier than the impact, and anything that modifies the ejecta must be more recent.

Sadly, a wide range of other factors complicate these rules of thumb. For instance, what factors may have affected the cratering rate in different parts of the solar system, or at different periods in its history? The vast majority of evidence for putting absolute, rather than relative, dates to such events comes from our own satellite, the Moon.

OPPOSITE The pattern of lunar cratering, coupled with geological evidence from the Moon's surface, reveals that the bombardment of our satellite climaxed with a violent peak around 3.9 billion years ago, before tailing off. Was this pattern common throughout the solar system?

The lunar record

The Moon is an ideal laboratory for studying the crater record, since it has been geologically inactive for a very long time. What's more, its lack of atmosphere means that craters on the moon remain pristine for many millions of years unless they are overwritten by later impacts. But most importantly, of course, the Moon is within reach – a dozen astronauts visited its surface between 1969 and 1972, and the rock samples that they brought back to Earth form the backbone to our understanding of solar system history.

The Apollo landings targeted six locations scattered across the lunar nearside, each selected for its geological significance. Safety considerations prevented a landing in the midst of the heavily cratered lunar highlands, but there were landings on their outskirts, on several of the dark lunar seas or maria, and close to mountain ranges and ejecta blankets associated with the formation of several major impact basins.

Back on Earth, the Moon rocks were carefully analysed, using techniques such as radiometric dating to identify precise ages. These revealed, for example, that most of the basaltic lavas forming the maria erupted from beneath the lunar surface between 3.5 and 3 billion years ago, indicating that the large impact basins into which they flooded must have formed before then.

In the mid-1970s, a group of scientists from the California Institute of Technology turned their attention to the dates of various impact melts (rocks melted and reformed during the impacts linked to the formation of the

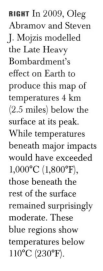

RIGHT In 2009, Oleg Abramov and Steven J. Mojzis modelled the Late Heavy Bombardment's effect on Earth to produce this map of temperatures 4 km (2.5 miles) below the surface at its peak. While temperatures beneath major impacts would have exceeded 1,000°C (1,800°F), those beneath the rest of the surface remained surprisingly moderate. These blue regions show temperatures below 110°C (230°F).

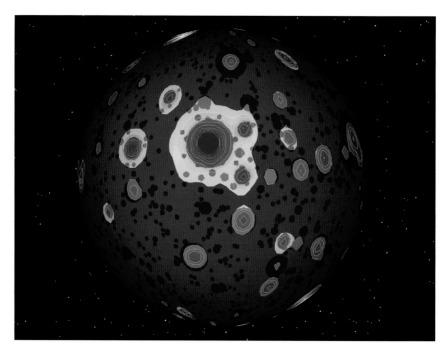

major basins), they noticed a remarkable pattern. Rock samples from widely separated parts of the Moon, linked to the formation of a dozen separate impact basins, had all crystallized in a relatively brief period between 3.8 and 3.9 billion years ago. The Caltech team proposed that this was evidence for a 'terminal lunar cataclysm' – a brief spike in the size and intensity of cratering that is now known as the Late Heavy Bombardment.

Doubts and causes

The evidence for the bombardment is widely, but not universally, accepted. Some sceptics believe that the melt samples are not as independent as they appear, and that, despite their wide distribution, they nearly all come from the single massive impact that formed the 1,300-km-wide (800-mile) Imbrium basin. Others believe the record has a built-in bias because later impacts would have destroyed the evidence of earlier ones. If this view is correct, then the impact rate would have declined steadily with the last major impacts around 3.8 billion years ago, rather than spiking at that time.

The only way to conclusively prove the existence of the Late Heavy Bombardment at this time is for humans or robotic probes to return to the Moon and collect rock samples from a wider range of locations. However, many of the doubts surrounding the issue have been driven by the lack of a plausible mechanism to trigger such a sudden and cataclysmic event.

Until recently, the somewhat vague explanation was that the bombardment somehow occurred as an abrupt clean-up operation, in which the debris and planetesimals not yet incorporated into the planets were rapidly absorbed. Fortunately in 2005, astronomers from Nice Observatory came up with a more detailed alternative, which blamed the bombardment on the migration of planets in the outer solar system, and proposed that most of the impacting bodies were icy bodies from the primordial Kuiper Belt (see page 253). If this theory is correct, then it has important implications for worlds across the solar system: it would imply that the Late Heavy Bombardment should have affected almost every planet and moon at about the same time.

'This "Planet V" theory suggests that there was originally a fifth rocky planet, smaller than Mars and orbiting somewhere between it and the asteroid belt.'

But there is an alternative explanation, curiously similar to the Nice model, but proposed a few years before it in 2002, by NASA scientists John Chambers and Jack Lissauer. This Planet V theory suggests there was originally a fifth rocky planet, smaller than Mars and orbiting somewhere between it and the asteroid belt. Initially, the planet's orbit was stable, but interactions with the inner planets destabilized it after about half a billion years, sending it ploughing into the asteroid belt with dramatic consequences. The Planet V hypothesis does not answer as many questions as the Nice model, but the different nature of the impacts involved in the two different scenarios may ultimately allow future lunar or planetary missions to discover which is more likely to be correct.

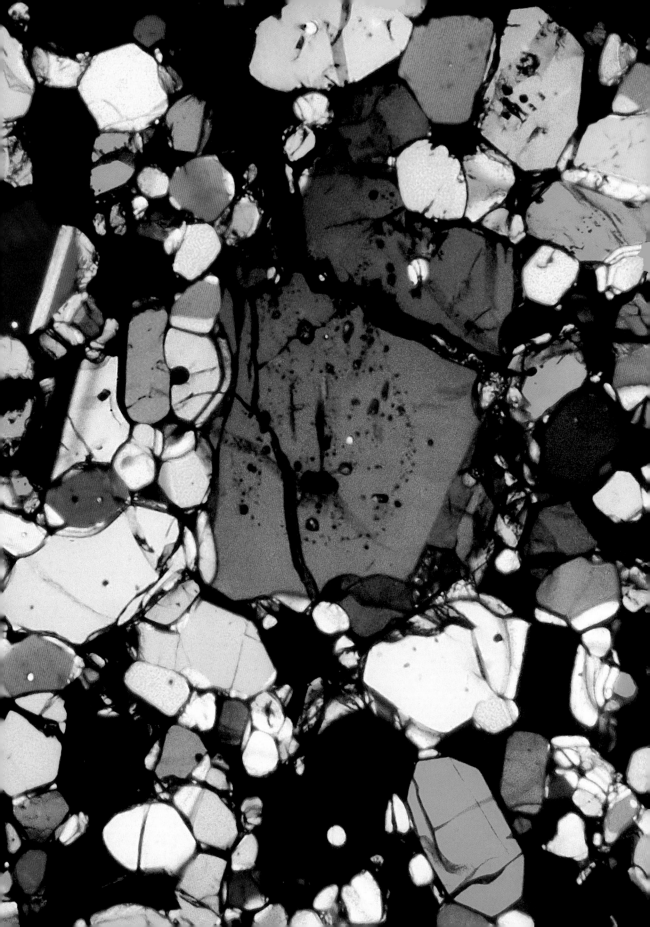

26 The composition of meteorites

DEFINITION FRAGMENTS OF ROCKY DEBRIS THAT SURVIVE A PLUNGE THROUGH EARTH'S ATMOSPHERE TO LAND ON THE SURFACE.

DISCOVERY THE IDEA THAT MATERIAL FROM SPACE WAS LANDING ON EARTH WAS FIRST PROMOTED BY ERNST CHLADNI AND JEAN-BAPTISTE BIOT AROUND 1800.

KEY BREAKTHROUGH IN THE MID-1800S, NEVIL STORY-MASKELYNE IDENTIFIED SEVERAL DIFFERENT TYPES OF METEORITE.

IMPORTANCE METEORITES OFFER ASTRONOMERS A RARE CHANCE TO STUDY THE RAW MATERIALS OF THE SOLAR SYSTEM UP CLOSE.

Many tonnes of material fall from space into Earth's atmosphere every day, but most burn up in the atmosphere. Only a few small chunks make it to the ground as meteorites – fragments of other worlds that give us a valuable glimpse of the raw material that formed the solar system.

Although meteoritic materials have been known since ancient times, the scientific study of meteorites only began in the early 19th century, when the idea that material was falling from space on a regular basis became widely accepted. And it is only in the last few decades that astronomers and geologists have come to recognize the treasure trove of information about the primordial solar system contained within these rare fragments.

Grouping meteorites

One of the first attempts to classify meteorites was made by Nevil Story-Maskelyne, curator of meteorites at the British Museum, in the mid-1800s. He developed the practice of slicing meteorites into thin sections and studying them through polarized light (light whose waves vibrate in a single plane) in order to highlight crystalline structures within them. Based on the differences he saw within them, Maskelyne grouped meteorites into three broad classes – the aerolites or 'stony' meteorites, the siderites or 'iron' meteorites, and the meso-siderites or 'stony-iron' meteorites.

While Story-Maskelyne's system is widely used to describe generalized meteorite types, it is too broad to be of much use for geological studies. Mineralogist Gustav Rose of the University of Berlin later modified it, recognizing the importance of chondrules (tiny spheres of rock within stony meteorites whose size is linked to the rate at which the meteorite's material

OPPOSITE Polarized light passing through a thin section of chondrite meteorite reveals contrasting colours that help identify the individual chondrules within it. These small fragments coalesced early in the solar system's history to form a rock that has remained unchanged for 4.5 billion years.

cooled during formation). Aristides Brezina, an Austrian student of Rose, later introduced the idea of classifying stony meteorites as chondrites or achondrites depending on the presence or absence of visible chondrules. Despite the advances of the 20th century, Rose and Brezina's scheme still offers a useful overview of the different types of meteorite.

Meteorite classes and their origin

Some 86 percent of all known meteorites are chondrites, usually with dark and crusty outer surfaces (created by charring during their descent through the atmosphere). Their interiors are a mass of chondrules, melted together at the edges, but preserving within them material from the protoplanetary nebula in which the planets formed. They are dominated by silicate minerals, but around 5 percent are 'carbonaceous' – rich in water and carbon-based organic molecules. The presence of these volatile, easily evaporated chemicals suggests that the carbonaceous chondrites were never heated beyond moderate temperatures, and so they preserve material from the early solar system in its most pristine state. One intriguing question is how the chondrites managed to become stuck together without thorough melting, but in 2005, Alan P. Boss of Washington's Carnegie Institution and Richard Durisen of Indiana University proposed an ingenious solution. They argued that the chondrites were bonded together by short-lived flash heating, caused by shock waves rippling through the protoplanetary nebula, generated by the formation of Jupiter.

'HED meteorites and a group of V-type asteroids are all thought to have been ejected during a massive impact that still scars Vesta's surface.'

Achondrites are the next most common, accounting for 8 percent of all discoveries. Lacking chrondules, they often resemble igneous rocks found on Earth, and show clear signs of processing by geological activity such as melting and volcanism. They are thought to have originated in the crust of planetesimals that grew large enough to produce geological activity, and were ejected from their parent worlds during impacts. A handful of achondrites are thought to have originated on the Moon and even Mars.

The irons account for 5 percent of all known meteorites (although their metallic nature makes them particularly noticeable, so they in fact may be rarer than this figure suggests). Dominated by iron, but often containing traces of nickel, their composition is very similar to the cores of the rocky planets. They frequently display elaborate criss-cross lines known as Widmanstätten patterns, which indicate that the metal grew into large crystals as it cooled slowly over several million years. All this evidence suggests that iron meteorites originated in the cooling cores of large planetesimals.

Finally, stony-iron meteorites account for just 1 percent of known falls, and contain a mix of metal and stony achondrite material. They are thought to have formed at the boundary between the core and mantle of large, well-differentiated planetesimals or asteroids.

Family histories

In the past few decades, new techniques have revealed more about the origins of meteorites. Measurements of oxygen isotope ratios can reveal the region of the protoplanetary nebula where a meteorite formed, while spectral analysis of asteroids has revealed that they tend to fall into broad groups analogous to the major meteorite classes. According to the widely used scheme developed by David J. Tholen of the University of Hawaii, 75 percent of asteroids fall into the C group, with dark, carbon-rich surfaces that can be linked to the carbonaceous chondrites. Within this group are several separate types, with members that have a shared surface chemistry. Beyond the C group, 17 percent of meteorites are of the S type, analogous to the stony meteorites. There are numerous less common types, including the iron-rich, M-type asteroids, which are similar to the iron meteorites.

In some cases, asteroids of a specific type and related meteorites can be traced back to a single parent body. The best examples are the Howardite-Eucrite-Diogenite or HED meteorites, a group of achondrites with a strong resemblance to Earth's own igneous rocks, which clearly originated in a geologically active parent body. HEDs account for more than half of the known achondrite meteorites, and in the 1960s, some believed that they originated on the Moon. However in 1977, astronomers Guy Consolmagno and Michael J. Drake constructed a detailed model of the parent world, and in 1979 Drake linked their origin to the large asteroid Vesta. Telescopic observations and a recent spaceprobe have since confirmed the presence of an enormous impact scar on Vesta (see page 181) – the likely origin of both the HED meteorites and a number of smaller 'V-type' asteroids.

ABOVE A polished section through an iron meteorite reveals characteristic structures known as Widmanstätten patterns. They form when molten metal is allowed to cool very slowly (for instance in the heart of a large asteroid), solidifying into exceptionally large crystals.

27 Water on the rocky planets

DEFINITION THE EXISTENCE OF WATER ON EARTH AND OTHER ROCKY PLANETS RAISES AWKWARD QUESTIONS ABOUT ITS ORIGINS.

DISCOVERY IN 1998, KIMBERLY CYR SHOWED HOW INFALLING ICY BODIES COULD HAVE ENRICHED INNER REGIONS OF THE PROTOPLANETARY NEBULA WITH WATER.

KEY BREAKTHROUGH RECENT STUDIES HAVE FOUND EVIDENCE FOR LIQUID WATER ON EARTH 4.4 BILLION YEARS AGO, INCREASING THE LIKELIHOOD THAT IT CAME FROM WITHIN OUR PLANET.

IMPORTANCE THE ORIGINS OF WATER ARE INTRINSICALLY LINKED TO THE BEGINNINGS OF LIFE ON EARTH.

The processes that gave rise to Earth and the other rocky planets generated intense heat that is thought to have driven any water out of their raw materials and away into space. So where did the water that once formed oceans on Venus, Earth and Mars come from?

Today, Earth is the only planet in the inner solar system with liquid water on its surface, covering some 71 percent of the planet and filling the ocean basins to an average depth of 3,700 m (12,100 ft). But there is strong evidence that Venus and Mars also had plentiful water in the past. In the case of Mars, much of this is now locked away in subsurface ice, while on Venus it has been driven away into space. Nevertheless, the presence of water on the inner planets presents a problem for models of the solar system's formation.

A damp start

Water in the form of ice would have been plentiful in all parts of the original solar nebula, but as temperatures rose near the centre as the Sun formed, much of it would have been heated above melting point and evaporated. Once driven into gaseous form, it would have been broken down into oxygen and hydrogen by solar radiation and driven outwards on the solar wind, as seems to have happened on Venus (see page 145). Ultimately, this created a frost line, between the orbits of Mars and Jupiter, which had a major influence on how the worlds to either side developed.

However, the presence of the frost line does not necessarily mean that the planets close to the Sun formed in an entirely dry state, since it only represents a theoretical distance at which small quantities of unprotected ice would evaporate. In practice, larger bodies of ice could survive for limited periods

OPPOSITE Water is a commonplace compound on the surface of Earth, but it nevertheless displays unique properties. It is one of the few substances that can exist in solid, liquid and gaseous phases in a relatively narrow range of temperatures, and the processes that transport it from one phase to another have helped shape our planet and others.

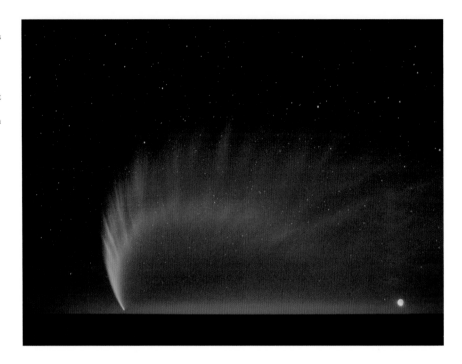

of time closer to the Sun, just as comets survive many passages through the inner solar system today. Indeed, according to modelling published in 1998 by Kimberly Cyr of the University of Arizona, the inner solar system would have been subject to a steady rain of small icy bodies a few metres across, sent spiralling back towards the Sun as they grew in size and were slowed down through friction with gases in the region beyond the frost line. As these ice chunks slowly evaporated, they would have created a water-enriched region in the protoplanetary disc closer to the Sun – steadily eroded by radiation and solar wind, but constantly replenished by new infalling material. The precise location of this region varies depending on factors such as the precise strength of the newly formed Sun, but it generally tends to encompass the region where Earth now orbits. There is also evidence that water survived within at least some meteorites and asteroids, and these too could have contributed to the raw materials of the inner planets.

Storms later?

The real challenge when it comes to explaining Earth's present-day water is that temperatures during our planet's formation were hot enough to melt rock. Even water chemically embedded in hydrated minerals would ultimately have been driven off by a process called outgassing, and vapour escaping into the primitive atmosphere should have been broken apart and blown away into space.

For this reason, most astronomers and geologists have until recently resorted to the idea that the planets were rehydrated after their formation by material from elsewhere in the solar system. The Late Heavy Bombardment, a series of cataclysmic impacts that seems to have reshaped the worlds of the inner solar system around 3.9 billion years ago (see page 105) seems to offer an obvious opportunity to return large amounts of water from comets or hydrated asteroids onto the surfaces of the rocky planets.

Astronomers can attempt to trace the origin of Earth's ocean water by comparing the ratios of normal hydrogen to deuterium (an isotope whose atoms weigh twice as much as hydrogen but share identical chemistry) in water from different parts of the solar system. This rules out many comets as a source of Earth's water, since they typically contain far higher levels of deuterium. According to Alessandro Morbidelli of the Nice Observatory, the deuterium ratios of carbonaceous chondrite meteorites offers a much better match, and so the bombarding objects are more likely to have been the closely related icy asteroids from beyond the frost line. The Nice model of planetary migration developed by Morbidelli and others (see page 101) even offers a mechanism by which such asteroids could have been disturbed and sent towards the inner solar system – the inward migration of Jupiter.

'The inner solar system would have been subject to a steady rain of small icy bodies a few metres across, sent spiralling back towards the Sun as they grew in size in the region beyond the frost line.'

Outlook cooler

However, the similarity in deuterium ratios does not necessarily prove the case for rehydration-by-bombardment as a whole. Kimberly Cyr's research has already shown that this region was also the likely source of Earth's original water, and the past few years have seen a number of geological studies suggesting that Earth got a lot cooler a lot earlier than previously thought. In particular, studies of microscopic zircon crystals discovered in the Jack Hills region of Western Australia, carried out by Mark Harrison of the Australian National University and Mark Watson of New York's Rensselaer Polytechnic Institute, suggest they formed in the presence of liquid water as early as 4.4 billion years ago.

The key to this unlikely discovery seems to lie in the complexities of Earth's early atmosphere. While initially it was too thin to prevent the loss of outgassed water vapour into space, other chemicals in the outgassed vapour, and particularly carbon dioxide, would have caused conditions to change rapidly. Since carbon dioxide is much heavier than water vapour, it would have persisted close to the surface, trapping heat from the Sun and creating an early greenhouse atmosphere around Earth. While this kept temperatures well above the normal boiling point of water, it also created a high-pressure environment where water was forced into liquid form. In this way, Earth could have developed oceans surprisingly early in its history. Conditions on this hot, moist Earth would ultimately have encouraged chemical weathering – a process that forms carbonate rocks and removes carbon dioxide from the atmosphere. However, it took the development of life to transform Earth into the world we know today.

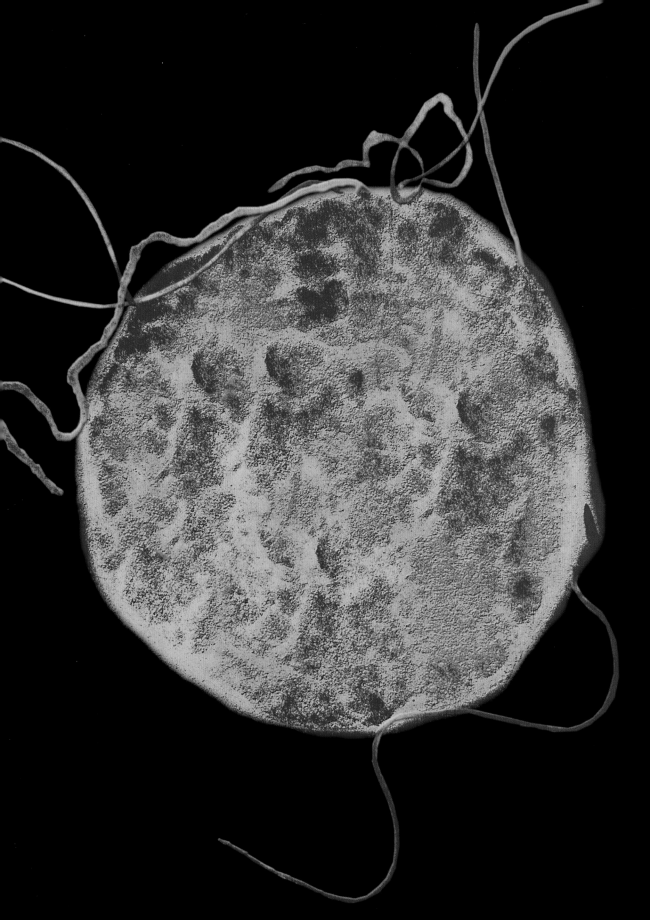

The origin of life

DEFINITION THE SIMPLE ORGANISMS AND ORGANIC CHEMICALS FROM WHICH LIFE ON EARTH BEGAN.

DISCOVERY THE IDEA OF A HABITABLE ZONE AROUND ANY STAR WAS INTRODUCED IN THE 1950S, INSPIRED BY THE IDEA THAT LIFE BEGAN IN WARM, SHALLOW SEAS.

KEY BREAKTHROUGH DISCOVERIES SINCE THE 1970S HAVE SHOWN THAT THE HABITABLE ZONE CONCEPT MAY BE OUTDATED.

IMPORTANCE UNDERSTANDING THE ORIGINS OF LIFE ON EARTH CAN HELP US TO PREDICT ITS EXISTENCE ELSEWHERE.

Earth is the only planet known to sustain life on its surface, but recent discoveries about the possible origins of life on our planet are transforming the way that scientists search for life elsewhere in our solar system and across the galaxy.

The fossil record of life on Earth has now been traced back through more than 3.6 billion years of history, although complex organisms such as animals and plants have only appeared in the last 600 million years or so. The earliest living things were simple, single-celled organisms so small and delicate that they leave only the slightest reminders in the fossil record – often in the form of chemical traces in the rock rather than true fossil imprints. What's more, several billion years of processing by Earth's tectonic and chemical cycles leaves very few rocks untouched from the earliest times. Those traces that have been found (most notably in Australia) suggest life emerged in the form of microbial mats – single-layered colonies of simple organisms on shallow, sunlit seabeds. Over time, as previous generations died and were buried beneath sand and silt, the newer generations flourished on top of them, gradually creating pillar-like, layered structures called stromatolites. Living examples of these strange organisms can be seen today in various locations, but most famously at Shark Bay in Western Australia.

Modelling the primordial soup

Stromatolite fossils seem to support the long-standing theory that life first took hold in warm shallow oceans. As early as 1952, American biochemists Stanley Miller and Harold Urey simulated the environment of the early Earth in laboratory experiments, and successfully generated organic chemicals such as the amino acids that form the basis of proteins. The idea

OPPOSITE In recent decades, the discovery of extremophile bacteria has helped transform our ideas about the conditions in which life can survive. For example *Sulfolobus acidocaldarius*, shown here, thrives in high temperatures and extreme acidity.

that life evolved in such an environment influenced early researchers into the possibility of extraterrestrial life, and the concept of the habitable or 'Goldilocks zone' – the region around a star where temperatures allow a planet of reasonable size to sustain a substantial atmosphere and liquid water on the surface – was born. One common criticism of the habitable zone concept is that it assumes all life in the Universe follows an Earth-like template and requires more or less Earth-like conditions to begin. But the realities of biochemistry are such that this is not as big an assumption as it might seem at first – for example, carbon is uniquely suited to forming complex molecules that are required for life, and water is also an ideal solvent in which organic chemical reactions can occur.

'Advocates of panspermia suggest that the basic components of life – organic chemicals and perhaps even entire cells – are widespread in the Universe, carried through space within comets and meteorites.'

A more valid criticism of the concept is that it is simply outdated. Discoveries elsewhere in our solar system (see pages 205 and 225) have revealed large bodies of liquid water far from the Sun. And new findings on Earth since the late 1970s have shown that extremophile organisms can thrive in apparently hostile environments such as deep-sea volcanic vents, extremes of acid and alkali, and hot subterranean rocks. Some biologists now believe that the environment around deep-sea vents, in particular, would have been far more suited to producing the first cells than shallow surface waters – and if this is true for Earth, why should we restrict the criteria for life on other worlds?

Life from space?

Regardless of where life on Earth began, it had to develop enormous complexity before the evolutionary mechanisms of self-replication and natural selection could have kicked into operation. An enormous gulf in complexity separates simple chemicals such as those produced in the Miller–Urey experiment from the advanced machinery of proteins and DNA required by even the simplest life, and some scientists estimate that the development of the first single-celled organisms by chance should have taken billions of years. Yet fossils show life appearing on Earth almost as soon as the surface could sustain it.

This apparent contradiction has led to a number of theories to explain how life managed to get started so quickly. Some evolutionists argue that life simply got lucky, or have proposed methods for making the trial-and-error process of creating the building blocks considerably easier. Others scientists, while still sticking to a general evolutionary approach, suggest there may be undiscovered principles beyond Darwinian natural selection that could have helped accelerate those vital early stages.

But there are also those who believe that life on Earth could have got a kick-start from the arrival of a ready-made starter kit from space. Advocates of this theory, known as panspermia, suggest that the basic components of life –

complex organic chemicals and perhaps even entire cells – are widespread in the Universe, carried through space in deep-frozen stasis within comets and meteorites. From here, these chance components are ready to spring into action when a chance impact sees them land in a hospitable environment.

While the idea of panspermia traces its origins back to the 19th century, it has only been given serious scientific consideration since the 1970s, when it was championed by British astronomer Fred Hoyle and his Sri Lankan colleague Chandra Wickramasinghe. Although claims of actual fossilized life forms within meteorites have generally been treated with scepticism, a number of new lines of evidence have come to light since then which suggest that, even if the idea remains unprovable, it is not entirely unfeasible. We now know that major meteorite impacts can certainly eject chunks of material from a planet's surface into interplanetary space, and we also know that there are various organisms (some surprisingly complex) that can survive exposure to the conditions of space for considerable periods, even without potential protection by layers of rock. What's more, a number of comets have now been identified whose orbits suggest they are interstellar wanderers passing through the solar system, rather than true members of the Sun's family. Most importantly, fragments of organic chemicals have been identified in distant nebulae and found within meteorites: in 2011, a team led by Michael Callahan of NASA's Goddard Space Flight Center even identified some of the building blocks of DNA within samples of carbonaceous meteorites.

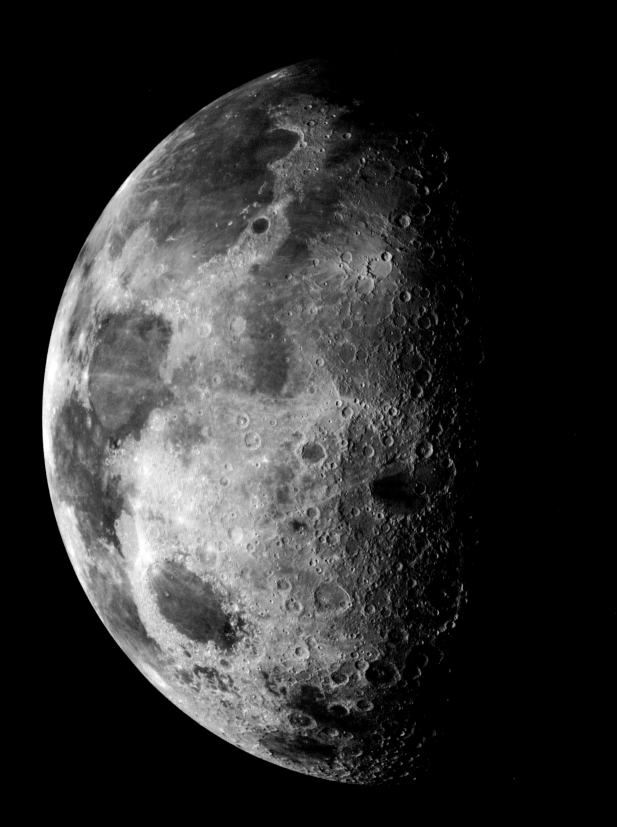

29 The birth of the Moon

DEFINITION THE MOON WAS CREATED IN A COLLISION BETWEEN A YOUNG EARTH AND ANOTHER WORLD THAT WAS THE SIZE OF MARS.

DISCOVERY ROCK SAMPLES BROUGHT BACK BY THE APOLLO LUNAR MISSIONS CONFIRMED THE MOON'S CHEMICAL COMPOSITION AND THE 'GIANT IMPACT' MODEL.

KEY BREAKTHROUGH A PROPOSAL THAT THE IMPACTING BODY ORIGINATED ELSEWHERE IN EARTH'S ORBIT MAY RESOLVE THE OUTSTANDING PROBLEMS AROUND THE GIANT IMPACT THEORY.

IMPORTANCE THE BIRTH OF THE MOON HAD A HUGE INFLUENCE ON THE HISTORY OF EARTH.

Earth's Moon is unique among the satellites of major planets – a world one quarter the size of its parent, and far larger in proportion to Earth than any other satellite. Such an unusual world requires an equally unique explanation for its origins.

The question of the Moon's origin has been a longstanding problem for astronomers. Of the other rocky planets, Mercury and Venus are moonless, while Mars has two tiny satellites that have long been considered as captured asteroids (though this is now in doubt – see page 173). The giant planets, meanwhile, all have their own families of satellites which, though sometimes even larger than our Moon, are at least in proportion to their parent worlds, and so likely formed from debris around the young gas giants in much the same way as the planets themselves formed around the Sun.

So how did the Moon form? The simplest explanation, called binary accretion, is that it was created in the same way as all the other major moons, originating from the same cloud of dust and gas as Earth, at more or less the same time. But why would Earth have had so much more excess material, in relation to its size, than the other planets?

The fission and capture hypotheses

An alternative model, put forward by British astronomer George Darwin (1845–1912), is known as the fission theory. Darwin correctly calculated that tidal forces between Earth and Moon are causing our satellite to recede at a rate of around 4 cm (1.6 in) per year, and are also slowing the rotation of Earth. He reasoned that perhaps the two worlds originated as one, and that this supersized planet rotated so rapidly that it developed a huge bulge on

OPPOSITE Seen from above the lunar north pole, the familiar face of Earth's Moon carries the signs of a long and violent history. But the origins of our satellite were only uncovered through computer simulations and analysis of rock samples brought back from the surface.

one side, which eventually ripped itself free and span into orbit. In support of his argument, Darwin pointed out the Moon's lower density, suggesting that it lacked a solid iron core and could have originated as a chunk of Earth's mantle. The fission hypothesis was popular through the early 20th century, with the Pacific Ocean basin sometimes pinpointed as the 'scar' left behind by the Moon's separation. However, by the 1930s, careful mathematical analysis had proved that Darwin's theory was essentially impossible.

'[Theia] grew to perhaps 10 percent of Earth's mass before its orbit became unstable and began to creep towards a slow but inevitable collision.'

A third possibility was that the Moon formed as an independent world somewhere else in the inner solar system, only to be captured into orbit around our planet. This capture hypothesis had problems of its own, however, since the chances of another planet approaching Earth on the right trajectory to be captured without catastrophically disrupting our own planet's orbit are very slim. As a result, the binary accretion model remained the best available theory for the Moon's formation, even though it raised many unanswered questions.

Evidence from Apollo

The Apollo missions that landed on the Moon between 1969 and 1972 brought some 382 kg (842 lb) of lunar rocks back to Earth. Over the next decade, evidence against binary accretion – or any of the previous alternatives – became overwhelming. Moon rocks had intriguing similarities and contrasts with those of Earth – for instance the ratios of oxygen isotopes within them suggested that both worlds formed in the same region of the solar system (ruling out the capture hypothesis). But the rocks contained very little water and evidence of a molten origin, suggesting that the Moon formed in a far more violent process than binary accretion. These significant differences also ruled out the fission hypothesis once and for all.

Fortunately, there was one other possibility – the so-called giant impact hypothesis. As early as 1946, retired Canadian geologist Reginald Aldworth Daly (1871–1957) of Harvard University suggested a modified version of Darwin's fission theory, in which the material that formed the Moon was thrown off Earth by a large impact rather than by rapid rotation. Although Daly's ideas had been largely ignored at the time, they fitted very well with the new evidence coming from the Apollo missions.

In the mid-1970s, two teams of American scientists began to investigate the theory further. William K. Hartmann and Donald R. Davis of the Planetary Science Institute in Tucson, Arizona, looked at it from the point of view of the planetary accretion model, pioneered in the Soviet Union by Victor Safronov (see page 78). They concluded that several smaller bodies could have formed in and around Earth's orbit, any of which could have become the impactor in Daly's theory. Meanwhile, A.G.W. Cameron and William Ward of Harvard were researching the nature of the impact itself, concluding

that it was probably caused by a Mars-sized body striking Earth at a tangent. The impact would have vaporized the outer silicate layers of the impactor, and a substantial amount of Earth's mantle, while allowing its iron-rich core to sink into the mantle of the damaged Earth. This would explain why the Moon apparently lacked an iron core.

A sibling for Earth?

Despite the work of these researchers, it was not until 1984, at an international conference in Hawaii, that the giant impact hypothesis was widely adopted. Today, it is the generally accepted model, and the impactor has even been given a name – Theia, after the mother of the Greek moon goddess Selene. However, there are still some significant unanswered questions. One issue is that lunar rocks are not quite as depleted of volatile chemicals as might be expected if the Moon formed in such a high-energy collision. Another is that the rocks show a uniform ratio of oxygen isotopes, implying that all the rock that went into the Moon originated in the same region of the solar system.

In 2005, Edward Belbruno and J. Richard Gott III of Princeton University proposed a potential solution to these problems. They outlined a model in which Theia formed at one of the Lagrangian points of Earth's orbit – gravitational 'sweet spots' where the forces of Earth and Sun are balanced, 60° behind or ahead of Earth itself. Here, it grew to perhaps 10 percent of Earth's mass before its orbit became unstable and began to creep towards a slow but inevitable collision. Belbruno and Gott's theory therefore not only explains the lack of isotopic differences in the lunar rocks, but also produces an eventual collision involving far less energy than if Theia came from elsewhere in the solar system, allowing more volatiles to survive.

ABOVE Maps of the Moon's near (left) and far sides show obvious differences – most clearly the absence of seas over much of the far side. Various theories have been put forward to explain this asymmetry, some of which trace it back to the conditions of the Moon's initial formation, or its immediate aftermath (see page 135).

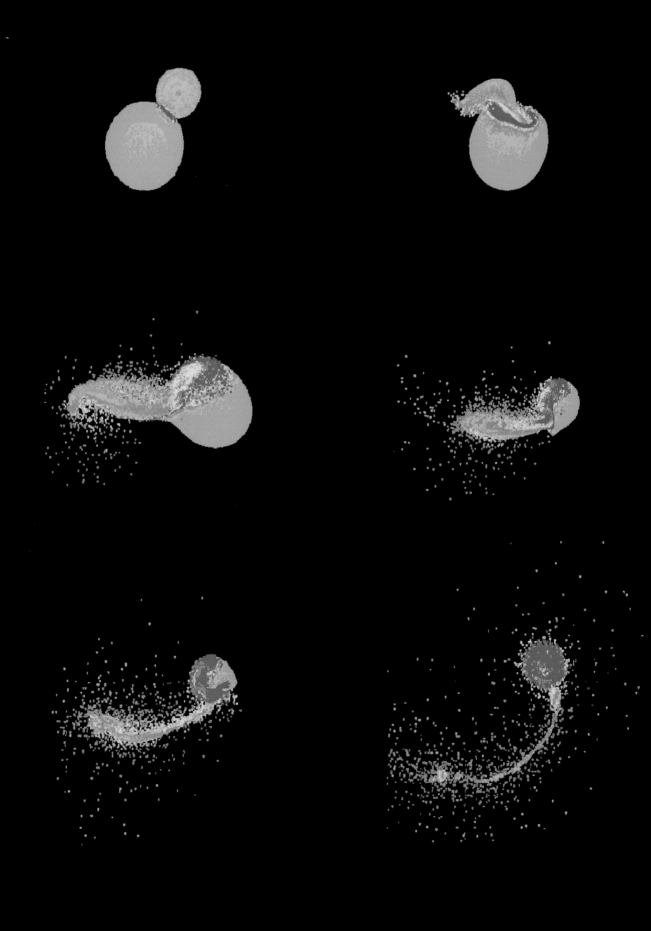

30 The remnants of Theia

DEFINITION POSSIBLE FRAGMENTS OF THE BODY RESPONSIBLE FOR
THE CREATION OF THE MOON, OR DEBRIS FROM THE COLLISION.

DISCOVERY IN 2008, SCIENTISTS SHOWED HOW MATERIAL THROWN
OUT BY THE THEIA COLLISION COULD HAVE SURVIVED AT THE
LAGRANGIAN POINTS OF THE MOON'S ORBIT.

KEY BREAKTHROUGH IN 2011, ANOTHER TEAM SUGGESTED THAT A
SUBSTANTIAL SECOND MOON OF EARTH MIGHT HAVE IMPACTED
WITH THE LUNAR FAR SIDE.

IMPORTANCE IF DEBRIS FROM THEIA COULD BE IDENTIFIED, IT
WOULD CONFIRM CURRENT THEORIES OF THE MOON'S ORIGIN.

Most astronomers now agree that our Moon was born out of an ancient
interplanetary collision between the primeval Earth and a Mars-sized world
called Theia. But could fragments of Theia, or its close relatives, still survive
in near-Earth space?

According to computer models of the giant impact hypothesis that resolves
most of the major questions about the nature of our satellite (see page 122),
the collision between Earth and the rogue planet Theia resulted in some
percent of Theia's mass ending up absorbed into Earth. While our planet
experienced a huge growth spurt that helped it reach its present size, the
other 2 percent of Theia, or a roughly equivalent amount of Earth's shattered
crust, was flung out into space.

Refugees from impact

Here, the debris met with different fates, depending on the speed with which
it was ejected. About half of it was moving fast enough to escape Earth's
gravity and enter an independent orbit around the Sun. Slight differences in
the speed of the fragments caused them to spread out in a doughnut-shaped
ring around Earth's orbit.

The remaining 1 percent of Theia's mass, meanwhile, lacked the energy
to escape, and so remained trapped in orbit around Earth at an estimated
distance of 20,000 km (12,500 miles). Here, it rapidly coalesced to form a
new satellite in anything between a few months and a few decades depending
on the predictions of various computer models. As the young Earth and
Moon orbited the Sun over the next few million years, they soaked up much
of the surviving material from Theia, while collisions among the remaining

OPPOSITE A computer
simulation by
Robin Canup of the
Southwest Research
Institute shows how
the initial impact of a
Mars-sized body with
the young Earth flings
a cloud of material
into orbit around the
planet, with much of it
escaping from Earth's
orbit completely.

fragments ground them down until little more than a fine powder remained. It's even possible that some of this material lingers today in the ghostly dust cloud that clings to the plane of Earth's orbit and creates a famously elusive glow in the night sky known as the *Gegenschein* or zodiacal light.

But according to recent studies, it's possible that a few larger fragments of Theia might have survived – perhaps even to the present day – in orbits that kept them safely away from the disruptive effects of Earth's gravity. And if not remnants of Theia itself, there might at least be small surviving asteroids that formed alongside the rogue planet.

Trojan moons

According to a theory proposed in 2008 by Jack Lissauer of the NASA Ames Research Center in California and John Chambers of the Carnegie Institution in Washington, DC, such fragments might have survived for a relatively brief time at the Lagrangian points of the Earth–Moon system – the locations 60° behind and ahead of the Moon's own location in its orbit, where the gravitational forces of Earth and Moon balance out. Here, Lissauer and Chambers speculate that debris from the initial collision could have coalesced into bodies up to 100 km (60 miles) across. By analogy with the Trojan asteroids that orbit the Sun in the Lagrangian points of Jupiter's orbit, these hypothetical bodies are called Trojan moons.

'The disruption of these secondary satellites could also have ejected them from Earth's neighbourhood into independent orbits around the Sun.'

Lissauer and Chambers suggest that the moons could have survived for perhaps 100 million years, before gravitational perturbations, caused either by the steady outward drift of the Moon's orbit, or perhaps by changes further out in the solar system (see page 101), ejected them from the Lagrangian points. In 2011, Martin Jutzi of the University of Bern, Switzerland, and Erik Asphaug of the University of California Santa Cruz published their calculations of what happened next. They estimated that a second satellite could have grown to a surprisingly large size – around 1,200 km (750 miles) across – and once disrupted from its stable orbit, would have approached the present Moon at a relatively low speed. Jutzi and Asphaug suggested that the impact happened on the far side of the Moon, smashing the smaller satellite apart and splattering its constituents across the lunar far side. This could explain the obvious differences between the near and far sides of the Moon, and in particular the fact that the crust on the lunar far side seems to be tens of kilometres thicker than it is on the near side.

However, the disruption of these secondary satellites could also have ejected them from Earth's neighbourhood into independent orbits around the Sun. In this case, it is possible that some fragments of these ancient lost worlds still await rediscovery as Near-Earth Asteroids, probably in elliptical orbits that cross Earth's own. One way of identifying such bodies would be to look for asteroids with compositions suspiciously similar to that of our own Moon.

A nearby phantom?

Another intriguing possibility is that fragments of Theia itself might have survived surprisingly close to Earth. In 2002, the Lincoln Near-Earth Asteroid Research (LINEAR) survey, a systematic hunt for Near-Earth Asteroids (NEAs) carried out by the Massachusetts Institute of Technology, discovered a 60-m-wide (200-ft) fragment of rock designated 2002 AA29. This small asteroid, with an estimated mass of 230,000 tonnes, follows an unusual 'horseshoe' orbit that normally comes within a few million kilometres of Earth at its closest approach. However, every couple of thousand years it moves into a temporary orbit around Earth itself, becoming a 'quasi-satellite' of our planet.

Although there are other asteroids with horseshoe orbits close to Earth (the most famous of which is probably Cruithne, sometimes misleadingly nicknamed a second moon), 2002 AA29's orbit is the most precise match for Earth's. J. Richard Gott and Edward Belbruno of Princeton University, who in 2005 were the first to propose that Theia formed at one of the Lagrangian points of Earth's own orbit (see page 123), have suggested that it may be a fragment of material that originated alongside Theia, or that it could even be a lump of debris thrown out by the impact of Theia and Earth.

If Gott and Belbruno's theory is correct, then 2002 AA29 may preserve pristine evidence of the exact material out of which Earth and Theia formed. What's more, the asteroid is on our planetary doorstep – a short hop away in space travel terms, and an intriguing potential target for future robot spaceprobes.

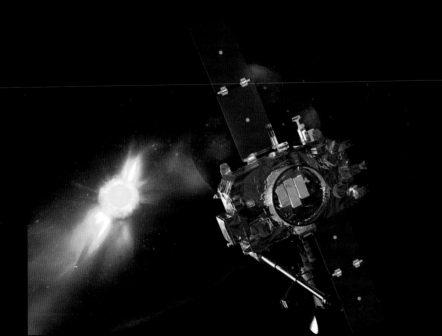

LEFT Alongside their primary mission to monitor the Sun, in 2009 NASA's twin STEREO satellites began a search for surviving fragments of Theia still trapped at the Lagrangian points of the Earth–Sun system.

31 Ice on the Moon

DEFINITION THE GROWING EVIDENCE FOR LARGE AMOUNTS OF
FROZEN WATER ON THE MOON.

DISCOVERY IN 1994, THE CLEMENTINE MISSION DETECTED
PERMANENTLY SHADOWED CRATERS WITH SMOOTH REFLECTIVE
FLOORS NEAR THE LUNAR POLES.

KEY BREAKTHROUGH IN 2009, THE CHANDRAYAAN-1 SPACEPROBE
DETECTED HYDRATED MINERALS SPREAD ACROSS LARGE REGIONS
OF THE LUNAR SURFACE.

IMPORTANCE FROZEN LUNAR WATER COULD ACT AS AN IMPORTANT
SUPPLY FOR FUTURE EXPLORERS OR COLONISTS.

Recent discoveries have confirmed the presence of substantial amounts
of ice buried in the lunar soil and, possibly, at the surface near the poles.
Identifying the quantities involved and pinpointing their precise locations
has important implications for the future of lunar exploration.

The rock samples returned to Earth by the Apollo astronauts in the 1970s
confirmed a bleak view of the Moon – for nearly all of its existence, it
seemed, our satellite had been a barren, airless ball of rock. The searing
temperatures involved in the process of the Moon's creation (see page 121)
ensured that any water present in the raw material was driven off into space.
And in the 4.5 billion years since then, fierce sunlight blasting the surface
ensured that any water that did reach the surface (dumped, for instance, by
comet impacts) was instantly boiled away into gas molecules that were split
apart and blown away on the solar wind. The Moon, it seemed clear, was
drier than the driest desert on Earth.

But since the 1990s, it has become clear that Apollo did not tell the whole
story. New evidence suggests that frozen water might still cling to the surface
in a few special places, and may even have been more widespread in the past.

Frozen poles

The idea that certain areas of the Moon could act as cold traps, allowing ice
to survive for billions of years, was initially proposed long before the Apollo
missions in 1961. Caltech researchers Kenneth Watson, Bruce C. Murray
and Harrison Brown realized that the relationship between Earth's orbit
and that of the Moon keeps the Sun's apparent path across the lunar sky
extremely close to the Moon's equatorial plane. As a result, the Sun passes

OPPOSITE In 2009 the
Moon Mineralogy
Mapper, a NASA
instrument carried
on board India's
Chandrayaan-1
satellite, confirmed the
presence of water ice
in lunar surface rocks.
This false-colour
image shows the
Moon's brightness at
three different infrared
wavelengths, with the
blue patches revealing
the presence of water
and related chemicals.

RIGHT NASA's Lunar
Reconnaissance
Orbiter imaged
the Moon's south
pole region over six
months to create this
'illumination map'
indicating the amount
of sunlight received
in different areas.
The map confirms
the theory that many
crater floors are in
permanent darkness.

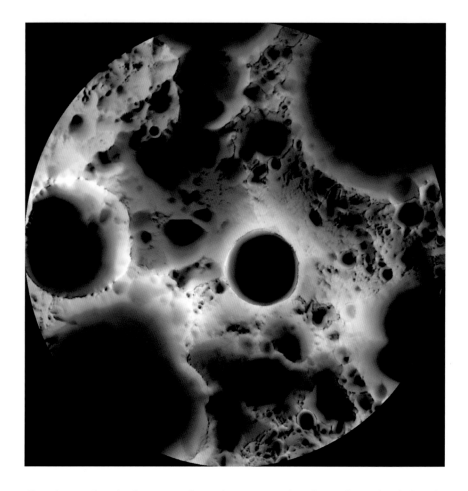

directly overhead when seen from the equator, but from the poles, it barely rises above the horizon at all. This allows deep craters at the lunar poles to remain in permanent shadow, with temperatures that never rise above approximately –220°C (–364°F).

However, these craters were seen at first as a mere curiosity. Little was known of the polar regions, the Apollo missions had shown that the heat of the Moon's formation had driven any native water out of the rocks, and no one could propose another mechanism to put water back on the Moon.

Things began to change following the 1986 passage of Comet Halley past the Sun, when a series of spaceprobe investigations triggered a renewed wave of interest in the nature of comets. Investigations of Halley and other comets since has proved that these icy bodies frequently dump water onto the planets. If such comets happened to crash into the lunar poles, then the possibility of ice surviving in permanent reservoirs seemed rather more likely. The surprise 1992 discovery (during radar mapping experiments) of possible ice in similar environments on Mercury fired interest still further.

Contradictory evidence

In 1994, the Clementine spaceprobe, the first lunar probe for a generation, arrived in orbit around the Moon, armed with remote sensing technology that had previously been used only for observing Earth. High-resolution images from the probe confirmed the suspected presence of permanently shadowed craters at the poles, while Clementine's radar detected what seemed to be highly reflective material in the same area.

Clementine's successor, Lunar Prospector, orbited the Moon for 19 months from 1998. Its neutron spectrometer instrument discovered a distinct enrichment in the amounts of hydrogen around the poles, most likely linked to the presence of ice in the lunar soil. To test the theory further at the end of its mission, NASA engineers steered Lunar Prospector to a deliberate demise, crashing into the dark floor of Shoemaker Crater near the lunar south pole. Earth-based telescopes watched the site in the hope that the impact would eject a substantial amount of lunar soil in a plume above the Moon, perhaps carrying ice within it. However the plume failed to appear, and so the experiment was inconclusive.

In the last few years a new wave of spaceprobes has taken up the search for lunar ice with varying results. Japan's SELENE spacecraft photographed the shadowed floor of the large crater Shackleton (illuminated by a dim glow of reflected sunlight) in 2008, but found no sign of surface ice (perhaps unsurprisingly, since any ice on the Moon is more likely to be mixed with rocks and dust in a form of permafrost).

'Deep craters at the lunar poles remain in permanent shadow, with temperatures that never rise above −220°C (−364°F).'

The search for lunar ice met with more success in 2009 thanks to Chandrayaan-1, India's first spaceprobe. This mission carried a NASA instrument called the Moon Mineralogy Mapper (M^3) – a spectrometer designed to analyse the lunar surface chemistry. M^3 detected hydrated minerals in the lunar soil or regolith at high latitudes, suggesting that the ground in these regions is a 'permafrost' mixture of rock and ice.

In 2009, NASA made a new and more sophisticated attempt at kicking up some lunar ice, with a spacecraft called LCROSS. This ingenious mission consisted of the burnt-out Centaur rocket stage (used to launch the spacecraft) and an instrument-packed 'shepherding spacecraft', placed on a collision course that smashed them both into the Cabeus crater on 9 October. Earthbound telescopes failed to detect the hoped-for plume of ice rising above the lunar south pole, but measurements of the Centaur impact taken by the shepherding spacecraft during the last six minutes of its life indicate that perhaps as much as 5 percent of the lunar regolith in Cabeus is composed of ice. Since Chandrayaan-1's data suggests Cabeus lies in a comparatively dry area, ice could be even more abundant elsewhere.

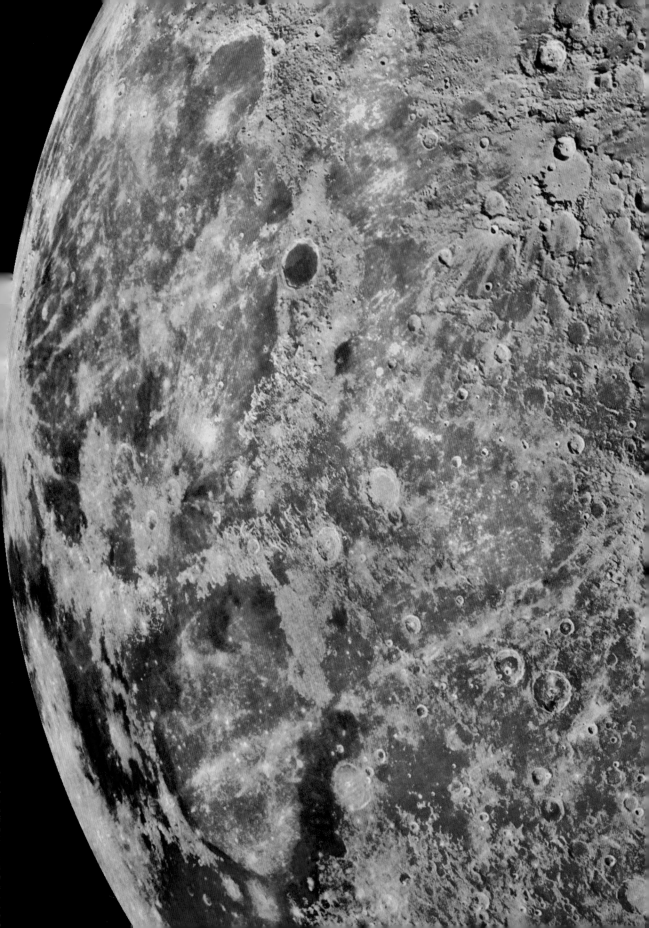

32

The dynamic Moon

DEFINITION RECENT EXPLORATION OF THE MOON HAS REVEALED A FAR MORE ACTIVE HISTORY THAN PREVIOUSLY SUSPECTED.

DISCOVERY THE LUNAR RECONNAISSANCE ORBITER, LAUNCHED IN 2009, HAS CONFIRMED A VARIETY OF PHASES OF VOLCANIC ACTIVITY IN THE MOON'S ANCIENT PAST.

KEY BREAKTHROUGH THE GRAIL SPACECRAFT, LAUNCHED IN 2011, WILL MAP THE MOON'S INTERIOR IN DETAIL.

IMPORTANCE UNDERSTANDING THE EARLY HISTORY OF THE MOON HELPS REVEAL ASPECTS OF EARTH'S OWN ORIGINS THAT HAVE BEEN CONCEALED BY LATER ACTIVITY.

NASA's Lunar Reconnaissance Orbiter has revealed that our satellite's history may be far more complex than previously thought, and raised some important questions. Now a new mission aims to use a pair of spacecraft to look deep into the lunar interior in the search for answers.

Launched in 2009, the Lunar Reconnaissance Orbiter (LRO) is packed with complex 'remote sensing' instruments for measuring characteristics such as the temperature of the lunar surface, its mineral composition and its topography. While such instruments are used routinely by satellites for studying our own planet, this is the first time such techniques have been applied extensively to the Moon, and the results have been impressive.

One of the main goals was to build up a map of mineral distribution. As is clear even with the naked eye, the lunar surface is divided into two broad types of terrain – dark, low-lying and relatively smooth seas or maria, and bright, heavily cratered highlands. Since before the Apollo missions, the generally accepted model of their formation has involved huge meteorite impacts creating basins that were subsequently flooded by lava eruptions. Rock samples brought back by the Apollo missions allowed geologists to date these events – the major impacts seem to have occurred around 3.8 billion years ago during the Late Heavy Bombardment (see page 105), while the lava erupted considerably later, between about 3.2 and 2.0 billion years ago. Investigations by LRO have found distinct differences in lava composition between the iron-rich centres of the seas, and their silicate-rich 'shores'. Areas that are particularly silicate-rich and iron-poor tend to appear reddish, and experts speculate that they may mark the last lava to erupt onto the lunar surface, at considerably lower temperatures than the first eruptions.

OPPOSITE In 1992, the Galileo spaceprobe turned its instruments on the Moon's north pole as it flew past on its way to Jupiter. This mosaic image exaggerates the natural colours to highlight different minerals in the lunar surface: blue and orange show volcanic material while pinkish hues mark material originating from the lunar highlands.

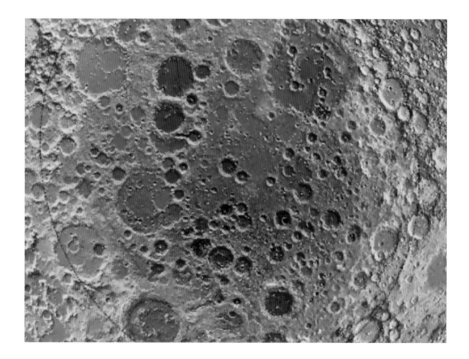

A shrinking world

In 2011, scientists using data from the LRO's Lunar Orbiter Laser Altimeter (LOLA) instrument announced another volcanic discovery: the presence of volcanic shields similar to those on Earth, Venus and Mars. Tens or even hundreds of kilometres across, these shallow domes form when runny, low-viscosity lava spreads across the surface instead of congealing near its origin, and may explain the concentration of some smaller-scale volcanic features.

Another LRO surprise has been confirmation that the Moon is shrinking. Long 'wrinkle ridges' that can be seen running across the lunar maria in the right lighting conditions are actually escarpments hundreds of metres high, created by compression of the crust. For a long time, these features were thought to have been formed like a skin on custard, as the surface of the lava seas solidified while the underlying material remained molten. However in the 1970s, American astronomer Peter Schultz identified spots where the ridges appeared to extend into the highlands, and in 1985, Alan Binder of the Lunar Research Institute proposed that the ridges were actually created by shrinking of the Moon's interior that forced the crust to compress. Now, high-resolution LRO images have shown that the ridges are more widespread than first thought, and in some cases run across relatively young craters, leading Tom Watters of the Smithsonian National Air and Space Museum and others to suggest that the Moon's slow shrinkage continues to this day.

Uneven seas

Perhaps the biggest mystery of lunar volcanism, however, is why the lunar seas are concentrated on the near side, while the far side, despite the presence of some large impact basins, is almost entirely made up of bright highland-style materials. One long-standing explanation suggests that the lunar interior is slightly asymmetrical, with the core pulled closer to Earth by tidal forces. As a result, reservoirs of hot magma forming at an equal distance from the core lay closer to the surface on the nearside, allowing them to erupt and form the maria. However, various alternative ideas have been proposed. Among the most recent is the idea that a second satellite of Earth, formed during the same impact that formed the Moon itself, 'splatted' across the lunar far side, raising its elevation so that any magma reservoirs ended up buried deep below ground (see page 126). Another idea, suggested by Justin Hagerty of the US Geological Survey and others, is that the distribution of magma itself was asymmetrical as a result of a huge impact that formed an enormous crater at the lunar south pole.

The existence of this crater, the South Pole-Aitken basin, was only confirmed by the Clementine and Lunar Prospector missions of the 1990s. With a diameter of 2,500 km (1,550 miles) and a depth of up to 13 km (8 miles), it is the second largest known crater in the solar system, and its formation would have had a traumatic effect on the entire Moon. It exposed a unique layer of iron-rich rock from the lower crust, and may have redistributed material in the lunar highlands to create notable differences between the mineralogy of the Moon's northern and southern hemispheres. Haggerty's team suggest that the shock waves it sent through the crust also opened fissures under the nearside, allowing magma rich in radioactive isotopes to penetrate these regions and, eventually, erupt onto the surface.

'A second satellite of Earth, formed during the same impact that formed the Moon itself, "splatted" across the lunar far side, raising its elevation.'

Haggerty's theory might also help to explain the strange features known as lunar mass concentrations of 'mascons'. First detected in 1968 from the deviations they caused in the Moon's gravity (and therefore in spacecraft trajectories), mascons seem to be concentrations of dense matter beneath the Moon's outer surface. Found predominantly beneath the maria and other large craters, they may be a result of compression in the rock beneath impact sites, but the process behind them is poorly understood. In September 2011, NASA launched a pair of spacecraft known as GRAIL (Gravity Recovery And Interior Laboratory) that will measure the mascons with far greater precision than ever before. Flying in parallel around the Moon, signals returned to Earth will allow precise measurements of their varying speeds, allowing astronomers to build up a gravity and density map of the Moon's deep interior.

The results may not just explain the origin of the mascons and the distribution of the lunar seas – they may also help explain the deeper effects of major asteroid strikes on the interior of any rocky world, perhaps determining whether a recent suggestion that asteroid impacts triggered the formation of Earth's own original continents could be correct.

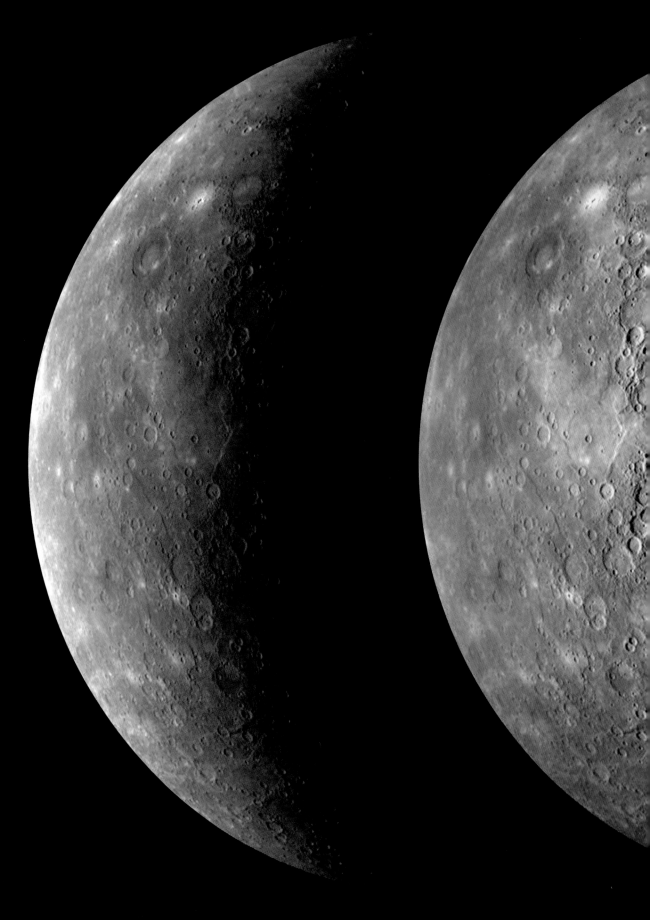

33

Mercury's complex past

DEFINITION THE INNERMOST PLANET, MERCURY, HAS NUMEROUS
STRANGE FEATURES THAT POSE UNANSWERED QUESTIONS.

DISCOVERY MERCURY HAS BEEN KNOWN SINCE ANCIENT TIMES, BUT
LITTLE WAS KNOWN ABOUT ITS LANDSCAPE UNTIL MARINER 10
FLEW PAST IN 1973.

KEY BREAKTHROUGH IN 2011, THE MESSENGER PROBE BECAME THE
FIRST SPACECRAFT TO ORBIT MERCURY.

IMPORTANCE MERCURY HAS THE POTENTIAL TO REVEAL A GREAT
DEAL ABOUT THE EVOLUTION OF THE ROCKY PLANETS.

Barely larger than Earth's Moon, Mercury is the smallest of the major planets, and the hardest to study from Earth since it always appears close to the Sun. However, two new spaceprobes should give us a better view of the planet's surface and reveal many of its secrets.

Like all the known planets, Mercury has been an intriguing target for observers ever since the telescope was invented in the early 1600s. But despite its relative proximity to Earth (92 million km or 57 million miles away at its closest), Mercury's tiny size made it an elusive and difficult target. The Moon-like pattern of phases caused by its orbit around the Sun was spotted early, but even seasoned astronomers using large instruments in the 19th and 20th centuries either saw nothing on the surface, or disagreed about what they did see. Until the late 1960s, when astronomers used giant radio telescopes to fire radar beams at Mercury and study the reflections, even some basic facts about Mercury, such as its diameter and rotation period, remained unclear.

So when interplanetary spacecraft became a reality in the 1960s, Mercury was an obvious destination. However, since this tiny world is so much closer to the Sun than Earth, it speeds around its orbit much faster than Earth – any visiting spaceprobe must not only escape from Earth, but also gain huge amounts of speed to catch up with Mercury.

Fleeting glimpses

The first spacecraft to reach Mercury – Mariner 10, launched in November 1973 – took an easier option, slotting into an elliptical orbit with a period of exactly two Mercury years (176 Earth days). This allowed it to fly

OPPOSITE A pair of images produced during MESSENGER's Mercury flyby of September 2009 show the planet in true and enhanced colour. Temperatures on this tiny planet range from a searing 430°C (800°F) to a chilling –200°C (–330°F).

past Mercury at high speed three times in 1974, sending back dozens of photographs and other data.

But the data returned by Mariner 10 was limited – not only by the speed of the flybys, but also by Mercury's unusual rotation. Tidal forces similar to those which have slowed the rotation of our Moon to match its orbit have also acted as a brake on Mercury's spin, so that it now has a day precisely two-thirds the length of its year. Since two Mercury years are equal to three Mercury days, Mariner's flybys always happened at the same point in the planet's rotation and with the same area illuminated. As a result, the three flybys could only map half of the planet's surface.

Nevertheless, Mariner revealed some intriguing features. Mercury looks superficially similar to our Moon, pockmarked with heavy craters and with some identifiable lava plains. However it also has unique structures called rupes – long, cliff-like faults that cross the surface and separate neighbouring areas of the landscape by steep scarps up to a kilometre (0.6 miles) high. As already suggested by radar observations, Mercury also proved to be far denser than the other rocky planets, and had a surprisingly strong magnetic field – evidence pointing to a large and partially molten iron core occupying up to 42 percent of its interior (compared to 17 percent in the case of Earth). US Geological Survey scientist Daniel Dzurisin suggested in 1978 that Mercury's large core could have given it an unusual geological history in which the planet first expanded and then shrank slightly. The splitting apart and later compression of the surface could explain the formation of the rupes features.

'Mercury's magnetic field is surprisingly dynamic: it frequently rearranges itself, forming twisted magnetic "tornadoes" that allow particles from the wind to rain down on the surface.'

But how did Mercury develop such a large core in the first place? An imbalance of iron close to the Sun in the early solar system could be ruled out by other lines of evidence and mathematical models of the protoplanetary nebula, so in 1988 a team led by Willy Benz of Harvard University suggested that the imbalance could be the result of a 'glancing blow' from a large planetesimal shortly after it formed. According to this model, Mercury was originally much larger, with a better proportioned mix of core and mantle materials. The collision stripped away much of the mantle, but left the core largely unscathed.

MESSENGER in orbit

The challenge in reaching Mercury's orbit meant that the planet was largely neglected in favour of other, more glamorous targets through the next three decades, and it was only in August 2004 that NASA launched a new probe, MESSENGER, on a protracted flightpath (involving multiple flypasts and gravity assists) that would allow it to gain sufficient speed to enter orbit around Mercury for the first time. MESSENGER (MErcury Surface, Space ENvironment, GEochemistry and Ranging) finally slipped into orbit in

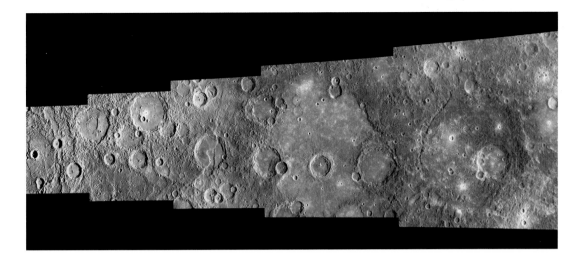

March 2011, armed with a wide array of instruments to study the planet. During the probe's first six months in orbit, it was able to photograph the entire planet in sunlight for the first time, confirming that Mercury's surface is largely volcanic, and that the volcanic material is basaltic in nature (similar to the volcanic rocks of Earth and the Moon). Among the intriguing new features discovered by MESSENGER is Apollodorus, a crater surrounded by a system of radiating faults that was immediately nicknamed 'the spider'.

In October 2011, results from the first phase of MESSENGER's mission were announced at the European Planetary Science Congress in Nantes, France. As well as stunning new images from both primary cameras and imaging spectrographs (designed to detect the chemical composition of the surface), the probe has also revealed surprising features of Mercury's magnetic field. Most notably, it is offset from the centre of the planet by almost 20 percent of Mercury's radius – giving it a surprising resemblance to the fields of Uranus and Neptune. While the unusual compositions of the ice-giant planets offer some explanations for their strange fields, the same excuses cannot apply to Mercury – so perhaps the strange offset is linked to the collision which created its outsized core?

MESSENGER's instruments have also shown that Mercury's magnetic field is surprisingly dynamic – driven by interactions with the solar wind, it frequently rearranges itself, forming twisted magnetic 'tornadoes' that allow particles from the wind to rain down on the surface. Such bombardment may assist in forming Mercury's exosphere – a tenuous halo of atoms such as hydrogen, helium, sodium and calcium that steadily leaks into space and must be constantly replenished. A process called 'sputtering' transfers momentum from the incoming solar wind to particles in Mercury's soil or regolith, allowing them to escape into space. In this way, astronomers suspect that the upper layers of Mercury's crust are chemically modified by the solar wind, and preserve traces of the Sun itself.

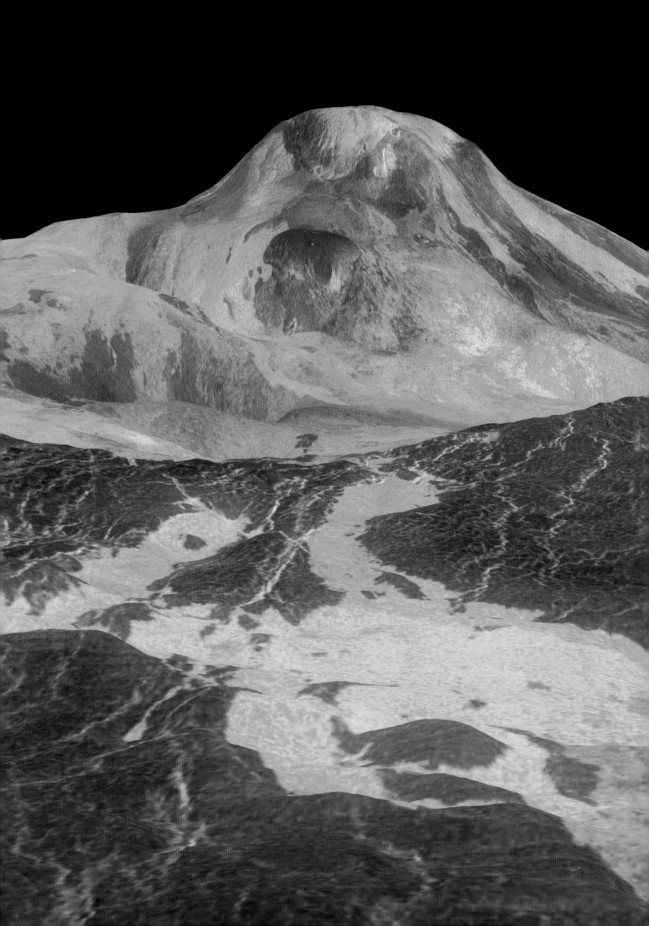

34 The volcanoes of Venus

DEFINITION THE HUGE VARIETY OF VOLCANIC STRUCTURES THAT
SHAPE THE SURFACE OF OUR NEAREST NEIGHBOURING PLANET.

DISCOVERY VOLCANIC HIGHLANDS WERE FIRST IDENTIFIED USING
EARTH-BASED RADAR IN THE 1970s.

KEY BREAKTHROUGH HIGH-RESOLUTION IMAGES FROM THE
MAGELLAN ORBITER SHOWED THE VOLCANOES IN DETAIL FOR
THE FIRST TIME.

IMPORTANCE DIFFERENCES IN VOLCANIC ACTIVITY BETWEEN
VENUS AND EARTH HELP US TO UNDERSTAND OUR OWN PLANET'S
GEOLOGICAL PROCESSES.

Radar mapping of the surface of Venus has revealed a planet covered in volcanoes of various kinds – the most of any planet in the solar system. These volcanoes have played a remarkable role in the planet's history, and some are probably active today.

The choking, opaque atmosphere of Earth's inner neighbour presented a fearsome barrier to early attempts to map or land on Venus. Despite the speculative maps drawn by some 19th-century astronomers, by the early 20th century it was clear that Venus was shrouded in brilliant clouds. It was only with the development of radar mapping techniques in the 1970s that astronomers were first able to pierce the cloud and reveal features of the surface below. The first radar maps, produced using signals beamed from the famous 300-m (1,000-ft) radio telescope at Arecibo, Puerto Rico, in the mid-1970s, were relatively crude, but allowed the identification of reflective features linked to highland areas. These were designated Alpha Regio, Beta Regio, Ovda Regio and Maxwell Montes (in honour of the Scottish physicist James Clerk Maxwell).

In 1978, NASA's Pioneer Venus spaceprobe put a radar in orbit around the planet for the first time, providing much higher-resolution images over the next decade. These revealed volcanic calderas on the Maxwell Montes peaks and elsewhere, suggesting that volcanoes were relatively common on Venus. They also revealed broad plains and deep canyons, but found no sign of tectonic faults: while Earth's crust is relatively thin and split into many separate, slowly drifting plates, that of Venus seems to be thicker, and is united in a single shell around the planet. Throughout the 1970s and 1980s, the handful of photographs sent back by the Soviet Venera landers (which

OPPOSITE This simulated view of Maat Mons, the highest volcano on Venus with a total elevation of 8 km (5 miles), combines radar altimetry data with other information gathered by the Magellan probe's synthetic aperture radar. Maat Mons is several hundred kilometres across, so vertical scale in the image has been exaggerated to make the overall shape clearer.

barely survived for a few minutes on the hostile Venusian surface) revealed a landscape of flat plains covered in fragments of volcanic rock.

Magellan's view

While early radar provided a general overview of the planet, and images from landers showed the local terrain, we had to wait until the 1990s to get our first glimpse of the wider Venusian landscape, courtesy of NASA's Magellan probe. This ambitious three-year mission carried high-resolution 'synthetic aperture' radar, previously only used for studying Earth, into orbit around Venus. Instead of firing only brief 'pings' of radio waves at the Venusian surface and detecting their reflections, Magellan's radar fired 'chirps' that took a longer time for the satellite to both send and receive – so long, in fact, that Magellan travelled some way along its orbit in the time taken to receive the signal back. Ingenious data-processing techniques back on Earth allowed the Magellan team to produce images with a resolution equivalent to the performance of a much larger radar dish. The radar also allowed scientists to analyse surface properties beyond simple topography, including the roughness, steepness and reflectivity of individual areas.

'When internal conditions become unsustainable, widespread volcanism erupts across the face of the planet, resurfacing the landscape in a few tens of millions of years.'

The maps and images created from Magellan's data during three years in orbit around Venus revealed it as a world dominated by volcanoes and their geological effects. Alongside mountainous shield volcanoes, Magellan revealed pit-like calderas, disc-like 'pancake domes', and networks of sunken cracks – radial arachnids and concentric, circular coronae – created by the welling-up and withdrawal of subsurface magma. More than 1,600 volcanic features have now been identified from Magellan images, and where volcanoes themselves were absent, lava plains were ubiquitous. Impact craters, meanwhile, are comparatively rare. This latter effect can be partly explained by the protective effect of the dense Venusian atmosphere, but a 1994 analysis by geologists from the United States Geological Survey and the University of Arizona showed that the number and distribution of craters was evidence for a catastrophic period of volcanic resurfacing around 300–600 million years ago. This event had covered most of the Venusian landscape with fresh lava, wiping out traces of earlier craters and leaving just a few older highland outcrops.

Magellan also confirmed the lack of large-scale tectonics on Venus, which at least offered some explanation for the widespread volcanism. On Earth, volcanic activity is largely concentrated along tectonic boundaries – mid-ocean trenches where the sea floor is spreading apart, and subduction zones where one segment of crust is forced below another, such as the Pacific 'Ring of Fire'. This provides a natural outlet for the escape of energy from Earth's interior. Venus, being only slightly smaller than Earth, is thought to generate a similar amount of internal heat, but the lack of tectonic boundaries on Venus turns the entire planet into a 'pressure cooker' with no such safety

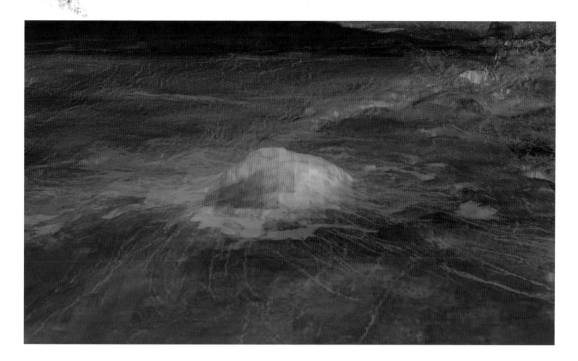

valve. As a result, when the internal conditions become unsustainable, widespread volcanism erupts across the face of the planet, resurfacing the entire landscape over a period of a few tens of millions of years.

Active volcanoes?

One major question that remains is whether the volcanoes are active today. Close analysis of radar images revealed delicate ash flows around the peak of Maat Mons – features that are likely to be eroded quite rapidly, and which therefore point to activity in the past few million years. The Soviet Venus landers Veneras 11 and 12 recorded lightning (possibly linked to rising clouds of ash) during their descent through the atmosphere above the Phoebe Regio highland region in 1978, and the European Space Agency's Venus Express mission has also recorded large amounts of lightning in the atmosphere. Further circumstantial evidence comes from a 90 percent drop in sulphur dioxide concentrations between 1978 and 1986, which may indicate the earlier measurement of this short-lived atmospheric gas was temporarily boosted by a major volcanic eruption.

In 2010, a team led by Suzanne E. Smrekar of NASA's Jet Propulsion Laboratory produced the most conclusive evidence for recent Venusian volcanism so far. Using the infrared spectroscope aboard Venus Express to peer through the clouds, they imaged nine potential hotspots – regions analogous to Earth's Hawaiian island volcanoes. Terrain in three of these areas proved to be unusually reflective compared to their surroundings, suggesting they have suffered little atmospheric weathering, and could be as little as a quarter of a million years old.

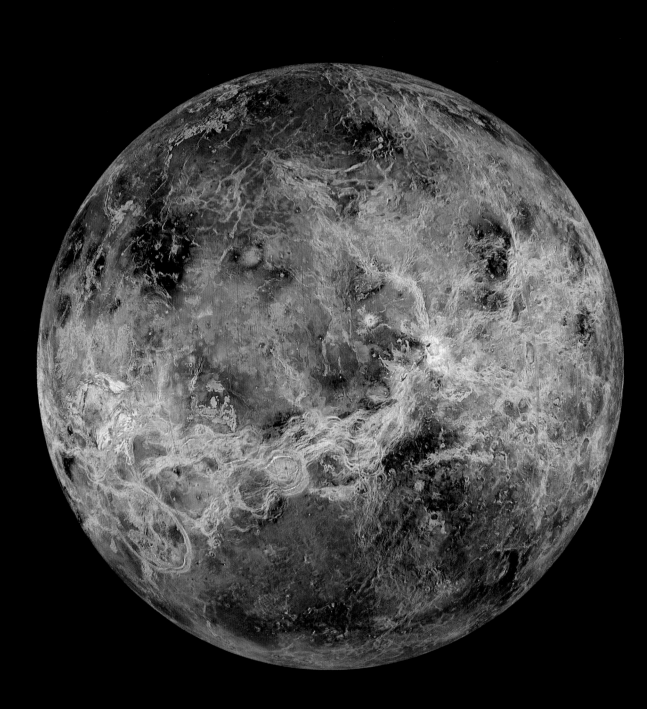

35 The Venusian hothouse

DEFINITION THE TOXIC ATMOSPHERE OF VENUS TURNS THE PLANET'S
SURFACE INTO A HELLISH, HIGH-PRESSURE OVEN.

DISCOVERY THE SCALDING TEMPERATURES BENEATH THE VENUSIAN
CLOUDS WERE CONFIRMED BY SPACEPROBES IN THE 1960s.

KEY BREAKTHROUGH IN 1986, JAMES F. KASTING SHOWED HOW
THE INCREASING HEAT OF THE SUN COULD HAVE TRIGGERED A
RUNAWAY GREENHOUSE EFFECT ON VENUS.

IMPORTANCE BY UNDERSTANDING THE EVOLUTION OF THE VENUSIAN
ATMOSPHERE, WE CAN LEARN MORE ABOUT EARTH'S OWN.

Venus is the nearest planet to Earth and the closest to it in size, yet history has taken it down a dramatically different path, transforming it into a toxic pressure cooker of a world. So just why did the two planets evolve in such radically diverse ways?

Named in ancient times after the goddess of beauty, Venus is the brightest object in the night sky after the Moon. It owes its brilliance not just to its proximity to Earth and the Sun, but also to a dense atmosphere that reflects 90 percent of incoming sunlight. Up until the early 20th century, astronomers hoped that the Venusian clouds might conceal a lush, tropical world, perhaps with abundant life. It was only in the late 1950s that astronomers turned their new radio telescopes towards the planet and detected emissions that indicated a surface temperature of several hundred degrees.

The soaring temperatures of Venus were confirmed by the first American and Soviet spaceprobes to fly past the planet in the early 1960s. Today we know that the planet's surface temperature is a scorching 460°C (860°F), but the planet's tremendous atmospheric pressure (more than 90 times Earth's) was only confirmed during Soviet attempts to put robot landers on the surface in the late 1960s. Several missions lost contact with Earth during their descent through the atmosphere, and it was only when Venera 7 sent back steady temperature and pressure readings for 23 minutes before it too ceased to function in December 1970, that engineers could finally be sure they had reached the surface.

Measurements taken from orbit and during these descents showed that the chemistry of the Venusian atmosphere is just as hostile as the temperature –

OPPOSITE Radar mapping by the Magellan probe reveals an entire hemisphere of Venus. While deep, ancient canyons run across parts of the surface, these appear never to have developed into full-blown tectonics, perhaps explaining the evolution of the Venusian atmosphere.

it is dominated by carbon dioxide, comprising 96 percent of the atmosphere, with smaller amounts of nitrogen and traces of sulphur dioxide (mostly in the clouds), argon, water vapour and carbon monoxide.

Complex weather

While Venus appears featureless in visible light, ultraviolet images reveal complex patterns in the atmosphere, dominated by huge chevron-shaped cloud structures that circle the planet in about four days. These stable large-scale features of the atmosphere can persist because of Venus's unusually slow rotation – the planet spins on its axis in 243 Earth days, while it takes only 224 days to circle the Sun. What's more, the rotation of Venus as seen from Earth is clockwise – reversed or retrograde compared with all the other planets.

'With no weathering mechanism, greenhouse gases produced by the planet's extensive volcanism accumulate in the atmosphere, accelerating the heating process.'

As a result of this unusual situation large-scale flows of air on Venus are driven mainly by the transfer of heat from the equator to the poles – the 'coriolis effects' that create winds parallel to the equators of fast-spinning planets such as Earth and Neptune are negligible. Nevertheless, wind speeds within the atmosphere reach an impressive 360 km/h (220 mph), and the upper atmosphere is said to super-rotate, on account of the fact that it moves much faster than the lower atmosphere or indeed the planet's surface.

The European Space Agency's Venus Express probe, which arrived in orbit around the planet in 2006, was equipped with a variety of instruments to probe the Venusian atmosphere in unprecedented detail. Among its discoveries were enormous eye-like polar vortices above the north and south poles, evidence for oxygen and hydrogen escaping into space, and clear signs that Venus was probably much cooler and wetter in the distant past.

Everything is connected

According to a model that is now widely accepted, Venus owes its current climate to a runaway greenhouse effect – a cycle in which a variety of atmospheric and geological effects heating the planet have reinforced one another in a spiral of positive feedback. Modelling carried out as early as 1986 by James F. Kasting of NASA's Ames Research Center showed that minor differences in the flux of solar radiation reaching an Earth-like planet could make a big difference to the amount of water evaporating from its oceans into the atmosphere. Throughout the history of the solar system, Venus has experienced just such an increase, as the Sun has brightened by an estimated 25 percent – more than enough, even without other effects, to turn its climate from temperate to torrid and to evaporate its oceans.

On Earth, increases in atmospheric water vapour tend to produce more precipitation, returning water to the ground and accelerating the chemical

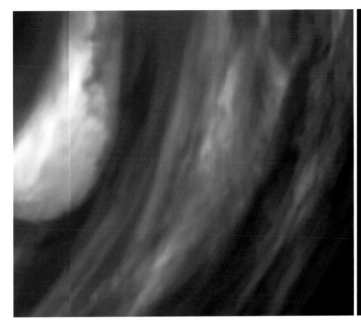

weathering of rocks – a process that locks up atmospheric carbon dioxide within carbonate minerals and therefore helps to reduce the heat-trapping effect of this important greenhouse gas. However on Venus, the lack of a substantial magnetic field permitted solar radiation to rapidly break the water vapour apart, allowing the fragmented hydrogen and oxygen to escape into space. With no weathering mechanism, greenhouse gases produced by the planet's extensive volcanism accumulate in the atmosphere, accelerating the heating process.

And the interconnections do not stop there. On Earth, oceans are thought to help lubricate the subduction zones where one tectonic plate is driven beneath another. The disappearance of water from Venus could have ensured that any nascent plate tectonics ground rapidly to a halt, creating the pressure-cooker volcano-driven geology that dominates the planet today (see page 141). The lack of a cooling process at the surface has also caused the temperature of the crust and upper mantle to rise significantly, reducing the temperature gradient from lower to upper mantle and therefore the amount of convection within it. On Earth, such convection is thought to play an important role in the formation of the magnetic field, so the lack of convection on Venus could help explain its missing magnetism.

Finally, this model also offers one explanation for the slow rotation of Venus, as the result of interaction between the thickening atmosphere and tidal forces from the Sun. However, that is not the only solution to be offered up for this particular problem – in 2006, Caltech researchers Alex Alemi and David Stevenson produced a model in which the same result could be created by a pair of giant impacts early in Venusian history.

ABOVE Images of Venus from ESA's Venus Express (left) and the Hubble Space Telescope (right) reveal large-scale structures in the planet's atmosphere. An infrared image from Venus Express's VIRTIS instrument shows a bright spot above the south pole, while the ultraviolet HST image reveals chevron-like circulation above the equator.

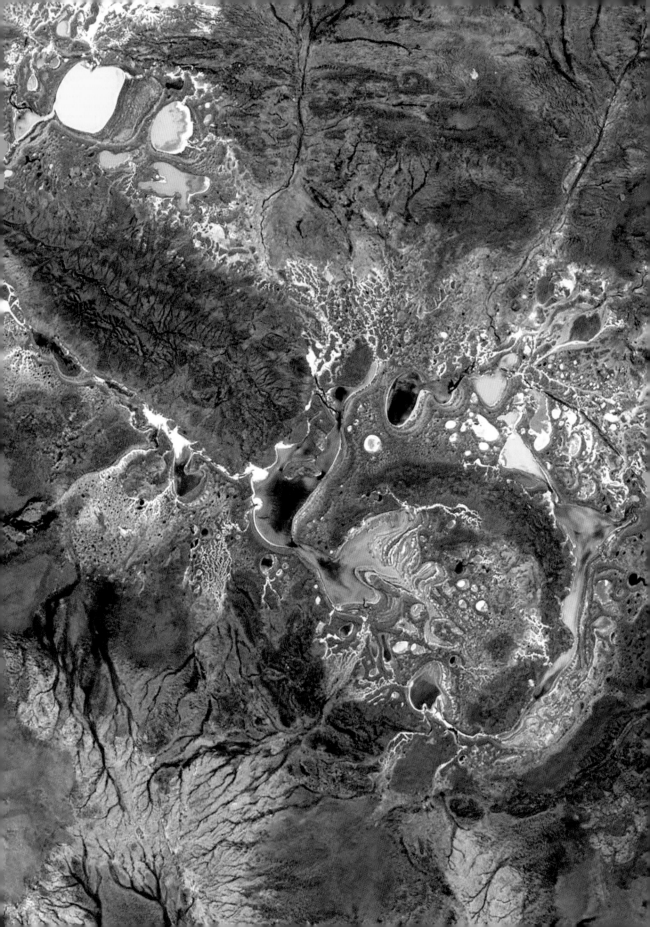

Impacts from space

DEFINITION OCCASIONAL MAJOR METEORITE IMPACTS THAT FORM CRATERS ON EARTH AND AFFECT GEOLOGY, CLIMATE AND LIFE.

DISCOVERY THE EXISTENCE OF METEORITES FROM SPACE WAS FIRST RECOGNIZED AROUND 1800.

KEY BREAKTHROUGH IN 1981, LUIS AND WALTER ALVAREZ PROPOSED THAT EXTINCTION OF THE DINOSAURS WAS LINKED TO A MAJOR IMPACT EVENT.

IMPORTANCE EVIDENCE FOR PAST IMPACTS FROM SPACE SUGGESTS THAT THEY COULD PRESENT A FUTURE THREAT TO OUR PLANET.

Material from space has rained down on the surface of Earth throughout its long history, ranging in size from dusty fragments that burn up in the atmosphere to large bodies that create widespread devastation. Yet the role of such impacts in shaping our planet has only recently been recognized.

Throughout much of history, astronomers and philosophers considered Earth and space as entirely separate realms, destined never to interact. Earth was seen as the realm of change and mutability, the heavens unchanging and eternal. Even when ideas about the nature of the cosmos began to change in the 17th century, the idea that objects from space could make their way to the surface of Earth remained unthinkable – despite numerous folk tales and ancient records of stones falling from the sky to suggest otherwise.

Things began to change in 1794, when German geologist Ernst Chladni suggested that strange nuggets of pure 'Pallas iron' might have their origins in space. Chladni's theories were widely mocked at first, but people began to take them seriously after French scientist Jean-Baptiste Biot conducted an exhaustive study of a shower of meteorites reported from the region of L'Aigle, in northern France, in April 1803. Scouring the countryside, Biot uncovered a distinctive 'strewn field' of 3,000 stones, consistent with the breakup of the fireball seen shortly before the rain of stones.

OPPOSITE Western Australia's colourful Shoemaker Crater was identified as an impact structure through the discovery of rock and mineral structures that are only generated by powerful shock waves. The 12-km-wide (7.5-mile) crater is probably around 1.6 billion years old.

Meteorite craters

At around the same time that the reality of meteorite falls became accepted, the discovery of asteroids increased the number of known objects in the solar system. Yet despite this, astronomers and geologists maintained a steadfast denial that larger rocks from space could impact on the surface of our planet.

RIGHT Today the
Chicxulub Crater
lies buried beneath
sediments around
Mexico's Yucatán
Peninsula, but this
map of gravity
anomalies across
the region clearly
reveals a ringlike
structure around
180 km (110 miles)
in diameter.

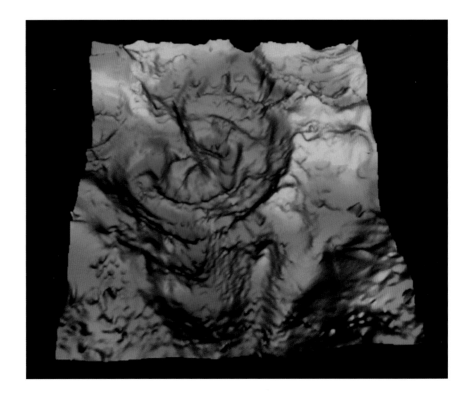

Most of the structures we now know to be impact craters were assumed, if they were recognized at all, to be volcanic in origin.

The famous Meteor Crater near Flagstaff, Arizona (also known as the Barringer or Canyon Diablo crater), offers a good example. Discovered by European settlers in the mid-19th century, it was generally assumed to be volcanic, and even American geologist Grove Karl Gilbert, one of the first people to propose an impact origin for lunar craters, blamed it on a gas explosion. In 1903, however, mining engineer Daniel Barringer bought the crater in the belief that it had been formed by a valuable iron-rich meteorite.

Barringer published his evidence for an impact in 1906, but his claims were undermined by three decades of failure to locate the bulk of the meteorite's remains. Today we understand that the shock wave that formed the crater would have vaporized the vast majority of the impactor itself. But it was only in the 1960s that planetary scientist Eugene Shoemaker clinched the case for an impact by locating shocked minerals, formed by the intense pressures and temperatures associated with the impact.

The Tunguska event

Meanwhile, another equally surprising discovery was being made halfway around the world. In 1908, a huge blast had laid waste to a vast area of forest in a remote region of Siberia in eastern Russia. Eyewitness reports linked it to a huge fireball-like meteor seen crossing the sky moments before the explosion, but the impact site was only visited for the first time in the late 1920s by Russian mineralogist Leonid Kulik. This time there was little doubt that the explosion was linked to an object from space, but the expected crater was nowhere to be found. The Tunguska event was generally attributed to an airburst – the explosion of a large chunk of space debris, tens of metres across, at an altitude of 5–10 km (3–6 miles). For a long time, this object was assumed to be a comet, but since the 1990s, several researchers have put forward evidence that it was more asteroid-like in composition.

Impacts and life

While astronomers were increasingly aware of our planet's vulnerable position, the geological establishment remained generally blinkered to the idea that impacts from space could have had widespread and long-lasting effects on Earth. Generations had been trained to view such catastrophist theories with suspicion, and as late as the 1960s, astronomers and geologists were still debating whether the countless lunar craters owed their origin to impacts or volcanoes. It was only in the 1970s, once rock samples returned by the Apollo Moon landings had been thoroughly studied, that the true timescale of lunar cratering became apparent. And although it was clear that the vast majority of impacts had occurred early in the solar system's history, it was also irrefutable that substantial impacts had continued right through the Moon's history. If the Moon had suffered continuous bombardment, then why should Earth be any different?

Matters came to a head in 1980, when a team led by Nobel-prizewinning physicist Walter Alvarez and his geologist son Luis put forward a daring hypothesis based on their studies of rock strata laid down some 65 million years ago, when the dinosaurs became extinct in the geological blink of an eye. Here, at the boundary between the Cretaceous and Tertiary periods of geological history, they found a layer of iridium-rich material embedded in rocks around the world. Iridium is a rare element on Earth, but far more common in asteroids and comets, so the Alvarez team concluded that the extinction of the dinosaurs coincided with a massive asteroid impact whose effects were felt around the world. The proposal was met with widespread scepticism, not least because the team could not identify a large impact crater of suitable age, but it inspired a new generation of geologists and palaeontologists to consider the possibility that the generally steady patterns of geological transition and evolution could sometimes be supplanted by brief cataclysmic events. Finally, in 1990, geologists identified the 180-km-wide (110-mile) Chicxulub Crater, buried beneath sediments on Mexico's Yucatán Peninsula, as the probable site of the Cretaceous–Tertiary impact. The idea that a single impact alone triggered the extinction of the dinosaurs and countless other species at the time remains controversial, but there is now little doubt that meteorite impacts do inflict cataclysmic damage on our planet from time to time.

'Finally, in 1990, geologists identified the 180-km-wide (110-mile) Chicxulub Crater on Mexico's Yucatán Peninsula, as the probable site of the Cretaceous–Tertiary impact.'

Periodic bombardments

DEFINITION CONTROVERSIAL THEORIES THAT EARTH SUFFERS
PERIODIC WAVES OF IMPACTS FROM SPACE THAT ARE LINKED TO
MASS EXTINCTIONS OF LIFE.

DISCOVERY DAVID RAUP AND JACK SEPKOWSKI FIRST CLAIMED TO
HAVE IDENTIFIED A CYCLE OF MASS EXTINCTIONS IN 1984.

KEY BREAKTHROUGH IN 2009, NASA LAUNCHED THE WISE SATELLITE,
CAPABLE OF IDENTIFYING A HYPOTHETICAL 'DEATH STAR' IN THE
OUTER SOLAR SYSTEM.

IMPORTANCE IF MASS EXTINCTIONS OCCUR IN REGULAR CYCLES, IT
WOULD ALTER OUR ENTIRE PICTURE OF THE HISTORY OF LIFE.

The discovery of a massive impact from space linked to the extinction of the dinosaurs sparked a wave of interest in the idea that similar impacts could mark other major events in the history of life, and set some astronomers wondering if an astronomical pulse lay at the heart of life's development.

During the early 1980s, the 'Alvarez impact hypothesis' for the extinction of the dinosaurs (see page 151) went rapidly from an unthinkable fringe theory to one of the most exciting ideas in science, triggering a wave of multidisciplinary research that ultimately linked the fields of palaeontology, geology and astronomy.

Geologists understandably began to look for evidence of impacts associated with other major changes in the history of life. While the disappearance of the dinosaurs is by far the best known of these 'mass extinctions', it is only one of many, and when the full range of species on Earth is taken into account, it is far from being the largest. One early target that showed promise was the so-called End-Eocene extinction, around 33.9 million years ago, which appeared to coincide with several impacts that, although smaller than the Cretaceous–Tertiary (K–T) event, could still have had devastating effects across wide regions.

A cycle of extinctions?

In the light of these new discoveries, in 1984 University of Chicago palaeontologists David M. Raup and Jack Sepkowski, specialists in large-scale patterns in the evolution of life, published a paper in *Nature* putting forward evidence for a periodic cycle or pulse in the diversity of life. Mass extinctions, they argued, occurred at intervals of roughly 26 million years.

OPPOSITE Every November, Earth ploughs through a trail of comet debris that produces the Leonid meteor shower. Do showers of much larger objects fall into the inner solar system on much longer timescales, triggering mass extinctions of life?

Understandably, this claim was enormously controversial from the outset, and has been subjected to enormous scrutiny in attempts to disprove it. Most recently, an analysis by Coryn Bailer-Jones of Germany's Max Planck Institute for Astronomy, published in 2011, argued that the supposed cycle is a statistical artifact. But nevertheless, Raup and Sepkowski's initial suggestion led to some equally remarkable attempts at explanation.

If the 26-million-year cycle does indeed exist, then it makes sense to look for a trigger factor somewhere beyond Earth. So far as geologists understand, our planet's internal processes do not obey such regular cycles, and, of course, the coincidence between extraterrestrial impacts and the K–T and End-Eocene extinctions is also suggestive. Since the 1980s, various claims have been made linking particular impacts to specific extinctions, but so far such connections have not been confirmed by further studies, and they remain dubious in the eyes of the scientific community. Meanwhile, other possible causes for extinctions – such as large-scale volcanism and major sea-level changes – seem to coincide with extinctions far more often. Even the extinction of the dinosaurs coincides with major eruptions in India's Deccan Traps, as well as the famous impact – it may be that, despite its iconic status, the Chicxulub impact is exceptional among extinction triggers.

'The climate crisis triggered by a major impact could have a severe effect on land plants and photosynthetic algae, and this in turn would devastate the animals reliant on them.'

Nemesis and others

Nevertheless, if there is a periodic cycle of extinction events, and if such a cycle turns out to be linked to extraterrestrial impacts, there is no shortage of potential mechanisms to explain the cycle. Perhaps the most famous of these, proposed by two separate teams of astronomers in the same issue of *Nature* as Raup and Sepkowski's original paper, is the 'Nemesis' hypothesis. This suggests that the Sun has an extremely faint companion star – a red or brown dwarf (see page 277) – following a multi-million-year orbit which disturbs the Oort Cloud of comets (see page 253) when close to perihelion. These disturbances send large numbers of comets plunging into the inner solar system, where they rain down onto the planets.

A variant on this idea invokes a massive but unseen planet in an orbit that grazes the inner edge of the Oort Cloud when close to its aphelion. The obvious question is why such a signficant object has not been discovered yet, but this is not insurmountable – Proxima Centauri, the closest known star to the Sun and companion to the brilliant Alpha Centauri system – was discovered more or less accidentally in 1915, and Nemesis would be far fainter than even Proxima. However, even a faint brown dwarf should emit significant amounts of infrared radiation, and most astronomers agree that the question of Nemesis's existence should be settled, one way or another, by the all-sky infrared survey currently being conducted by the WISE (Wide-Field Infrared Survey Explorer) satellite, launched in 2009.

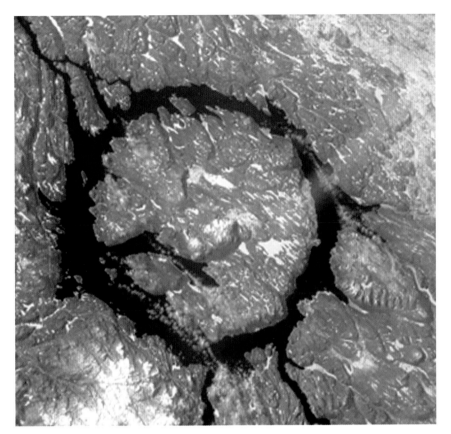

LEFT Canada's ring-shaped Manicouagan Lake is a huge flooded impact crater, some 70 km (44 miles) across, that was created around 215 million years ago. Manicouagan is just one of five craters of similar age aligned in a chain that stretches around the world – almost certainly the result of impacts from a single broken-up comet or asteroid.

Should Nemesis finally be disproved, however, the 'Shiva hypothesis', put forward by Michael Rampino of New York University, offers an alternative explanation for cyclic extinctions, based on our solar system's movement through the Milky Way. The Sun takes 200 million years to circle the galaxy, but a wobble in its orbit carries it through the dense plane of the Milky Way's disc every 30 million years. During these passages, Rampino argued, close encounters with stars and other massive objects are more likely, and could potentially raise tides to disturb comets in the Oort Cloud.

But if the possibility that impacts have affected the development of life on Earth throughout its history remains controversial, the idea that it happens on occasion, at least, has become far more acceptable. In addition to the significant effects of a large-scale impact itself, the possible after-effects include tsunamis, wildfires, and the injection of huge amounts of debris into the upper atmosphere, blocking out sunlight and triggering global cooling. The climate crisis triggered by a major impact could have a severe effect on plant life such as land plants and photosynthetic algae, and this, in turn, would devastate the entire pyramid of herbivorous and carnivorous animals reliant on them. As we learn more about the ecological relationships that shape our world, it becomes ever clearer that extraterrestrial events can have devastating consequences.

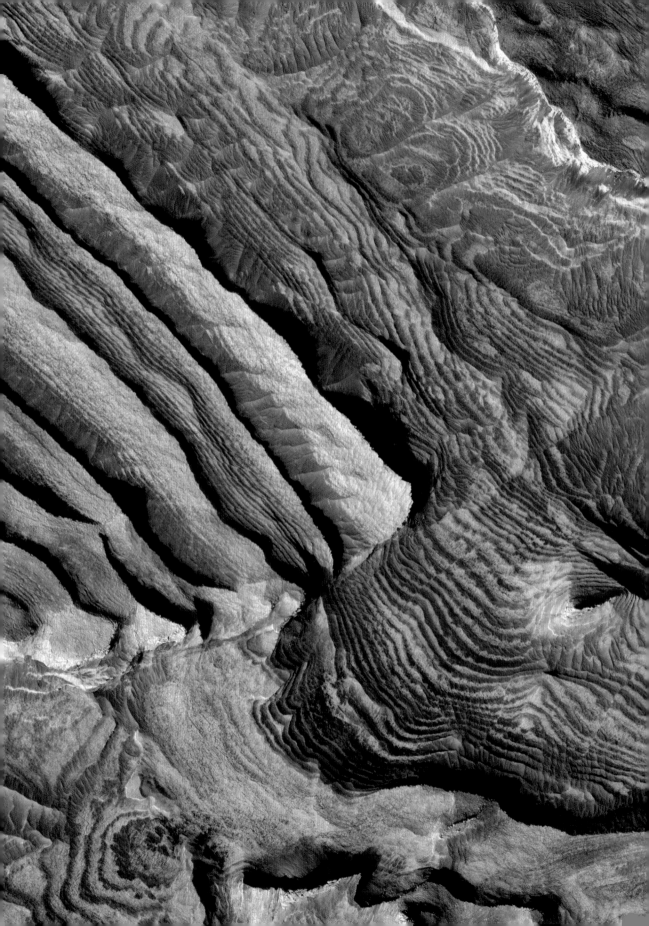

38 The active history of Mars

DEFINITION NEW EVIDENCE THAT MARS HAS A FAR MORE COMPLEX HISTORY THAN PREVIOUSLY SUSPECTED.

DISCOVERY THE 1997 ARRIVAL OF MARS GLOBAL SURVEYOR BEGAN A NEW WAVE OF EXPLORATION THAT IS STILL CONTINUING.

KEY BREAKTHROUGH IN 2008, THREE TEAMS OF ASTRONOMERS SUGGESTED THAT A HUGE IMPACT TRANSFORMED MUCH OF THE MARTIAN NORTHERN HEMISPHERE INTO A GIANT IMPACT BASIN.

IMPORTANCE UNDERSTANDING THE GEOLOGICAL HISTORY OF MARS HAS IMPORTANT IMPLICATIONS FOR FUTURE COLONIZATION AND FOR THE CHANCE THAT LIFE EVOLVED ON THE PLANET.

Since the late 1990s, a series of robot missions to Mars has imaged its surface in increasing detail, revealing the Red Planet's fascinating history. Mars Global Surveyor, Mars Express and a series of Mars landers and rovers have helped provide answers to some long-standing questions.

After the success of the Viking orbiters and landers in the 1970s, attempts to study Mars in more detail were frustrated throughout the next two decades by a series of failed American and Soviet spaceprobes. It was only in 1997 that exploration resumed in earnest, with the success of the Mars Pathfinder mission to land a miniature rover on the surface of Mars, and the arrival of the Mars Global Surveyor satellite in orbit around the planet.

The view from orbit

Mars Global Surveyor (MGS) carried with it a suite of instruments that took full advantage of technological improvements since the 1970s. Its cameras were capable of resolving features as small as 1.5 metres (5 ft) on the lunar surface, while its laser altimeter fired pulses of infrared radiation towards the Martian surface ten times per second and detected their reflections in order to map changes in Martian topography of as little as 37 cm (17 in). Among its other instruments was the Thermal Emission Spectrometer (TES), capable of mapping the mineral composition of the Martian surface.

Over nine years of operation, MGS mapped the Martian surface in unprecedented detail. It revealed complex structure in the polar ice caps, delicate erosion features linked to past (and possibly present) water on the surface (see page 165), dune fields, layers of sediment and the dark tracks left by dust devils that disturb the Martian sands. Altimetry, meanwhile, revealed

OPPOSITE This stunning image from Mars Reconnaissance Orbiter shows complex layered terrain in Becquerel Crater just north of the Martian equator. Rocks in this region of Mars have built up from layered sediments, with patterns apparently linked to long-term cycles in the planet's axial tilt. False colours distinguish sand (blue) from exposed rock (pale pink).

that the visible difference between the plains of the northern hemisphere and the southern craters is reflected in the planet's elevation and the thickness of its crust, which varies from around 50 km (30 miles) up to 125 km (80 miles) in the southern hemisphere.

In 2008, three groups of scientists published papers in *Nature* supporting a surprising explanation for this Martian dichotomy – they propose that it was caused by a giant impact involving a huge asteroid more than half the size of Earth's Moon. Computer modelling shows that the huge impact caused by such a world striking Mars at 6–10 km/s (3.7–6 miles per second) at a glancing angle could create an impact basin some 10,600 km (6,600 miles) long and 8,500 km (5,300 miles) wide, nicknamed the Borealis Basin. Within this region and its surroundings, the Martian crust would have become a sea of molten rock, which eventually solidified to form the smooth, rolling plains of the present northern hemisphere. One puzzling aspect of this theory is that the lack of cratering on the plains implies that the impact occurred surprisingly late in the planet's history: if this is the case, then the Late Heavy Bombardment (see page 105) could not have concealed the ejecta blanket that the Borealis impact would have spread across the planet. One solution to this dilemma would be if the impact occurred early in the Late Heavy Bombardment period, but the magma ocean somehow remained in a molten state until this phase of the solar system's history was nearly over.

Mars in three dimensions

Launched in 2003, the European Space Agency's Mars Express reached the Red Planet in a little over six months thanks to a favourable alignment of Earth and Mars. Among the instruments it carried were a ground-penetrating radar capable of searching for frozen water beneath the surface (see page 166), a spectrometer for mapping minerals, and an innovative stereo camera, capable of producing detailed images from slightly different viewpoints that could then be combined to produce a three-dimensional image of the Martian surface, resolving features down to 2 metres (6.7 ft) in size.

Amongst the probe's major discoveries in more than eight years of operation have been the confirmation of frozen water in Mars's south polar ice cap (previously it was only known in the northern polar

cap – see page 166), and the identification of methane in the planet's atmosphere. This chemical breaks down rapidly in the Martian air, so it must have been produced recently – a discovery that has important implications for our view of Mars since the only known mechanisms for generating methane are volcanic activity or the action of living organisms.

Mars is famously peppered with towering volcanoes, including Olympus Mons, the tallest in the solar system at 27 km (19 miles) high. They were initially thought to be long-extinct, but high-resolution images from MGS, Mars Express and Mars Reconnaissance Orbiter have revealed fields of smaller volcanic cones close to the Martian north pole that appear to have been active in the relatively recent past. Smooth areas with very little impact cratering on the flanks of major volcanoes, including Olympus Mons itself, suggest that even these have occasionally erupted in the last 2–4 million years.

> 'The Martian crust would have become a sea of molten rock, which eventually solidified to form the smooth, rolling plains of the present northern hemisphere.'

Explorers on the surface

Meanwhile on the surface, Mars Pathfinder paved the way for a series of more ambitious landers. While NASA's Mars Polar Lander and ESA's Beagle 2 both crashed onto the surface, the Phoenix mission landed successfully near the north polar cap in 2008, and operated successfully for several months before the onset of the polar winter, successfully confirming the existence of ice in the Martian permafrost. In 2004, meanwhile, the Mars Exploration Rovers *Spirit* and *Opportunity* landed in different regions of the planet's mid-latitudes. *Spirit* landed in a 10-km-wide (6-mile) crater called Gusev, in an area that appeared to have been affected by running water in the past, while *Opportunity* landed on the smooth Meridiani Planum region, and coincidentally rolled into a small crater.

Both rovers were spectacular successes, outlasting their initial planned 90-day missions many times over. *Spirit* confirmed geological processes that could only have occurred under water and found evidence for hot springs, while *Opportunity* uncovered more water-formed minerals and identified the first sedimentary rocks on Mars. Communication was only lost with *Spirit* in 2010, while *Opportunity* was still going strong in late 2011.

39 Martian climate change

DEFINITION SIGNS THAT MARS IS CURRENTLY GOING THROUGH A SUBSTANTIAL LONG-TERM TEMPERATURE INCREASE.

DISCOVERY IN 2001, MARS GLOBAL SURVEYOR IDENTIFIED THE DISAPPEARANCE OF SEMI-PERMANENT CARBON DIOXIDE ICE AROUND THE PLANET'S SOUTH POLE.

KEY BREAKTHROUGH LONG-TERM CHANGES TO PLANETARY ORBITS AFFECTING CLIMATE WERE IDENTIFIED BY MILUTIN MILANKOVIC IN 1912.

IMPORTANCE CYCLES IN THE MARTIAN CLIMATE SHOW THAT THE RED PLANET WAS FAR MORE HOSPITABLE TO LIFE IN THE PAST.

In the past decade, evidence from Martian orbiters and landers has suggested that the Red Planet, like Earth, is currently going through a period of rapid climate change. What's more, it's also clear that Mars is subject to long-term climate cycles that may render it far more hospitable at times.

Earth-based astronomers have long understood that Mars has a complex short-term climate cycle, clearly visible from Earth in the waxing and waning of the polar ice caps as carbon dioxide frosts evaporate in spring and accumulate in autumn. With an axis tilted just slightly more than Earth's, it goes through the familiar cycle of seasons throughout an orbit that lasts 687 Earth days. However this orbit is also markedly elliptical, ranging between 207 million km (129 million miles) and 249 million km (155 million miles) from the Sun, and as a result there is a distinct difference between seasons in the northern and southern hemispheres.

In the north, seasonal variations are reduced because Mars is closer to the Sun during winter and further away in summer. In the south, however, the seasons are exaggerated because Mars is closer to the Sun in summer, and further away in winter. In addition, the distance to the Sun has an overall heating effect that tends to raise enormous dust storms around the time of perihelion (closest approach to the Sun). Fine Martian sand can be lofted into the upper atmosphere, where it lingers for weeks and has a further warming effect on the planet.

But as well as these short-term changes, we are now learning that Mars is undergoing climate change on far longer timescales. In 2001, NASA scientists directed the cameras aboard Mars Global Surveyor towards a section of the

OPPOSITE Evaporating carbon dioxide ice produces strange pits in the polar cap as the Martian south pole moves into spring and begins to warm. Long-term variations in the size of such pits suggest that Mars is significantly warmer now than it was just a few years ago.

south polar ice cap that they had imaged previously – a group of small pits in the permanent carbon dioxide ice that seemed to persist even as the deeper winter frosts came and went. What they saw came as a surprise: the pits had now expanded and merged together, indicating that a large area of Martian ice had disappeared, sublimating into the atmosphere.

This was the first hint that Mars is undergoing a period of rapid global warming, and apparently clinching proof came in 2007, when comparison of temperature measurements taken by the Viking Orbiters of the 1970s with those from more modern probes revealed that Mars today is 0.5°C (0.9°F) warmer than it was three decades ago. If this temperature increase continues, Mars could lose its south polar cap completely. But what is driving climate change on Mars, and how far could it go?

Cycles of change

Astronomers believe that the long cyclical changes in Martian climate are caused at least in part by variations in the planet's orbit – so-called Milankovic cycles, discovered by Serbian geophysicist Milutin Milankovic in the early 20th century. Milankovic was looking for evidence to explain apparent cycles in Earth's own recent climate, and invoked three major variations in Earth's orbit – the 'precession of the equinoxes' that causes the direction of the planet's tilted axis to change over 25,800 years, a slower oscillation in the degree of axial tilt (affecting the severity of the seasons), and a slow 'flexing' in the shape of Earth's entire orbit.

'Frozen carbon dioxide sublimating from the south pole will thicken the atmosphere and increase the Martian greenhouse effect, trapping more solar heat and increasing the current planetary warming.'

Fortunately for us, the effects of these cycles on Earth are comparatively small, due in part to the regulating presence of the Moon. But nevertheless, the small alterations they make to the amount and distribution of heat from the Sun striking our planet can have a noticeable effect on climate when other factors put Earth in a vulnerable state.

On Mars, however, the Milankovic effects have a far bigger effect. The Martian orbit can flex between a near-perfect circle and its current noticeable ellipse, and as described previously, the relationship between the planet's orbit and axial tilt tends to increase seasonal change in one hemisphere and diminish it in the other. As Mars goes through its 175,000-year cycle of precession, this situation will reverse, while the 100,000-year and 2.2-million-year cycles of eccentricity will gradually circularize the planet's orbit. Finally, the planet's axial tilt varies between around 15° and 35° in a 124,000-year cycle, so, at times, the seasons are far more extreme than they are today.

Feedback mechanisms

Milankovic cycles are one important factor influencing variations in the Martian climate, but the situation is also complicated by natural feedback

mechanisms in which a change to one element of the climate system produces an effect that may either reinforce or counter the original change. For instance, frozen carbon dioxide sublimating from the south pole will thicken the atmosphere and increase the Martian greenhouse effect, trapping more solar heat and increasing the current planetary warming. In turn, this could lead to higher winds, whipping up dust storms whose heating effect will increase the warming still further.

Another potential feedback mechanism comes from the mysterious source of Martian methane (see page 171). In 2009, a team led by Michael Mumma of NASA's Goddard Space Flight Center announced the results of several years of careful observations using NASA's Infrared Telescope Facility and the Keck Telescopes based on Mauna Kea, Hawaii. They discovered that huge plumes of methane are emitted in spring and summer, apparently emerging from areas that are rich in subterranean ice. One of these methane outbursts released an estimated 19,000 tonnes of the gas, which is a far more effective greenhouse gas than carbon dioxide. If the mechanism that releases it into the atmosphere responds favourably to increased temperatures, then the methane emission is only likely to accelerate in the future, increasing the planet's general warming trend. Eventually, however, the inevitable Milankovic cycles suggest that Martian climate change will reverse, and the planet will gradually slip back into the deep freeze.

ABOVE This unnamed crater close to the north pole of Mars shelters a frozen ice lake around 10 km (6 miles) across. Ice can also be seen on parts of the wall – the pattern of distribution is probably linked to the amount of sunlight striking different parts of the crater, and is therefore linked to long-term Milankovic cycles in the Martian orbit.

40 The waters of Mars

DEFINITION INCREASINGLY SUBSTANTIAL EVIDENCE THAT WATER HAS FLOWED ON THE SURFACE OF MARS IN THE RECENT PAST.

DISCOVERY IN 2000, MARS GLOBAL SURVEYOR PHOTOGRAPHED 'GULLIES' THAT MAY HAVE BEEN CAUSED BY ESCAPING WATER.

KEY BREAKTHROUGH IN 2011, MARS RECONNAISSANCE ORBITER TRACKED DARK SEASONAL MARKINGS THAT ARE PROBABLY CREATED BY BRINE SEEPING FROM BELOW THE SURFACE.

IMPORTANCE CONFIRMATION OF LIQUID WATER ON MARS TODAY WOULD REVOLUTIONIZE THE PROSPECTS FOR THE SURVIVAL OF MARTIAN LIFE AND ASSIST WITH FUTURE HUMAN EXPLORATION.

After decades of argument, evidence from the Mars Reconnaissance Orbiter and other missions now conclusively points to the fact that water not only played a key role in Martian history, but is also sometimes present on the surface today.

The location of Mars in our solar system has always suggested that it might harbour water – either on the surface or just below. In the 1870s, Italian astronomer Giovanni Schiaparelli claimed to have seen long, straight lines or *canali* linking darker patches of the Martian surface. He interpreted them as natural channels between standing bodies of water, but others, inspired in part by their misinterpretations of the Italian word *canali*, suggested they were artificial canals. The most elaborate version of this theory was developed by American astronomer Percival Lowell, who saw the canals as the work of intelligent Martians moving water from polar ice caps to equatorial deserts.

Needless to say, Schiaparelli's *canali* turned out not to exist, and today they are generally assumed to have been some kind of optical illusion. Nevertheless, astronomers still assumed that Mars might show some signs of flowing water through much of the 20th century. It was only when the early spaceprobes of the 1960s and 1970s sent back pictures of a cold, dry world that these hopes were dashed. While Mars experiences surface temperatures that range from –90°C (–130°F) to 20°C (68°F), its low atmospheric pressure (around 0.6 percent of Earth's) means that any liquid water exposed at the surface would rapidly evaporate or boil into the atmosphere.

Nevertheless, Mars certainly had some water, albeit frozen into the north polar ice cap and largely buried beneath frosty layers of carbon

OPPOSITE The Valles Marineris canyon system forms a scar across some 4,000 km (2,500 miles) of the Martian surface. While it formed as a result of geological faulting in the planet's crust, it also shows clear signs of being shaped by water running from the surrounding plains down into the valley.

dioxide dry ice. Some astronomers argued that sinuous valleys amid the southern highlands and teardrop-shaped scars on the northern plains were evidence that standing bodies of liquid water had been plentiful in the Martian past, but believers in a cold, dry Mars suggested they were more likely to be the result of occasional melting of subsurface ice, perhaps driven by volcanic activity.

Gullies and glaciers

The tide began to turn early in the 21st century, thanks to images returned by the Mars Global Surveyor and Mars Express orbiters. In 2000, NASA announced the discovery of extremely young gullies on the sides of a canyon called Gorgonum Chaos – features that were probably formed by liquid seeping from the canyon rim and running towards its base. While sceptics pointed out that the gullies could be formed by escaping liquid carbon dioxide, optimists pointed out that they looked like they had emerged from an aquifer or water table just below the Martian surface.

'The rover's study of distinctive haematite spheres or "blueberries" revealed that they and many of the other rocks in the area had formed within a standing body of water.'

In 2003, NASA's Mars Odyssey mission identified the chemical signature of widespread water beneath polar and mid-latitudes – accounting for perhaps half the content of the soil by mass. However, much of this is believed to be locked away in hydrated minerals such as clays, or at least frozen solid. The Phoenix lander, which touched down near the north polar cap in 2008, found ice just a few inches below the dusty soil.

In fact, Phoenix's discovery may point to a remarkable hidden secret. New images from the Mars Reconnaissance Orbiter (MRO) have shown areas where impacts have blasted away the characteristic red soil to reveal ice just beneath the surface. In 2009, MRO's radar also helped to identify the presence of large amounts of ice in structures called lobate debris aprons, and close-up images from the probe's HIRISE camera have revealed glacier-like features across a wide range of Martian landscapes. Mars Express, meanwhile, has even identified patterns similar to pack ice close to the equator in the southern Elysium Planitia. While the vast majority of these features are covered with soil and rock, could it be that this is just a thin layer hiding the reality of a world dominated by ice and glaciers?

A watery present?

Meanwhile, the discovery of spectacularly layered sedimentary rocks in MGS images appeared to be more evidence for large bodies of standing water, perhaps even oceans, in the Martian past. Once again there were 'dry' alternative – sediments can build up from countless layers of thin, wind-driven dust, and even volcanic ash can produce similarly layered structures over time. However when further studies revealed clay-like minerals within these layers, the evidence for a watery origin strengthened. Clinching

LEFT The dark brown features extending from beneath this crater rim, named 'recurring slope lineae' or RSLs, offer the most convincing evidence yet for the presence of persistent water on the Martian surface.

the case, however, required the up-close chemical analysis of the Mars Exploration Rovers *Spirit* and *Opportunity*. *Spirit* landed in Gusev Crater, a suspected dried-up lake, but found that it had been covered by lava at some later point in its history. However, when one of the rover's wheels jammed and began scraping along the ground, geologists discovered that the rocks it uncovered had been penetrated by a hot salty spring at some point in the past. *Opportunity*, meanwhile, landed on Meridiani Planum in a region rich in the iron compound haematite. The rover's study of distinctive haematite spheres or 'blueberries' revealed that they, and many of the other rocks in the area, had formed within a standing body of water.

In August 2011, the MRO team announced perhaps the most promising development yet – convincing evidence for water flowing on the Martian surface today. Observing a number of highland craters several times through a Martian year, MRO scientists noticed dark features emerging from outcrops of bedrock in the crater rims, and moving gradually downslope along narrow channels from late spring to late summer, before fading away in the winter. Named recurring slope lineae or RSLs, these features cannot be formed by the relatively explosive action of liquid carbon dioxide, and since pure water would freeze rapidly in the locations observed, the best explanation for their origin seems to be the seepage of brine (whose salt content lowers its freezing point). If the presence of water on the Martian surface can be confirmed with further observation, it will be a major breakthrough.

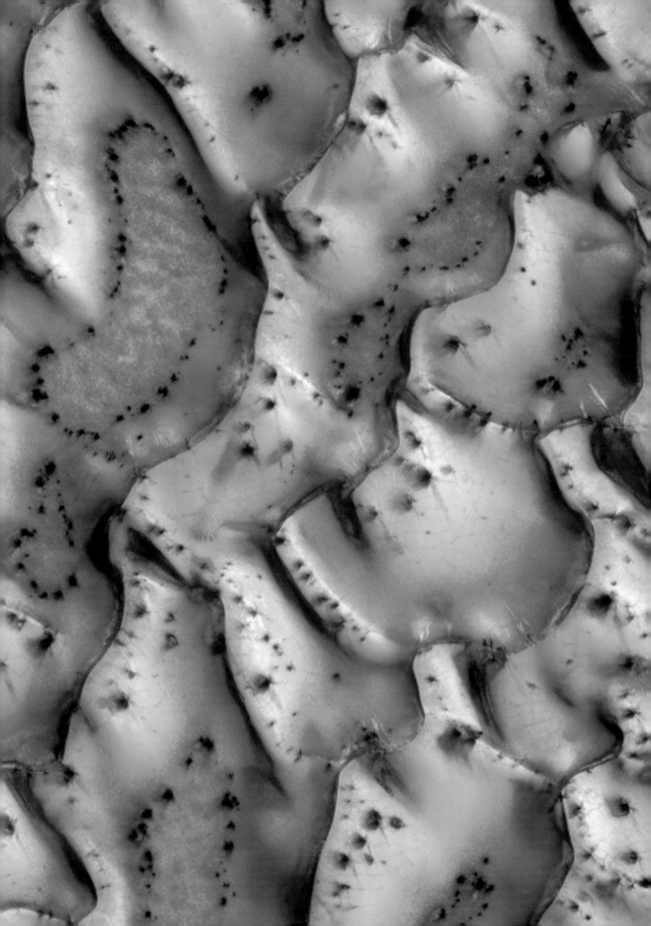

41

The possibility of life on Mars

DEFINITION CONTROVERSIAL EVIDENCE FOR LIFE ON MARS IN THE DISTANT PAST, AND PERHAPS EVEN TODAY.

DISCOVERY EXPERIMENTS ON BOARD THE VIKING LANDERS OF THE 1970S PRODUCED CONFLICTING RESULTS.

KEY BREAKTHROUGH IN 2008, HUNGARIAN ASTRONOMERS SUGGESTED SPIDER-LIKE MARKINGS AROUND THE SOUTH POLE COULD BE CREATED BY PHOTOSYNTHETIC MICROBES.

IMPORTANCE THE DISCOVERY OF LIFE ON ANOTHER WORLD WOULD HAVE HUGE SCIENTIFIC AND PHILOSOPHICAL IMPLICATIONS.

Mars is the most hospitable of the other planets even today, and in the past was probably far more Earth-like, with plentiful liquid water on its surface. So could life have begun to evolve on the Red Planet, and might it still cling on in today's more hostile environment?

The possibility of Martian life has fascinated astronomers for centuries. Famous observers of the early telescopic era, such as Christiaan Huygens, and William Herschel, believed that Mars was probably home to intelligent beings. Shifting dark patches on the surface were interpreted as seasonal changes in the vegetation, and the later reports of artificial-looking channels or *canali* sparked a wave of speculation that continued into the Space Age. However, the first spaceprobe images of Mars suggested that it was a cold, dry and dead world, and it was only with the arrival of the Viking landers in 1976 that scientists were able to investigate the possibility of life in detail.

A controversial experiment

Each of the Vikings carried a suite of experiments to test for life, either by directly detecting carbon-based organic chemicals in the soil, or by looking for signs of gas being released by microorganisms when a soil sample was fed with nutrients and incubated. While most of the tests proved negative, one known as the 'Labelled Release' (LR) experiment, produced puzzling results – at first, it appeared that something in the soil sample was indeed processing the nutrients and releasing gas, but when a second dose of nutrient was added to the sample a week later, there was no further gas release.

Both Viking landers found similar results, and most of the mission scientists eventually concluded that this behaviour indicated that some unknown

OPPOSITE According to Hungarian scientists, these spectacular 'starburst' or 'spider' features, formed by sublimation of carbon dioxide from beneath the surface of Mars, might gain their colour from photosynthetic microbes.

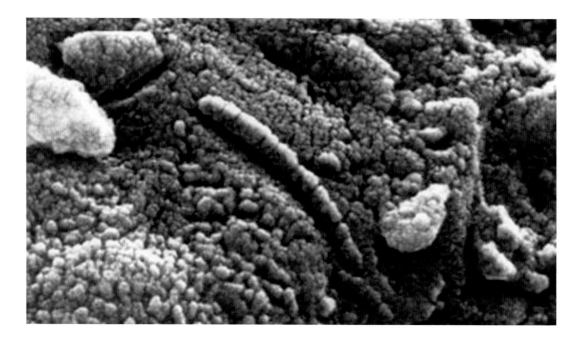

chemical in the soil, rather than a living organism, was responsible for the initial release of gas. However several scientists, including Gilbert Levin, designer of the LR experiment, have doubts about this conclusion.

But if the results of Viking's search for present-day life remain inconclusive, the decades since have seen a wealth of discoveries suggesting that Mars was far more hospitable in the past – so could life have developed then? Testing the habitability of the past environment is one of the main goals of NASA's *Curiosity* rover, scheduled to operate on Mars from late 2012.

'Fossils' from Mars

In the summer of 1996, headlines around the world reported the discovery of possible traces of life in an ancient fragment of Mars, discovered as a meteorite in Antarctica. Catalogued as ALH 84001, this meteorite fell to Earth some 13,000 years ago after 15 million years in space – but its interior preserved Martian rock unchanged for more than 4 billion years. Now a group of experienced NASA scientists claimed to have detected minerals and chemicals within the rock that would, on Earth, be accepted as products of bacteria. Electron microscope images showed worm-like structures in the rock, typically just a few tens of nanometres (billionths of a metre) across. The NASA team tentatively suggested that they could be microfossils – the remains of tiny bacteria, far smaller than any known from Earth at that time.

Given the claims being made for ALH 84001, the scientific community subjected the evidence to harsh scrutiny. Some lines of evidence soon collapsed as scientists found ways to produce the same chemicals without organic intervention. Others, such as the alleged fossils, were generally disregarded because they implied the existence of tiny nanobacteria that would be too small to exist and replicate according to our current understanding. However no experiment has yet replicated these structures by other means, and recent discoveries have boosted evidence for nanobacteria on Earth.

The strongest remaining evidence that life might once have existed in ALH 84001 comes from carbonate and magnetite minerals, deposited in distinct patterns that suggest they could be the ghostly traces of ancient bacteria. In 2001, a second NASA team claimed to have mimicked these patterns without organic processes, in Mars-like conditions, but the original group insisted the comparison was inaccurate. While the balance of scientific opinion remains sceptical, the debate is unlikely to be settled for good without more samples of Martian rock to examine.

Life today?

Since the speculation over ALH 84001 died down, attention has returned to the prospects for life on Mars today. The increasing evidence for water beneath the surface suggests that Mars is far more hospitable to life than previously suspected. The discovery of the remains of ancient hot acid springs by the *Spirit* Mars rover, and of extremophile microorganisms surviving in similar environments on Earth (see page 118), has improved the chances still further.

'The results of Viking's search for present-day life remain inconclusive, but the decades since have seen a wealth of discoveries suggesting that Mars was far more hospitable in the past.'

Some of the most intriguing evidence has recently come from ESA's Mars Express probe, which entered orbit around Mars in late 2003 and almost immediately identified the presence of methane in the Martian atmosphere. Since solar radiation should cause methane to disintegrate on a relatively short timescale, any methane now present must be constantly generated at an estimated rate of 270 tonnes per year. There are only two feasible sources for producing the gas – ongoing volcanic activity, or colonies of methane-producing microbes.

In February 2005, ESA scientists announced the discovery of formaldehyde, another short-lived gas that can be replenished by either volcanism or life. Intriguingly, however, both gases are found in the same areas of Mars, and often associated with known sources of water vapour and subsurface ice, which may indicate that microbes are the more likely source.

In 2008, a team of Hungarian scientists led by András Horváth of the Budapest Observatory made the fascinating suggestion that we may already have seen traces of microscopic life on Mars. They argue that the dark spider-like features and blotches associated with the evaporation of carbon dioxide around the south pole could be caused by photosynthetic microbes flourishing in the brief Martian spring. If this extraordinary claim is borne out, it would be an uncanny echo of earlier theories about shifting vegetation on the Martian surface.

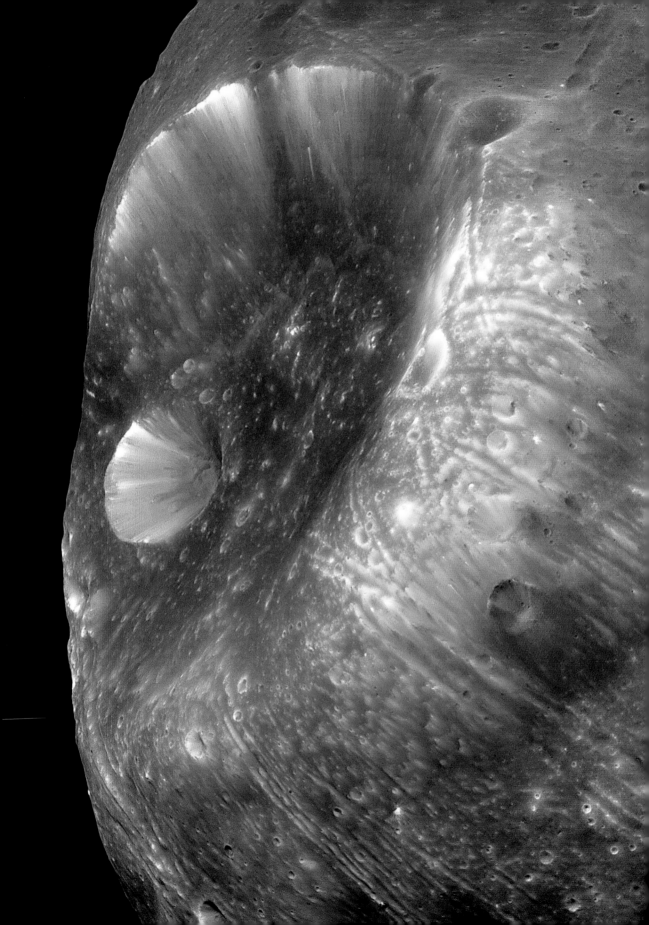

42

The origin of the Martian moons

DEFINITION CHANGING IDEAS ABOUT THE ORIGIN OF THE TWO SMALL SATELLITES OF MARS.

DISCOVERY THE MARTIAN MOONS WERE DISCOVERED BY ASAPH HALL IN 1877 AND LONG ASSUMED TO BE CAPTURED ASTEROIDS.

KEY BREAKTHROUGH A 2010 ANALYSIS SUGGESTS THAT PHOBOS AND DEIMOS ORIGINATED RATHER LIKE EARTH'S MOON, AS DEBRIS THROWN OFF DURING AN IMPACT ON MARS.

IMPORTANCE THE MARTIAN MOONS MAY PRESERVE MATERIAL FROM THE ANCIENT SURFACE OF MARS.

The two small moons of Mars are unlike anything found elsewhere in the solar system. Long assumed to be captured asteroids, recent analysis of both their orbital characteristics and their compositions has suggested that they may have a more dramatic origin.

Although the existence of two moons around Mars was predicted as early as the 1600s by no less an authority than Johannes Kepler (see page 14), the reasoning behind it (based on the numerical gap between the single satellite of Earth and the four moons of Jupiter) was little more than guesswork. Nevertheless, it influenced generations of astronomers, and satirists including Jonathan Swift and Voltaire. And ultimately, it inspired astronomer Asaph Hall, whose detailed searches from the US Naval Observatory in Washington, DC, resulted in the discovery of two small satellites in orbit around the red planet in August 1877.

Phobos and Deimos were puzzling from the outset. Not only are they tiny, with average diameters of 22 km (13.5 miles) and 12.5 km (7.8 miles) respectively, but they orbit extremely close to Mars itself, at 9,400 km (5,800 miles) and 23,500 km (14,600 miles) from the planet's centre. This means that Phobos circles Mars in just 7 hours 39 minutes (more than three times faster than the planet rotates), and Deimos in 30 hours 18 minutes. At the time, the preferred explanation for the origin of satellites was the 'fission hypothesis' (see page 121), but the speedy orbit of Phobos presented a major problem for the idea that the two Martian moons were ejected from a fast-spinning early Mars. Instead, there seemed to be two possible explanations for their origin – either they formed from debris left behind after the formation of Mars, or they were captured from elsewhere in the solar system.

OPPOSITE A close-up image from the HIRISE camera aboard NASA's Mars Reconnaissance Orbiter reveals colourful detail in Stickney Crater on Phobos. The groove-like parallel scars running across the moon's surface can also be clearly identified.

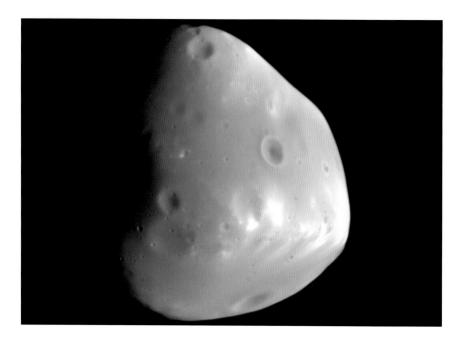

Viking and after

When NASA's twin Viking spaceprobes arrived in Martian orbit during mid-1976, they provided the first detailed views of the two satellites (although Mariner 9 had returned a handful of low-resolution images a few years previously). Phobos proved to be dark, elongated and heavily cratered, with one particular bowl-shaped crater, Stickney, some 9 km (5.6 miles) in diameter. The satellite's mass, meanwhile, proved to be remarkably low, suggesting that its interior is highly porous and contains up to 30 percent empty space. Aside from its craters, the most striking features of Phobos's surface were a number of grooves or streaks, up to 200 metres (660 ft) across and 20 km (12.5 miles) long, which seemed to radiate from around Stickney and were generally assumed to be linked to its formation.

Deimos, meanwhile, was also dark and cratered, but was slightly more regular in size, and significantly smoother, apparently due to surface dust levelling out the relief. It was also even more porous, with an average density just a little greater than that of water. One theory put forward to explain this dusty surface is that Deimos may have been struck by a single large impact relatively late in its history, throwing out a large amount of debris that later fell back to blanket the surface.

Based on the first spectral analyses of the satellites' surfaces, astronomers concluded that the two asteroids were made of primitive 'carbonaceous chondrite' material, similar to that of the C-type asteroids (see page 187) and therefore that they were probably captured asteroids themselves. Later spectral studies using the Hubble Space Telescope and others revealed that the moons were distinctly reddish in colour, with a close resemblance to D-type asteroids, which typically lurk in the outer reaches of the asteroid belt. These asteroids seem to contain substantial amounts of ice, which would make them even more primitive and unaltered than C-types. According to one theory, these unusual asteroids may be migrants from the Kuiper Belt, disturbed during the early phase of planetary migration (see page 101). If this is the case, then Phobos and Deimos could have remarkably exotic origins.

However, the moons' orbits still present a significant problem – both follow near-perfect circular paths above the Martian equator, which suggests some mechanism must have modified their orbits from the tilted ellipses that are by far the most probable result of a capture scenario. The relatively low mass and sparse atmosphere of Mars mean that explanations relying on either tidal forces or atmospheric drag to do this job face problems. Another possibility, first mooted by Geoffrey Landis of NASA's John Glenn Research Center in 2002, is that the moons both originated in binary asteroid systems, split apart and captured into orbit around Mars. The forces involved in separating the components would tend to pull the captured bodies into circular orbits, but still require a quite precise set of conditions for the initial capture.

'The moons bear a close resemblance to D-type asteroids that may be migrants from the Kuiper Belt. If this is the case, then Phobos and Deimos could have remarkably exotic origins.'

Recent surprises

Phobos and Deimos remained intriguing mysteries throughout the 1980s and 1990s, in large part due to a string of failed American and Soviet/Russian Mars probes. However, they have been studied in some detail by several NASA missions since the late 1990s, and these have revealed some unexpected surprises. One of the most significant is that the grooves of Phobos are not, as previously thought, radiating from Stickney but are in fact aligned with the moon's direction of travel, and centred on its leading point. This suggests they may have been created as the moon ploughed through debris in its orbit – perhaps on as many as a dozen separate occasions.

Even more surprisingly, in 2010, an international team led by Marco Giuranna of the Italian National Institute for Astrophysics published a study that dramatically overturned previous ideas about the moons' composition. Based on results from spectrometers aboard NASA's Mars Global Surveyor and the European Space Agency's Mars Express probe, they showed that the surface of Phobos could not, in fact, be matched to any known class of chondritic meteorite, and, in particular, that areas close to Stickney were rich in phyllosilicate, a hydrated mineral found on the surface of Mars. Based on this evidence, it seems that Phobos and Deimos may not in fact be captured asteroids after all – instead, they might be debris ejected from Mars itself during a large interplanetary collision (similar to the process that formed our own moon). According to this theory, it's even possible that the two moons formed within short-lived Martian rings, and that the last remnants from these rings were responsible for creating the distinctive grooves on Phobos.

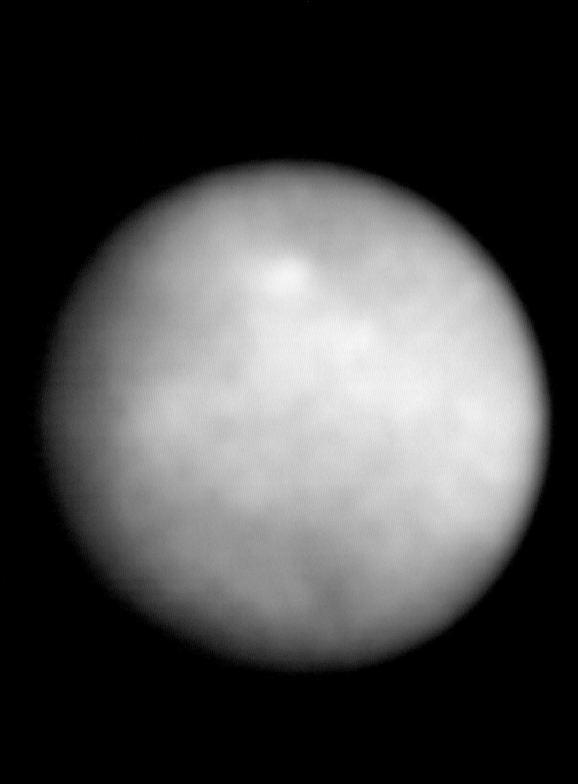

43

Ceres

DEFINITION THE LARGEST MEMBER OF THE ASTEROID BELT, CERES HAS RECENTLY BEEN RECLASSIFIED AS A DWARF PLANET.

DISCOVERY CERES WAS FIRST OBSERVED BY GIUSEPPE PIAZZI IN 1801.

KEY BREAKTHROUGH IN 2003, ASTRONOMERS USED THE HUBBLE SPACE TELESCOPE TO MAP CERES FOR THE FIRST TIME.

IMPORTANCE IF CERES IS A SURVIVING PLANETESIMAL FROM THE SOLAR SYSTEM'S FORMATION, IT COULD BE A TREASURE TROVE OF INFORMATION ABOUT THE RAW MATERIALS OF OUR OWN PLANET.

The solar system's main asteroid belt forms a broad ring around the Sun between the orbits of Mars and Jupiter. Most asteroids are kilometre-scale fragments of ancient rock, but the largest of them, the dwarf planet Ceres, seems to be an intriguing and complex world.

Ceres was the first asteroid to be discovered, spotted by Italian astronomer Giuseppe Piazzi on 1 January 1801, at a time when many astronomers were convinced there should be a 'fifth planet' in the unusually large gap between Mars and Jupiter. Indeed, Ceres was considered to be a new planet at first, until further discoveries over the following decades relegated it to just the first and largest among countless asteroids. However, it was clear from the outset that the new world was smaller than any of the other planets – astronomers estimated it to be a few hundred kilometres across.

Today, the diameter of Ceres is known to be around 950 km (590 miles), making it by far the largest object in the asteroid belt. It contains roughly one third of all the mass in the belt and has sufficient gravity to have pulled itself into a spherical shape. This means that, according to the new classification of solar system objects agreed by the International Astronomical Union in 2006, Ceres is now classed as a dwarf planet (a spherical body, orbiting the Sun, that has not cleared other objects from around its orbit).

Mysterious world

But while Ceres' promotion to a planet of sorts may be largely a matter of semantics, it happens to have coincided neatly with a renewed wave of interest in this strange little world, and discoveries that suggest it is not quite the barren ball of rock we might expect.

OPPOSITE This Hubble Space Telescope image represents our best view of Ceres so far. It clearly shows the dwarf planet's reddish surface, as well as bright patches that are probably caused by ice.

The recent discoveries have come largely from Hubble Space Telescope (HST) observations, which have resolved Ceres into a disc with distinct, if blurry, surface features. Between December 2003 and January 2004, a team of astronomers including Peter Thomas of Cornell University used the HST to take a series of 267 images of Ceres through a complete rotation. While the individual images are unavoidably pixelated, they showed a number of bright and dark surface features. Perhaps most importantly, though, they revealed Ceres' near-perfect spherical shape, with a slight equatorial bulge. This kind of shape indicates that the asteroid has a differentiated interior separate into layers – in other words, like the major worlds of the inner solar system, it went through considerable evolution early in its history.

Studying the surface

Earlier spectral analysis put Ceres among the C-type asteroids – worlds whose surfaces are covered in carbon-rich minerals, thought to be related to the carbonaceous chondrite meteorites (see page 110). In general, carbonaceous chondrites are assumed to be almost unchanged samples of the raw material left over from the solar system's formation, and until the new evidence for a differentiated interior emerged, Ceres was generally assumed to be an exceptionally large example of such a C-type asteroid.

'Most astronomers now agree that Ceres is probably the largest remaining planetesimal, surviving in a primitive state from the origins of the solar system some 4.5 billion years ago.'

However the situation now appears to be much more complex. In 2006, astronomers studying the infrared spectrum of Ceres announced the discovery of evidence for hydrated minerals in the crust – carbonates and clays with molecules of water locked up in their mineral structure. This suggests that the material that formed Ceres was rich in ice and water vapour, fitting with its position close to the frost line in the early protoplanetary nebula (see page 97). Further evidence for an icy nature comes from the Hubble images – dark patches with bright centres are probably craters that pierced the relatively dark outer crust to expose fresh ice beneath. Another prominent bright spot on the surface is probably a large region of highly reflective ice.

A changing world?

Intriguingly, infrared photographs of Ceres taken with the Keck telescopes in Hawaii have shown variations in the light and dark patches over time, and there is some evidence that Ceres might have a thin atmosphere of water vapour. Ceres is surprisingly warm for a world that never comes within 2.5 astronomical units (AU) of the Sun, with surface temperatures reaching around –35°C (–31°F) at times – just enough for ice to sublimate from its surface. If this theory is correct, then the changing patterns of brightness on the surface could be due to evaporation and condensation of frost.

According to several recent models of its evolution, Ceres may have an internal structure of separate layers, with a rocky core, an icy mantle around

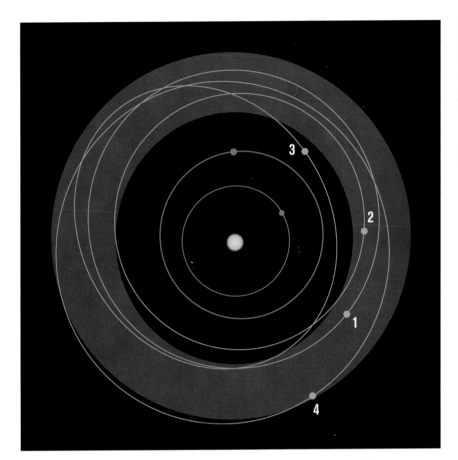

100 km (60 miles) deep and, possibly, even a liquid ocean layer. While the dwarf planet is almost certainly geologically dead today, it's possible that, early in its history, heat from the core could have triggered icy volcanic activity similar to that seen among the moons of the outer solar system.

Given its size and location in the solar system, most astronomers now agree that Ceres is probably the largest remaining planetesimal, surviving in a remarkably primitive state from the very origins of the solar system some 4.5 billion years ago. While the size to which it grew was limited by the relatively sparse supply of rocky material in this region of the protoplanetary nebula and the disruptive influence of Jupiter's gravity, Ceres was fortunate to survive intact, while most of its siblings fell into elliptical orbits that either ejected them from the solar system completely, or saw them collide and coalesce to form the modern rocky planets. An alternative and far more surprising idea, put forward by William B. McKinnon of Washington University in 2008, is that Ceres might be an ice dwarf from the Kuiper Belt, similar to Triton and Pluto (see pages 245 and 249), and introduced to the asteroid belt during the migration of the outer giant planets (see page 101). Whatever its true origin, Ceres promises to be a fascinating target for the Dawn asteroid probe when it enters orbit around it later this decade.

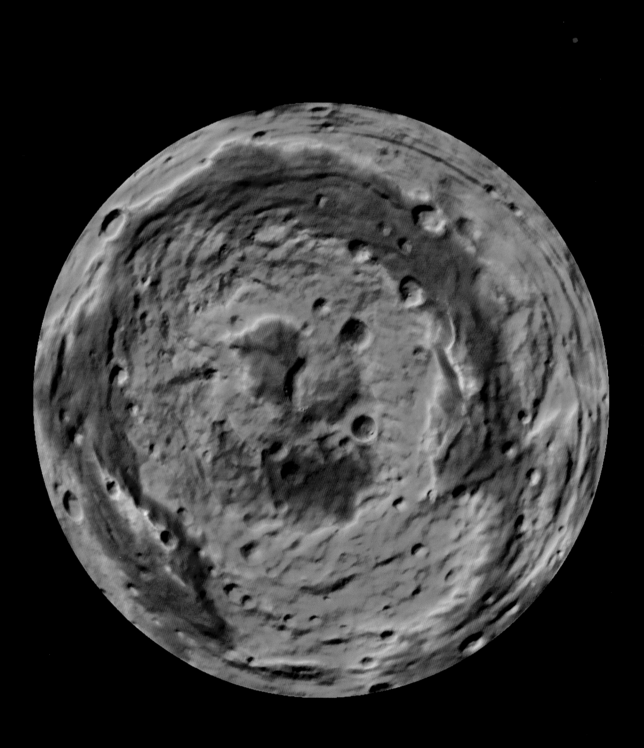

44 Vesta's volcanic surface

DEFINITION THE SECOND LARGEST ASTEROID SHOWS CLEAR SIGNS OF GEOLOGICAL ACTIVITY IN ITS PAST.

DISCOVERY VESTA WAS DISCOVERED BY GERMAN ASTRONOMER HEINRICH OLBERS IN 1807.

KEY BREAKTHROUGH SPECTRAL OBSERVATIONS BEGINNING IN 1970 ESTABLISHED THE UNUSUAL IGNEOUS NATURE OF VESTA'S SURFACE ROCKS.

IMPORTANCE THE PROCESSES THAT KEPT VESTA ACTIVE ALSO AFFECTED THE ROCKY INNER PLANETS, AND CAN PROVIDE RARE INFORMATION ABOUT CONDITIONS IN THE EARLY SOLAR NEBULA.

The strange asteroid Vesta is an intriguing relic from the early days of the solar system, battered by volcanic activity and an enormous impact. And, within its rocks, it may also hold a vital clue to the cataclysmic events that created our solar system.

The second largest world in the asteroid belt, Vesta is very different from Ceres. While its larger neighbour's surface appears largely unchanged since the early days of the solar system (see page 177), Vesta's landscape is covered in igneous rocks similar to those that erupt from volcanoes on much larger rocky worlds. These rocks are considerably more reflective than the carbon-rich minerals of Ceres, and they make Vesta the brightest of all the asteroids.

Early observations

Vesta was the fourth asteroid to be discovered, identified by German astronomer Heinrich Olbers in 1807. Olbers had already discovered and named the second asteroid, Pallas, so he gave the famous mathematician Carl Gauss the honour of naming his new find. Gauss chose to name it after the Roman goddess of the hearth and home.

The new asteroid's brightness made it a good target for astronomers hoping to discover its physical properties. Edward C. Pickering of Harvard College Observatory made the most accurate early estimate of Vesta's size at around 513 km (319 miles) in 1879, and he went on to make precise photometric measurements of its brightness. By the 1950s, researchers were able to estimate Vesta's rotation period based on minute changes to its brightness, and in 1966, German-American astronomer Hans Hertz was able to calculate Vesta's mass by measuring its effect on a smaller nearby asteroid

OPPOSITE This false-colour elevation map was made using stereo cameras as NASA's Dawn probe orbited above Vesta's south pole in 2011. It clearly shows the rim of the huge Rheasilvia impact structure, some 500 km (310 miles) across.

RIGHT A view across Vesta's southern hemisphere from Dawn clearly shows the raised central peak of Rheasilvia, some 23 km (14 miles) above the surrounding crater floor.

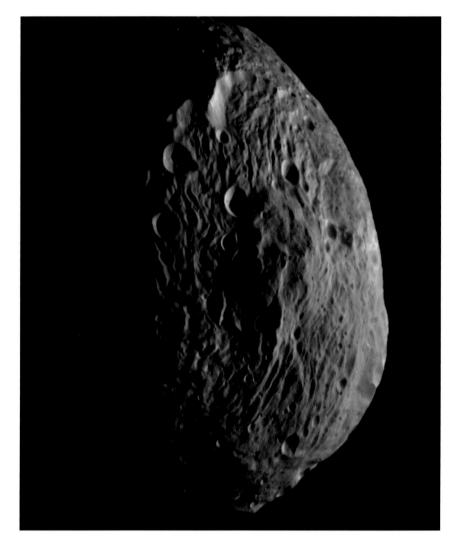

Vesta proved to be about as dense as Mars, a surprisingly high density for an asteroid. Spectroscopic observations by Tom McCord of the Massachusetts Institute of Technology and colleagues revealed its unusual surface in 1970, and Vesta was soon recognized as prototype for a class of V-type asteroids.

Vesta up close

Most early models of Vesta assumed that the asteroid was large enough to be spherical, but in 1989 technological advances allowed its shape to be resolved, and showed that, while Vesta's equatorial diameter is 550 km (342 miles), the distance across its poles is just 462 km (287 miles).

When astronomers turned the Hubble Space Telescope's cameras towards Vesta for the first time in 1996, they discovered the reason for Vesta's asymmetry – its south pole is scarred by an enormous impact crater. Now known as Rheasilvia, the impact has gouged a huge hole in the surface, some

460 km (290 miles) across and 13 km (8 miles) deep, with a distinctive peak in the centre rising back to 23 km (14 miles) above the crater floor.

Vesta's unusual features made it a prime target for NASA's Dawn mission, a robotic spaceprobe that arrived at Vesta in July 2011. Dawn will map Vesta from orbit for a year before moving on to a planned rendezvous with Ceres in 2015. Initial observations have confirmed the traumatic effect the formation of Rheasilvia had on the entire asteroid, revealing grooves around Vesta's equator that were probably created by shock waves from the impact. They also confirmed that the crater penetrated through Vesta's outer crust, revealing a section through several different layers of crust rocks, into the top of a mantle rich in the mineral olivine. Material ejected from this impact is believed to account for the other V-type asteroids, and also the related 'HED' meteorites found on Earth (see page 111). This makes Vesta one of the few asteroids whose composition can be studied in laboratory conditions.

Solar system archaeology

Vesta's volcanic surface and unusually dense interior suggest that it is a rare survivor from a family of similar planetesimals that formed early in the solar system's history. In order to melt in the way they did, these igneous asteroids must have formed in regions of the solar nebula enriched with radioactive materials – isotopes such as aluminium-26. In 1999, a study of the Piplia Kalan HED meteorite by Gopalan Srinivasan and colleagues at India's Physical Research Laboratory showed that in order to get the full benefit from heating as the radioactive atoms decayed, Vesta and its siblings must have come together very soon after this material was injected into the solar nebula.

'Vesta's south pole is scarred by an enormous impact crater. Now known as Rheasilvia, it has gouged a huge hole in the surface, 460 km (290 miles) across and 13 km (8 miles) deep.'

As heat from decaying isotopes spread through their rocks, the interiors of Vesta-like asteroids melted and separated into layers of different densities, forming a core of molten iron and nickel beneath a churning mantle of olivine. As these asteroids cooled again and began to form solid crusts, their mantles were still hot enough to power volcanic activity for some time before they too solidified. Over the aeons since their formation, most of these metal-cored asteroids have long since been shattered to pieces – only Vesta has survived.

In 2011, astronomers Alan P. Boss of Washington's Carnegie Institute, and Matthias Gritschneder of the University of California at Santa Cruz independently went in search of the source of the radioactive material that powered this activity. Using different modelling techniques, they both concluded that it was produced in a supernova that exploded around 15 light years from the solar nebula, and injected into the nebula by the expanding shock wave about 20,000 years later. Since the asteroids and planets must have begun to form very shortly after this, it may just be that Gritschneder and Boss have found a trace of the event that created our solar system itself.

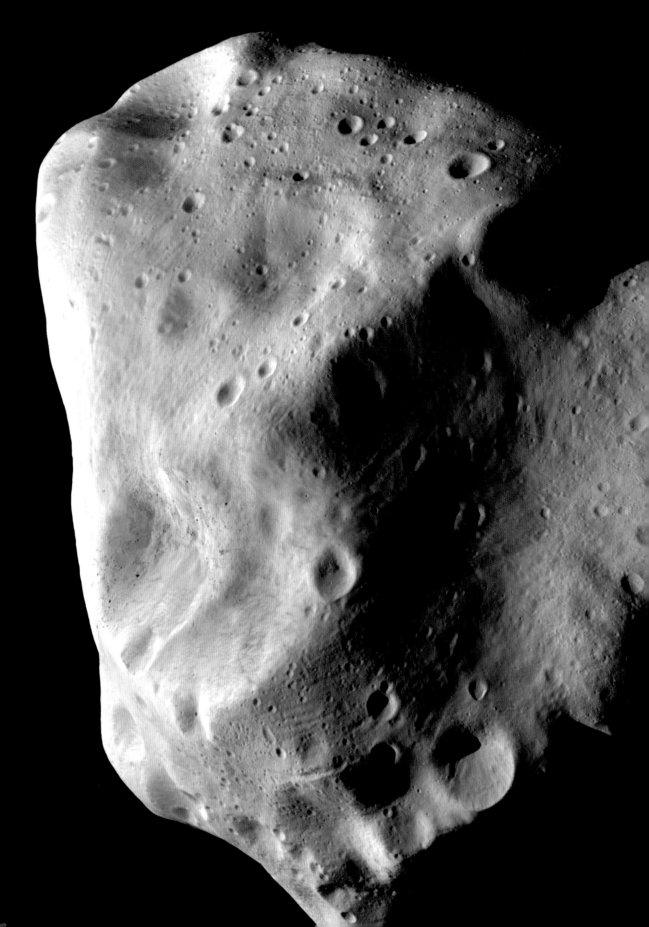

The evolution of asteroids

DEFINITION EVIDENCE THAT ASTEROIDS ARE CONSTANTLY EVOLVING, DYNAMIC BODIES.

DISCOVERY THE FIRST ASTEROIDS WERE DISCOVERED IN THE EARLY 1800s.

KEY BREAKTHROUGH AROUND 1918, KIYOTSUGU HIRAYAMA SHOWED HOW CERTAIN ASTEROID 'FAMILIES' COULD BE TRACED BACK TO THE BREAK-UP OF LARGER BODIES.

IMPORTANCE ESTABLISHING THE ORIGINS OF ASTEROID FAMILIES ALLOWS ASTRONOMERS TO RECONSTRUCT ANCIENT PLANETESIMALS FROM THE EARLY DAYS OF THE SOLAR SYSTEM.

Sandwiched between the orbits of Mars and Jupiter, the asteroid belt has long been seen as a relic filled with debris from the early days of the solar system. Recent discoveries, however, have cast it in a different light, as a region whose objects are constantly changing and evolving.

Following the discovery of a handful of bright asteroids such as Ceres and Vesta in the early 1800s, technological improvements throughout the 19th century saw the number of known asteroids rise into the hundreds and eventually thousands. Today there are thought to be around 1.7 million objects larger than 1 kilometre (0.6 miles) across within the main asteroid belt, as well as countless smaller fragments.

At first, astronomers hoped that the orbits of all these different worlds might all be traced back to a common origin in the break-up of an ancient 'fifth planet' predicted by theories of the time. However, it soon became clear that the orbits of individual asteroids had little in common with each other except for the fact they were hemmed in by the gravity of Jupiter on the outer edge, and Mars on the inner side. In reality, the asteroid belt marks a region where Jupiter's powerful gravity, combined with a lack of raw material, actually prevented the formation of a small rocky planet. So for a long time, it seemed that the asteroids were simply random fragments of debris left over from the early days of the solar system. It turned out that this was far from the truth.

Straying from the belt

The fact that not all asteroids remain with the main asteroid belt is an important clue to the dynamic nature of their orbits. The first of these Near-Earth Objects (NEOs) to be identified was Amor, discovered by Belgian

OPPOSITE The European Space Agency's Rosetta comet probe sent back this image of asteroid 21 Lutetia in July 2010. Lutetia is a dense metal-rich asteroid that has been heavily cratered, but not completely fragmented, during its long history.

astronomer Eugène Joseph Delporte in 1932, and hundreds are now known. Despite their name, few NEOs present a threat to our planet – most stay well beyond Earth's orbit, or follow tilted paths that keep them at a safe distance.

'Not every collision results in a neat fragmentation – measurements indicate that some asteroids shattered with too little force to fly apart completely.'

Asteroids in such stray orbits are living on borrowed time. Close encounters with planets will disrupt their orbits on timescales of millions of years, either sending them spiralling towards a collision with the Sun, pushing them into a 'Trojan' orbit at a safe distance from the planet (see page 126), or ejecting them from the solar system altogether. The fact that plenty of NEOs still exist is a sign that some process is replenishing them, and this is probably linked to the 'Kirkwood gaps' found in certain regions of the main belt – empty zones that correspond to resonant orbits, where an asteroid's orbital period would be a neat fraction of Jupiter's. Any object venturing into one of the gaps will find itself repeatedly and systematically disturbed by Jupiter's gravity, pushing it into the elliptical orbit of an NEO.

Finding asteroid families

Around 1918, Japanese astronomer Kiyotsugu Hirayama made an important breakthrough that revealed how asteroids in differing orbits might share a common origin after all. He recognized that many of an asteroid's orbital characteristics were not constant. Instead they changed in long osculating cycles under the influence of the Sun, the planets, and even other asteroids.

Hirayama also identified another set of orbital characteristics that remain stable over far longer periods, known as the proper elements. When the distribution of these proper elements was studied, it soon became clear that some 35 percent of all asteroids are clumped together in distinct families.

More than 20 asteroid families are now known. Some are associated with major asteroids such as Pallas, Vesta and Hygiea, with the smaller members originating as fragments chipped off the larger world by impacts. Other families have no particularly dominant member and probably originated in the fragmentation of a single larger body.

In December 2010, astronomers got a rare insight into these collisions when Steve Larson of the NEO-hunting Catalina Sky Survey project noticed that the main-belt asteroid Scheilla had taken on a comet-like appearance. Comparison with previous images showed that a cloud had developed around the asteroid in the previous month, and close-up images from ground-based observatories and the Hubble Space Telescope confirmed that the cloud was composed of large debris fragments rather than comet-like gas. According to the latest models, Scheilla was hit by a smaller asteroid, roughly 35 metres (100 ft) in diameter, travelling at a speed of 5 km/s (3 miles per second). Collisions between asteroids may be rare on a human timescale, but they are inevitable on the much longer timescales of solar system history. And not

LEFT In January 2010, the Hubble Space Telescope photographed a newly discovered comet-like object called P/2010 A2. It proved to be the first evidence for a recent collision between asteroids.

every collision results in a neat fragmentation – spaceprobe measurements indicate that some asteroids, such as Mathilde and Itokawa, shattered with too little force to fly apart completely. Instead, their weak gravity pulled them back together, creating a low-density rubble pile.

Asteroid types

Asteroids can also be classified by their surface properties, discovered by analysing their spectra (see page 25). The main classes of asteroids show a clear relationship to the main types of meteorite found on Earth (see page 109), and fall into three main groups: C-type, S-type and M-type. C-type asteroids are dark and carbonaceous, with surfaces covered in light-absorbing, carbon-based molecules. S-types are brighter, with silica-based rocks and minerals familiar from the larger planets. A bias toward S-types close to the Sun and C-types further away probably reflects differences in the protoplanetary nebula from which the asteroids formed. Finally M-type asteroids are predominantly metallic – mostly large fragments of iron.

Despite this broad simplicity, there are many additional complications – and to add to the problems, there is no single agreed list of asteroid classifications, with numerous proposed subtypes and a handful of distinctive minor groups that appear to sit outside the three main types altogether. Similarities in surface between the members of asteroid families tend to confirm their origin within a single parent body, but in some cases families have members of several different mineralogical types. This suggests they probably originated from the destruction of much larger asteroids with layered internal structures – a group of lost worlds of which Vesta (see page 181) may be the sole survivor.

46 Jupiter's interior

DEFINITION A MYSTERIOUS INTERNAL POWER SOURCE THAT HELPS DRIVE COMPLEX WEATHER SYSTEMS IN JUPITER'S UPPER ATMOSPHERE.

DISCOVERY JUPITER'S UNUSUAL HEAT OUTPUT WAS FIRST IDENTIFIED THROUGH INFRARED IMAGING IN 1966.

KEY BREAKTHROUGH IN 1995, THE GALILEO ATMOSPHERIC PROBE DROPPED THROUGH JUPITER'S CLOUDS, RETURNING VALUABLE INFORMATION ABOUT ATMOSPHERIC CONDITIONS.

IMPORTANCE UNDERSTANDING JUPITER'S INTERIOR COULD RESOLVE UNANSWERED QUESTIONS ABOUT THE GIANT PLANET'S FORMATION.

The largest planet in the Solar System, Jupiter is an immense gas giant wrapped in colourful cloud bands, wracked with powerful storms and heated by an internal energy source. However, we still know little about the planet below its surface layers.

While the fine details of Jupiter's atmosphere are in a state of constant flux, its overall structure has remained the same ever since Gian Domenico Cassini and Robert Hooke drew the first telescopic maps of the planet in the 1660s. The dominant features are dark and light stripes known as belts and zones – names that suggest the darker bands are relatively localized features above a more uniform light background. In fact, the reverse is the case – the Voyager spaceprobe flybys of the late 1970s showed that the dark brown and bluish belts were clearings that revealed clouds at deeper levels of the atmosphere, while the creamy-white zones were in fact areas of higher-altitude cloud obscuring the darker material below.

Belts and zones

As with all planets, Jupiter's climate is governed by the movement of heat from warmer to colder areas. On Earth, each hemisphere displays three cells in which warm air rises up at low latitudes, cools, and sink down closer to the poles. Jupiter's bands are formed by similar cells that are more numerous because the Jovian atmosphere is so much denser and deeper than Earth's.

The boundaries between belts and zones give rise to Jupiter's most complex weather. High-speed jet streams running along each boundary strip away streamers of high, light cloud into ragged 'festoons', that hang above the deeper neighbouring cloud layers. Small storms are constantly coming and

OPPOSITE Jupiter's spectacular weather systems are captured in this long-range view of the planet, taken by the Cassini spaceprobe as it flew past on its way to Saturn in December 2000.

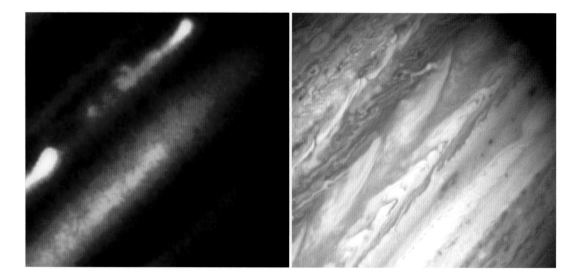

going over periods of days or weeks, but larger and more prominent ones tend to be rarer. They usually appear as white spots sitting on the boundary between belts and zones, where the opposing winds along the northern and southern edges power their rotation.

Atmospheric chemistry

As a mixture of gases is carried upwards in each convective band, pressure drops and the atmosphere cools, allowing various gases to condense into clouds. Spectroscopic analysis and laboratory modelling of these clouds show that water condenses at the lowest altitude, forming a deep base layer that usually remains unseen. Somewhat higher up, ammonium hydrosulphide condenses to form the belt clouds. Finally, ammonia condenses at even higher altitudes, creating the zones. The lower cloud bands of the belts have a tendency to move westward with Jupiter's general rotation, but at higher altitudes, coriolis forces generated by the planet's rapid spin become greater, and tend to drive the winds of the zones in the opposite, eastward, direction.

While these are the major chemical components of Jupiter's clouds, they raise an interesting question, since they should all form white clouds. The colourful blues, oranges, creams and reds that are actually seen probably come from small traces of other chemicals. The bruises that spread through the planet's atmosphere in the aftermath of the Comet Shoemaker–Levy 9 impact in 1994 (see page 197) dredged up chemicals from the deep interior, including carbon disulphide, hydrogen sulphide, and pure sulphur, which may contribute to these colours.

In October 1995, Galileo mission's atmospheric probe, a heavily shielded ball of scientific instruments weighing some 339 kg (746 lb), plunged into the outer layers of Jupiter's atmosphere, returning data for 58 minutes during a parachute descent before it finally failed under pressures equivalent to

23 Earth atmospheres. Although the probe recorded high winds of up to 725 km/h (450 mph), it encountered few clouds and no sign of water vapour, challenging accepted models of the planet's atmosphere. It was only later that further analysis revealed that the probe had, by chance, fallen through a dry and relatively cloudless 'hot spot' in the Jovian atmosphere.

Inner mysteries

Much of Jupiter's activity is powered by energy radiating from its deep inner layers. Infrared images of the giant planet show that it emits more heat than it receives from the Sun – an apparent imbalance that was first discovered by Frank Low of the University of Arizona in 1966. Overall, Jupiter is thought to have an internal power source that generates about the same amount of energy as the planet receives in solar radiation. As with the other giant planets, the source of this internal energy is thought to be a mix of residual heat from the planet's formation, coupled with slow contraction of the planet under gravity – the Kelvin–Helmholtz mechanism first suggested in the late 19th century as a possible energy source for the Sun itself. Cooling of the planet's outer layers causes a drop in pressure that shrinks the planet slightly, heating up the interior layers – in order to produce the internal energy so far measured, Jupiter must be shrinking by roughly 2 cm (0.8 in) per year.

The precise structure of Jupiter's deep interior remains uncertain. Beneath the activity of the outer atmosphere, the planet's inner layers are thought to be composed mostly of hydrogen, which becomes a liquid under pressure about 1,000 km (600 miles) into the planet. Much further down, the hydrogen disintegrates into electrically charged ions, creating a sea of liquid metallic hydrogen that is thought to generate the planet's powerful magnetic field.

'The "bruises" that spread through the planet's atmosphere in the aftermath of the Comet Shoemaker-Levy 9 impact dredged up chemicals from the deep interior.'

The planet was long assumed to have a central rocky core about the size of Earth and much more dense, and this was apparently confirmed with gravitational measurements taken by the Galileo spaceprobe. However, models of Jupiter's formation in which it was born from a single rotating gas cloud (see page 98) suggest that it might have no core whatsoever. At the other extreme, modelling work carried out at the University of California at Berkeley in 2008 suggests the core could be twice the size previously suggested, containing up to 18 times the mass of Earth.

One way to resolve uncertainties about Jupiter's interior would be to use seismology techniques similar to those that have proved successful in probing the Sun (see page 86). Astronomers have searched in vain for signs of global oscillation in Jupiter's atmosphere since the 1970s, but it was only in 2011 that a team led by Patrick Gaulme of the University of Paris reported success. Combined with data from the Juno spaceprobe, scheduled to enter orbit around Jupiter, in 2016, this technique may finally resolve some of the outstanding questions about the giant planet.

47 Red spots of Jupiter

DEFINITION JUPITER'S RED SPOTS ARE ENORMOUS LOW-PRESSURE STORMS IN THE PLANET'S SOUTHERN HEMISPHERE.

DISCOVERY THE GREAT RED SPOT HAS BEEN OBSERVED SINCE THE MID-19TH CENTURY AND, PERHAPS, SINCE THE MID-17TH.

KEY BREAKTHROUGH IN 2005, ASTRONOMERS SAW A LARGE WHITE STORM, OVAL BA, TRANSFORM INTO A NEW RED SPOT.

IMPORTANCE THE ATMOSPHERE OF JUPITER IS THE MOST COMPLEX IN THE SOLAR SYSTEM, WITH LESSONS FOR OUR STUDIES OF ALL OTHER PLANETARY ATMOSPHERES.

Jupiter's Great Red Spot is the most famous storm in the solar system – an anticyclone twice the size of Earth that has probably persisted for several centuries. But recent observations have shown that not all red spots on the giant planet are quite as long-lived.

Although astronomers only recognized and named the Great Red Spot (GRS) as recently as 1878, during a period when it was particularly noticeable, the spot and its accompanying 'hollow' in Jupiter's cloud bands had certainly been observed for at least half a century before, and have a prehistory going back considerably further. Italian astronomer Gian Domenico Cassini discovered a dark spot in Jupiter's southern hemisphere in 1665, and he and others continued to observe it through to 1713, when it disappeared. The precise relationship of Cassini's spot to the modern GRS is still uncertain – although it appeared in the same region of the planet, it had different dimensions and circled the planet at a different rate.

Astronomers soon developed several ways to account for the appearance of the GRS. One popular model saw it as a floating island amid a Jovian ocean, while another theory suggested it was an atmospheric disturbance formed above some feature on the hypothetical solid surface beneath the clouds.

A storm the size of Earth

However, as telescopes improved and photography allowed the preservation and later study of images showing the spot's behaviour, the evidence increasingly pointed towards the idea of the GRS as an anticyclone – a low-pressure weather feature which, thanks to the coriolis forces generated by Jupiter's rapid rotation, spins anticlockwise in the southern hemisphere.

OPPOSITE A spectacular enhanced-colour view of Jupiter's Great Red Spot, captured by the Voyager 1 spaceprobe in 1979, shows enormous folded cloud structures around the planet-sized storm.

Since the 1970s, spaceprobe images have confirmed that the Great Red Spot is indeed a huge anticyclone, with a diameter up to twice that of Earth. Circling the planet between the South Equatorial Belt (SEB) and the South Tropical Zone, its uppermost clouds rise some 8 km (5 miles) above the surrounding cloud bands, while it sits in a hollow in the SEB that plunges to a depth of around 50 km (30 miles), revealing some of the planet's lowest visible cloud layers. The spot rotates once every seven days, and wind speeds along its edges reach 430 km/h (270 mph).

Despite its apparent longevity, the GRS is constantly changing – computer models and laboratory tests both suggest that it is a free-floating eddy in the upper atmosphere, not reliant on any kind of driving force from beneath the surface. The speed with which it circles the planet varies considerably and is apparently linked to changes in the appearance of the SEB. And the spot's own influence extends deep into the planet: it is thought to gets its colour when a soup of complex, sulphur-rich chemicals, dredged up from deep within the Jovian atmosphere by a powerful updraft, are modified by exposure to ultraviolet sunlight. However the GRS can alter dramatically in both size and intensity, sometimes fading almost completely from view, leaving only the hollow within the SEB to mark its position. It's thought that only the most intense low-pressure areas can reach far enough into Jupiter's atmosphere to bring up the red-staining material, so perhaps the occasional pale spells mark periods when the GRS is weaker than usual. In 2010, infrared observations of the spot using the European Southern Observatory's Very Large Telescope revealed unexpected structure within the spot – the central region appears cool compared to the edges, but the deepest red patch within the eye of the storm is itself relatively warm (although the temperature differences involved are a matter of a few degrees at most).

'The Little Red Spot got caught up in the ferocious winds that still surround the Great Red Spot, and was torn to shreds, with its remnants circling the GRS for a short time before they were totally absorbed.'

New Red Spots

While the GRS was long assumed to be one of a kind, in the past decade, astronomers using the Hubble Space Telescope have been surprised to observe not one, but two other red spots in Jupiter's atmosphere. The first and largest of these, technically known as 'Oval BA' but commonly nicknamed 'Red Spot Jr', formed from the merger of three smaller white ovals that had formed around 1939 and spent several decades circling to the south of the GRS. As the ovals coalesced in 1998 and 2000, they at first formed a single white storm, which began to turn red in 2005. Astronomers such as Santiago Pérez-Hoyos of the University of the Basque Country believe that the mechanism involved in the spot's colour change is similar to that which colours the GRS itself. By 2008, Oval BA was spinning more rapidly, and had grown in size to almost the diameter of Earth. And in the same period that Oval BA has been growing, the GRS has been shrinking – according to a study carried out by scientists at the University of California

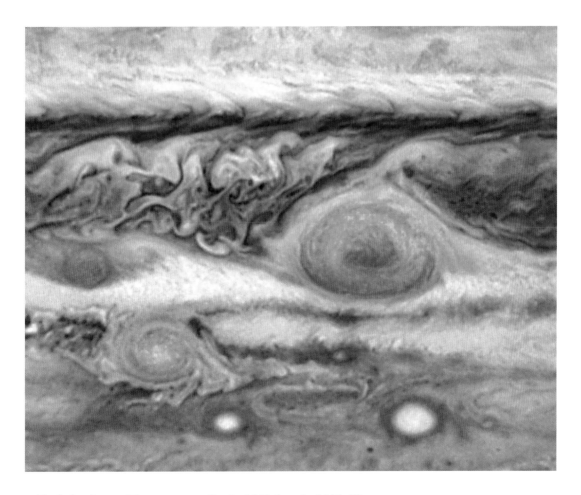

at Berkeley it was 15 percent smaller in 2007 than in 2000. The team suspect that the triple-storm merger may have opened the way for large-scale climate change across Jupiter's southern hemisphere, which is now being manifested in a variety of ways. Since the formation of Oval BA, it has passed close to the GRS on several occasions but so far the two systems have survived their encounters unscathed.

Meanwhile, in May 2008, another Berkeley team led by Imke de Pater reported that a smaller white oval in Jupiter's South Tropical Zone had turned red in new HST images. Known as the South Tropical Little Red Spot (LRS) and nicknamed 'Baby Red Spot', it offered a fascinating example of the fate that can befall storms on Jupiter.

Barely a month after the colour change, the LRS got caught up in the ferocious winds that still surround the Great Red Spot, and was torn to shreds, with its remnants circling the GRS for a short time before they were totally absorbed. The fate of the LRS is typical of many Jovian storms – it seems that large spots such as the GRS and Oval BA maintain their energy by feeding on smaller ones.

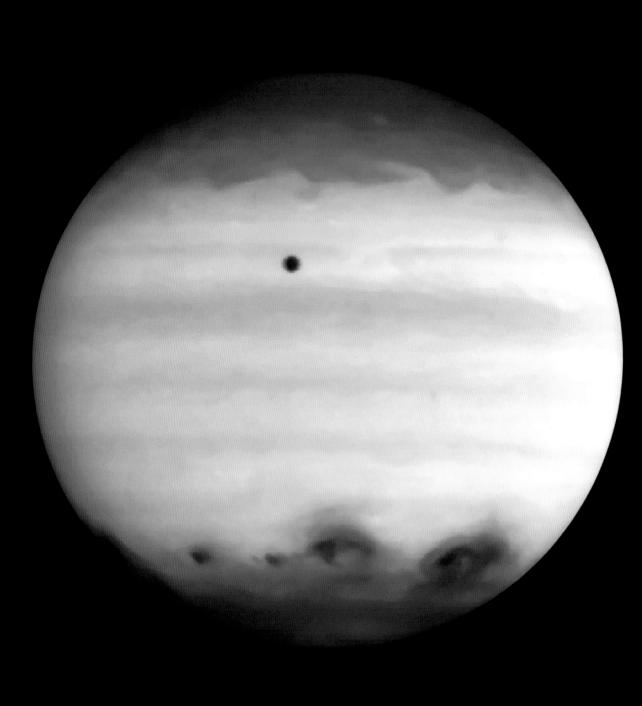

48 The Jovian gravity shield

DEFINITION JUPITER'S IMMENSE GRAVITY PULLS COMETS TO THEIR DOOM ON A REGULAR BASIS.

DISCOVERY IN 1994, COMET SHOEMAKER–LEVY 9 PLOUGHED INTO JUPITER'S ATMOSPHERE CAUSING SPECTACULAR EXPLOSIONS.

KEY BREAKTHROUGH IN 2009 AND 2010, ASTRONOMERS DETECTED FURTHER IMPACTS ON JUPITER.

IMPORTANCE SOME ASTRONOMERS THINK JUPITER'S GRAVITY SHIELDS THE INNER SOLAR SYSTEM FROM COMET IMPACTS.

Jupiter exerts an enormous gravitational influence across a large region of the outer solar system, frequently interacting with smaller objects and sometimes pulling them to their doom. But does it also play a key role in protecting the worlds of the inner solar system?

As in the case of impacts on Earth (see page 149), it has taken a long time for astronomers to recognize the significance of collisions in the evolution of our solar system. In particular, the last couple of decades have seen a shift in the perception of cometary and asteroid impacts from comparatively rare events in historical terms, to surprisingly – even alarmingly – frequent ones.

Discovering a doomed comet

Perhaps the biggest change in our perception came in July 1994, when fragments of Comet Shoemaker–Levy 9 (SL-9) smashing into Jupiter triggered the largest explosions ever seen in the solar system. The comet, discovered in March 1993 by Carolyn and Eugene Shoemaker and David H. Levy, had immediately stood out as something unusual – instead of a point-like nucleus and spherical coma, it appeared to have a bar-like structure. It also appeared very close to Jupiter, and further observations confirmed that it was actually in orbit around the giant planet. When the Hubble Space Telescope turned its powerful gaze on the comet, it showed that SL-9 was not a single object, but instead a 'string of pearls' – a series of fragments, each up to 2 km (1.2 miles) across, following the same path through space.

When SL-9's orbit was traced back, it turned out to have passed very close to Jupiter during July 1992, when tidal forces from the giant planet had torn it to pieces. Further analysis showed that SL-9 had probably been captured

OPPOSITE This ultraviolet image of Jupiter was captured by the Hubble Space Telescope on 21 July 1994, and reveals the prominent atmospheric 'bruises' created by the impact of the fragmented comet Shoemaker–Levy 9.

into orbit around Jupiter in the 1970s and, more significantly, that it would not persist for long in its present orbit – in fact, the comet was doomed to an imminent collision with the gas giant in barely a year's time.

This unique opportunity to observe a major extraterrestrial collision as it happened saw professional and amateur astronomers around the world train their telescopes on Jupiter for an unprecedented observing campaign. The observing priorities of the HST and other astronomical satellites were reassigned, and the Jupiter-bound Galileo spaceprobe also directed its cameras towards the planet. The geometry of the comet's orbit meant that its fragments would crash into Jupiter's southern hemisphere just on the far side of the planet as seen from Earth, but within view of Galileo. Predictions of what would be seen varied wildly, from spectacular explosions and permanent disruption to the Jovian system (perhaps replenishing the planet's tenuous ring system), to nothing at all.

The great crash of 1994

In the event, the event proved to be spectacular. The first impact sent a huge fireball thousands of kilometres above the Jovian cloudtops, at temperatures of up to 24,000°C (43,000°F). Over the next few days, some 20 more fragments smashed into Jupiter, the largest of which, 'fragment G', unleashed an explosion roughly equivalent to 6 million megatons of TNT or 600 times the world's entire nuclear arsenal). As the impact sites rotated onto the near side of the planet, they revealed dark, ring-like 'bruises' spread across thousands of kilometres, stirring up material from deep within the planet and providing a unique glimpse into the depths of Jupiter's atmosphere.

'Large impacts occur on Jupiter at a much higher rate than they do in the inner solar system – several thousand times higher according to some estimates.'

Despite the scale of disruption caused by the impacts themselves, Jupiter showed itself to be remarkably resilient. Its bruises dissipated over a matter of weeks, and global and regional changes to the atmospheric temperature and chemistry disappeared within a year. Although the comet did not inject significant amounts of new material into the Jovian rings, it does seem to have had a long-term effect on them – in 2011, a team of astronomers led by Matthew Hedman and Mark Showalter of NASA's Cassini imaging team identified a corrugated pattern of spiral ripples in the rings. Inspired by the discovery of similar patterns in Saturn's C and D rings (see page 217), they suggested that the ripples had been caused by tenuous clouds of material drifting towards the planet and colliding with the ring material. By comparing images of the rings taken by the Galileo probe in 1996 and 2000, Showalter was able to date the origin of the ripples to 1994.

How big and how often?

While the SL-9 impact was undoubtedly fascinating, it was generally thought to be a rare event, on a scale that might happen just once in a millennium. However, recent discoveries have suggested that is far from

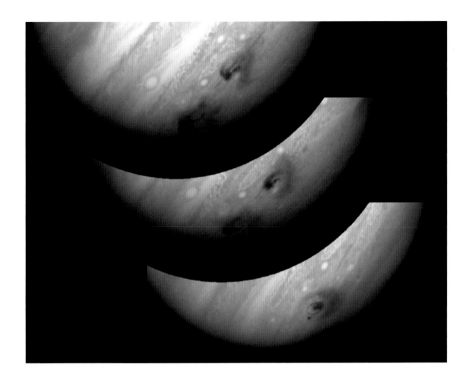

the case. In July 2009, a new 'bruise' was seen on Jupiter, thought to be the result of a somewhat denser object (probably a small asteroid) crashing into the atmosphere. In 2010, amateur astronomers spotted two bright flashes on Jupiter that did not develop bruises – probably caused by smaller meteors exploding in the atmosphere. And using 2007 images from the New Horizons probe, in 2011 Mark Showalter was able to identify two more recent patterns of 'ring ripples' – evidence of further comet crashes that were completely missed by observers on Earth.

It seems clear, then, that large impacts occur on Jupiter at a much higher rate than they do in the inner solar system – several thousand times higher according to some estimates. And this is not simply because the giant planet presents a bigger target – instead, Jupiter's enormous gravity has a disruptive effect on a large proportion of objects passing close to it, drawing many of them to their doom. Some astronomers have speculated that this 'comet catching' effect could reduce the number of impacts on worlds in the inner solar system, and possibly be a key factor in allowing the stable development of life on Earth.

However, the reality of Jupiter's influence might not be so clear cut. Recent work by J. Horner and B.W. Jones of Britain's Open University has suggested that in some models, giants in a planetary system can actually *increase* the flux of asteroids or comets sent towards their star. Nevertheless, the evidence so far suggests that, within our own solar system, Jupiter's effect is, on balance, benign.

49 The volcanoes of Io

DEFINITION POWERFUL VOLCANISM GENERATED BY TIDAL FORCES AFFECTING JUPITER'S INNERMOST MOON.

DISCOVERY VOLCANIC ACTIVITY ON IO WAS DISCOVERED FOLLOWING THE VOYAGER 1 FLYBY OF MARCH 1979.

KEY BREAKTHROUGH IN 2011, ASTRONOMERS SHOWED THAT IO PROBABLY HAS AN OCEAN OF MOLTEN ROCK BENEATH ITS SURFACE.

IMPORTANCE IO DEMONSTRATES THE POTENTIALLY HUGE POWER OF TIDAL FORCES ACTING ON THE SATELLITES OF LARGE PLANETS.

Io is renowned as the most volcanic world in the solar system, with a tortured surface that is continuously reshaped by sulphur-rich eruptions. But planetary scientists are still struggling to understand the mechanism that powers Io's violent activity.

Io is the innermost of the four giant moons that dominate Jupiter's satellite system. First observed by the great Italian astronomer Galileo Galilei shortly after the invention of the telescope in the early 1600s, they are traditionally known as the Galilean moons. Even before the Space Age, a few vital facts about Io had emerged. Spectroscopic observations of its light suggested that the moon was devoid of water ice, in stark contrast to its neighbouring outer moons – instead, it appeared to be rich in sodium and above all sulphur. Visual observations suggested distinct differences across the surface – most notably a brighter band around the equator and darker poles. In the 1960s, radio-telescope observations showed that Io has an influence on Jupiter's powerful magnetic field, creating pulses in radio noise that vary with a period that matches Io's orbit.

Volcano world

In the early 1970s, NASA's Pioneer 10 and 11 spaceprobes flew close to Io and helped to refine estimates of its size, mass and density, showing that it is the densest of the Galilean moons. However, they encountered belts of fierce radiation around Io's orbit, which prevented them from returning detailed images. These had to wait until the Voyager 1 flyby of March 1979. The first close-up pictures showed a multicoloured surface of yellows, browns, reds and whites, scarred and pitted, but apparently devoid of impact craters. The best explanation was that Io's surface was being resurfaced on a

OPPOSITE This enhanced-colour view from the Galileo spaceprobe emphasizes colour differences across Io's sulphurous yellow surface. Volcanic activity on Io is so widespread and constant that many areas changed beyond recognition in the 15 years between the Voyager flybys and Galileo's arrival.

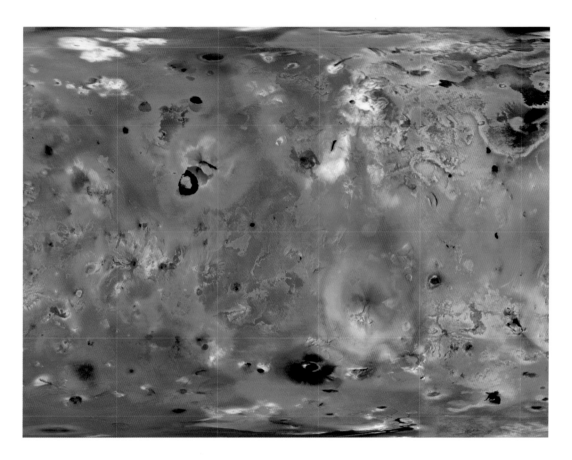

ABOVE A global projection of Io's surface reveals prominent features coloured by the presence of different sulphur compounds. The prominent red ring surrounds the volcanic centre Pele.

comparatively short timescale by volcanic activity, and this was dramatically confirmed shortly after the flyby when NASA engineer Linda Morabito, studying images of Io backlit by the Sun, discovered a huge plume of material erupting into space above the planet. Further analysis of the images confirmed the presence of nine volcanic plumes, flinging sulphur compounds hundreds of kilometres above the surface. As the plumes fall back onto Io, they blanket the landscape in sulphurous frosts that owe their colours to the variety of different crystalline structures, or 'allotropes', adopted by sulphur.

When Voyager 2 made its own flyby four months later, the effect of this volcanism was dramatically demonstrated – Io's features had already changed significantly from the previous encounter. When the Galileo probe arrived in orbit around Jupiter in 1995, it found Io transformed again, confirming that the moon is the most volcanically active world in the solar system.

While most of the satellites of the outer solar system are made from a mixture of ice and rock (as we might expect from their position beyond the frost line of the primordial protoplanetary nebula – see page 97), Io is different. It is composed mostly of silicate rocks and contains little water – presumably most of it was driven off early in Io's history by the internal heat that powers the volcanic activity.

But with a diameter barely larger than Earth's own moon, why should Io be so geologically active? It cannot be driven purely by heat left from the satellite's formation or generated by radioactive minerals still trapped inside (since much larger moons such as Ganymede show far less activity).

In fact, the true driving force behind Io's volcanism was identified even before the Voyager 1 flyby in a paper published by Stan Peale, Patrick Cassen and R.T. Reynolds of the University of California at Santa Barbara and NASA's Ames research centre. They predicted that Io's location in the Jovian system would see it pummelled by intense tidal forces generated by its interactions with Jupiter, Europa and Ganymede. The tug of the outer satellites prevents Io from settling into a perfectly circular orbit, and so it experiences constantly changing gravitational pull, causing the surface to flex by as much as 100 metres (330 ft) on its Jupiter-facing side. Similar tidal heating affects many other moons in the outer solar system (notably Europa, Enceladus and Triton – see pages 205, 225 and 245), but is at its most dramatic on Io.

'Close-up images of the surface revealed the presence of towering mountains that seem to be created as Io's crust moves around, stretching in some places and crumpling in others.'

Venturing closer

Based on the discovery of copious sulphur plumes and frosts, scientists assumed that lava erupting from Io's volcanoes would also be composed of easily melted sulphur compounds, and therefore would be relatively cool. However, infrared measurements made by Earth-based telescopes and confirmed by the Galileo probe showed that the surface lavas are hotter than expected, and actually composed of melted silicate rock.

During Galileo's initial mission the probe was deliberately kept at a safe distance from the dangerous radiation belts around Io. It was only in 1999 that the spacecraft's orbit was changed to bring it closer to the volcanic moon, allowing it to take close-up images of the surface. These revealed the presence of towering mountains that seem to be created as Io's crust moves around, stretching in some places and crumpling in others.

Galileo completed its mission in 2003, but provided a wealth of data that scientists back on Earth are still analysing. In 2011, a team led by geophysicist Krishan Khurana of the University of California at Los Angeles announced they had finally resolved a long-standing puzzle around Io's relationship with Jupiter's magnetic field. Distortions in the field close to the moon, detected by Galileo's magnetometer, had previously been blamed on Io's tenuous atmosphere, but Khurana's team showed they could be better explained by an induced magnetic field generated by fluid within the moon. Similar fields around Europa, Ganymede and Callisto are relatively easy to explain through the presence of liquid water oceans, but recent advances in mineral physics have shown that molten rocks can fulfil the same role in certain conditions. As a result, it now seems likely that Io conceals a global ocean of molten magma, perhaps up to 50 km (30 miles) deep in places.

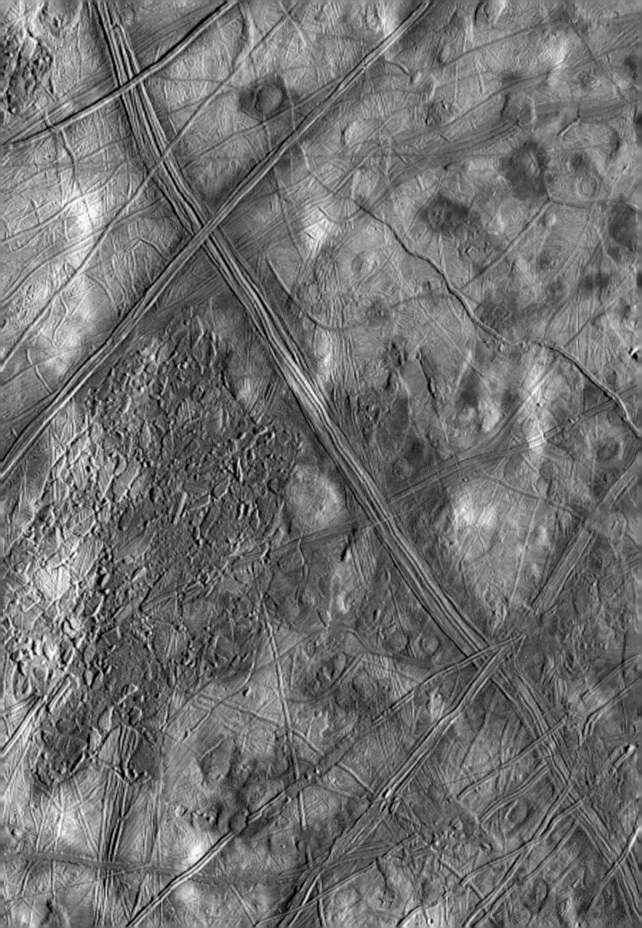

Europa's icy ocean

DEFINITION A DEEP OCEAN THOUGHT TO LIE HIDDEN BENEATH THE ICY CRUST OF JUPITER'S GALILEAN MOON EUROPA.

DISCOVERY THE YOUNG AGE OF EUROPA'S ICY CRUST WAS CONFIRMED BY THE GALILEO SPACEPROBE IN 1995.

KEY BREAKTHROUGH A 2001 STUDY OF CRATERS ON EUROPA'S SURFACE PUT A LOWER LIMIT ON THE THICKNESS OF THE CRUST.

IMPORTANCE EUROPA'S OCEAN IS A POTENTIAL HAVEN FOR LIFE ELSEWHERE IN THE SOLAR SYSTEM, BUT OUR ABILITY TO CONFIRM THIS IN THE FUTURE WILL DEPEND ON THE DEPTH OF ICE ABOVE.

Europa is the second closest to Jupiter of the four large 'Galilean' satellites, orbiting between volcano-wracked Io and the larger, more sedate Ganymede and Callisto. Like all Galilean satellites, we knew very little about it until the Voyager spaceprobes flew past Jupiter in 1979.

The Voyagers revealed a curious iceball – a world that seemed white and featureless at first glance, but which enhanced photographs revealed to be crisscrossed with countless brownish streaks named *lineae* (from the Latin for 'line'), and stained in pink and blue patches. Craters were few and far between, while in some places the terrain was eerily reminiscent of jumbled Arctic pack ice. Strangest of all was Europa's smoothness – its surface is the flattest of any world in the solar system and, relative to its size, it is smoother than a cueball. Astronomers were startled to find a world the size of our Moon, with no substantial mountains or cliffs, deep trenches or craters, just rolling hills and valleys with the occasional sunken pit marking the ghost of a meteorite impact.

It seemed clear from the outset that there was only one explanation – Europa's surface was a dense layer of ice, able to slip, slide, creep and rearrange itself like the ice in glaciers on Earth. Any underlying landscape must be buried so deeply that the ice filled in its depressions and smoothed out its bumps, leaving nothing but a smooth, almost featureless landscape.

Waterworld?

But was there land underneath at all? The discovery of volcanic activity on Europa's inner neighbour Io (see page 201) had surprised almost everyone, but the same model that explained Io's activity through the heating effect

OPPOSITE This false-colour image of Europa's surface from the Galileo spaceprobe shows pure ice in blue tones and impurities in red and brown. Long linear features and spot-like 'freckles' indicate the upwelling of material from Europa's hidden ocean.

of Jupiter's tides also predicted that Europa took a similar pounding, and so should be only slightly less active. This led to the theory that Europa's interior might be warm enough to maintain an ocean of liquid water, of which the icy crust was just the top surface. A concealed ocean would naturally provide a smooth surface on which the icy crust could form, explaining Europa's flat landscape. It might also explain the mysterious scars and packice-like regions that covered the surface.

Although the theory rapidly became popular (especially among science-fiction writers), planetary scientists had a long wait to find out if they were right. Then in 1995, the Galileo probe finally reached Jupiter and swung into orbit at the beginning of an eight-year programme of study. Galileo was able to visit Europa repeatedly, flying past at much closer range than the Voyagers had, and revealing unseen surface detail. The scarcity of craters on Europa soon confirmed that its surface was quite young in planetary terms – between 20 and 180 million years old.

'Astronomers were startled to find a world with no substantial mountains, deep trenches or craters, just rolling hills and valleys with the occasional sunken pit marking the ghost of a meteorite impact.'

It was another instrument, however, that finally confirmed liquid beneath the crust. Galileo's magnetometer picked up a weak magnetic field around Europa. The shape and strength of the field revealed that it was induced – rather than being generated by molten or solid iron in the moon's core, it was being created by a conducting fluid, most likely a salt-water ocean, interacting with the much stronger field of Jupiter itself, as Europa swept round its orbit. Galileo also found that, despite sometimes reaching widths of 20 km (12.5 miles), the cracks in Europa's surface are actually as smooth as the rest of the moon – they stand out mostly because they are stained with chemicals such as magnesium sulphate and other sulphur compounds. The probe also discovered new types of terrain, including brownish spots called *lenticulae* (freckles), and jumbled chaos regions where blocks of ice seem to be jammed together and thrown on top of each other.

Beneath the surface
In 2001, University of Arizona scientists Elizabeth Turtle and Elisabetta Pierazzo used images from Galileo to put a lower limit on the thickness of Europa's ice. By searching for impact craters large enough to have a raised peak at their centre, they were able to study the nature of the ice beneath which the crater formed. The process of crater formation on any world naturally pushes up a central peak made of the deepest material beneath the impact site, so if a crater was large enough and the crust thin enough, the central peak might be disrupted by the existence of water or simply warm ice below the impact. However, even Europa's largest central-peak crater, the 24-km-wide (15-mile) Pwyll, turned out to have a fairly normal peak. This suggested that Europa's hard, cold outer crust must be at least 4 km (2.5 miles) thick beneath Pwyll.

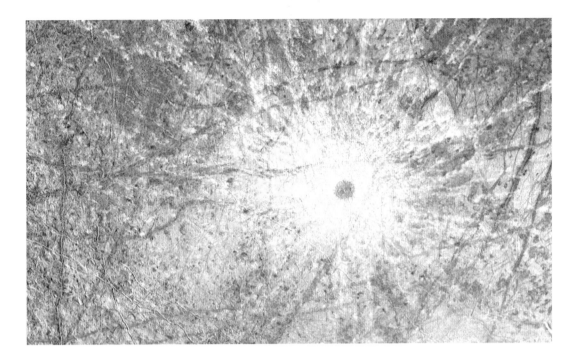

Despite this evidence, planetary geologists are still arguing over the precise thickness of the icy layer, and its structure. These arguments are tied to different explanations for the surface features. Supporters of the thin crust model suggest that the *lineae* are formed when water escapes through cracks in the surface, and the *lenticulae* are created in a similar way as rising currents of water melt their way through the ice. According to them, the crust may be as little as 200 m (650 ft) deep in places. Thick-crust advocates, in contrast, explain both the *lineae* and the freckles by rising currents through the crust. They believe that it could be up to 30 km (19 miles) deep in total, with an outer shell of cold, hard ice above an inner layer of warmer, more mobile ice that occasionally forces its way upwards.

The chaos terrain is perhaps the most difficult for either side to explain. The 'thin crust' model suggests that these regions are a result of catastrophic melting of the surface – the jumbled blocks are effectively icebergs set adrift by this sudden melting, and then re-frozen into the ice. The 'thick crust' model again suggests that the blocks have been jumbled and uplifted thanks to rising currents of warm ice several kilometres below. But both theories have trouble explaining all the features present in these regions.

However thick Europa's crust may be, it almost certainly covers an ocean up to 100 km (62 miles) deep, with a volcanic sea floor beneath. Such an ocean must hold at least twice the amount of water present in Earth's oceans, and makes Europa a fascinating target for future planetary probes, especially since it raises the intriguing possibility that life might thrive around the sea-floor volcanoes in the same way that it does in Earth's deep oceans.

ABOVE An enhanced-colour image from NASA's Galileo probe reveals the range of brownish freckles and lines on Europa's bright surface. The large crater Pwyll, with a central diameter of 40 km (25 miles) is thought to be one of the youngest features on Europa, and is still surrounded by a spray of brilliant white ejecta material.

51 The seas of Ganymede and Callisto

DEFINITION BURIED LAYERS OF WATER THAT LIE BENEATH THE
SURFACE OF JUPITER'S OUTER GALILEAN MOONS.

DISCOVERY MAGNETIC FIELD MEASUREMENTS FROM THE GALILEO
SPACECRAFT REVEALED DISTURBANCES CAUSED BY CONDUCTING
FLUID INSIDE BOTH MOONS.

KEY BREAKTHROUGH THE PRESENCE OF LIQUID WATER MAY BE DUE
TO THE STRANGE PROPERTIES OF ICE AT HIGH PRESSURES.

IMPORTANCE THE PRESENCE OF LIQUID WATER ENVIRONMENTS ON
BOTH WORLDS MAKES THEM POSSIBLE HABITATS FOR LIFE.

Jupiter's two largest moons are today immune to the tidal heating that
shapes Io and Europa, but nevertheless they are very different, both from
one another and from their inner neighbours. One surprising similarity,
however, is that they may both have hidden oceans beneath their crusts.

Ganymede and Callisto orbit well beyond Europa, and far enough from
Jupiter to avoid the crucial influence of its tides. However, while Callisto is
a heavily cratered ball of rock and ice that seems to have changed very little
since its formation, the slightly larger Ganymede (the largest satellite in the
entire solar system, bigger than the planet Mercury) shows clear signs of a
geologically active past. Its surface is a jumbled mixture of darker cratered
and lighter, less cratered terrains, often blurring together at the edges.

The density of both worlds suggests that, like Europa, they are essentially a
mix of rock and water ice. In fact, despite Europa's icy appearance, it seems
that Ganymede and Callisto contain significantly more ice overall (a roughly
50/50 mix of water ice and silicate rock). In Ganymede's case, the moon
has undergone at least partial differentiation, with rocky material sinking
towards the core and ice concentrating in the crust.

Diverse worlds

The most prominent features on Ganymede are craters (concentrated in,
but not exclusive to, the older and darker terrain), and ridges and grooves
that form long strips within the lighter terrain. The parallel ridges, called
sulci (from the Latin word for groove) are thought to mark regions where
the crust has stretched apart. They appear to be analogous to the ridges that
form on Earth's ocean floors where two sections of crust are pulled apart

OPPOSITE A Galileo
image of Ganymede's
surface reveals a
complex web of dark
and light terrains that
shows clear signs of
tectonic activity. Such
geological changes
must have been driven
by internal heat from
within the giant moon.

and new volcanic material wells up from beneath to fill the gap. In order to fuel this activity, it seems that Ganymede's interior must have been warmer in the past than it is today. This allowed an icy equivalent of Earth's own tectonic activity to develop, perhaps driven by currents of warm material rising up through the moon's interior and causing the ancient, cratered crust to shift and split apart.

In contrast, Callisto has a dark, uniform surface, broken only by the bright splashes of icy ejecta within and around its craters. It is thought to be the most heavily cratered world in the solar system, peppered to saturation point by the countless impacts collected during a life as a 'sitting duck' for asteroids and comets pulled in by Jupiter's powerful gravity.

'The ocean forms a couple of hundred kilometres inside the moons, where a transition between low-pressure forms of ice and unusual high-pressure "polymorphs" is accompanied by a sudden drop in melting point.'

But how did Ganymede become warm enough for tectonic processes to briefly take hold, while the slightly smaller but otherwise similar Callisto did not? The contrast between the moons is too large to be explained by the slight difference in size and internal heat, so some other force must be at work. One possible solution would be if Callisto formed unusually slowly, but finding a mechanism to achieve this presents its own problems.

In 1997, Adam Showman and David J. Stevenson of Caltech, along with Renu Malhotra of the Lunar and Planetary Institute, showed that orbital changes early in the history of the Galilean moons offered a possible solution. According to their model, the moons probably formed somewhat closer to Jupiter than their present positions and, as they spiralled outwards, they went through a series of close encounters with each other that prevented the orbits of the inner three from becoming perfectly circular. This process, called orbital pumping, still takes place between Io and Europa, and the slightly elliptical orbits that result are largely responsible for the strong tidal forces each moon experiences. Ganymede and Callisto, in contrast, today have near-perfect circular orbits, but if Ganymede experienced similar pumping early in its life, this may have been enough to heat its interior and power its tectonic activity. A little of Ganymede's internal heat remains today, and as a result the moon seems to have a small core of molten iron that allows it to produce its own magnetic field.

Hidden oceans

Perhaps the most surprising recent discovery about these two outer moons, however, has been the evidence that they each possess a subterranean ocean beneath their solid crust. The discovery was made using readings from the magnetometer carried aboard the Galileo spaceprobe, which toured the Jupiter system between 1995 and 2003.

The magnetometer was designed to measure changes in Jupiter's powerful magnetic field, created by its interactions with magnetism and other effects

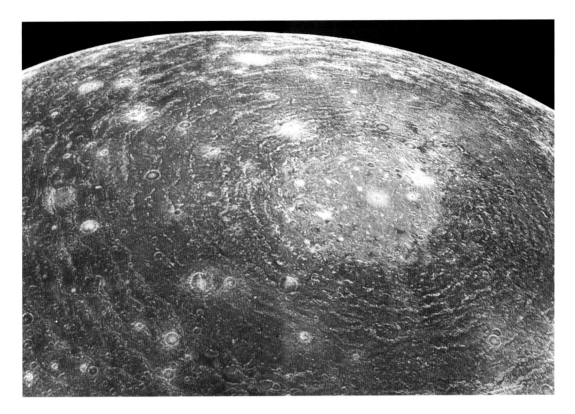

ABOVE The enormous
Valhalla impact
structure may be the
largest crater in the
solar system – from
edge to edge, this
shallow, multi-
ringed basin is about
3,800 km (2,360 miles)
across. The bright
plain at its centre
indicates an upwelling
of fresh material from
beneath the crust.

around the moons. However alongside Ganymede's expected internal magnetic field, it found that there was also a weak but distinctive 'induced' field. This type of magnetism is produced by electric currents that flow when a conducting fluid moves through a stronger magnetic field: its presence suggests that Ganymede's interior contains a conducting fluid such as water.

While Ganymede's active past makes the presence of liquid water today somewhat less surprising, the discovery of a similar field around Callisto was far more of a shock: at the time scientists believed that it was a uniform mix of rock and ice all the way through.

Astronomers believe that maintaining liquid water on the outer moons requires a very different mechanism from that which warms Europa's ocean. One possibility, proposed for Ganymede as early as the 1980s, is that the ocean forms a couple of hundred kilometres inside the moons, where a transition between familiar low-pressure forms of ice and unusual high-pressure 'polymorphs' is accompanied by a sudden drop in melting point. With the addition of residual heat (from the satellites' formation and radioactive materials in their mantles) and small amounts of 'antifreeze', in the form of chemicals such as ammonia or sulphate salts, this transition may be enough to create a thin liquid ocean. However conditions in these buried oceans would be far more hostile than those on Europa, and the chances of life somehow evolving on Ganymede or Callisto seem remote.

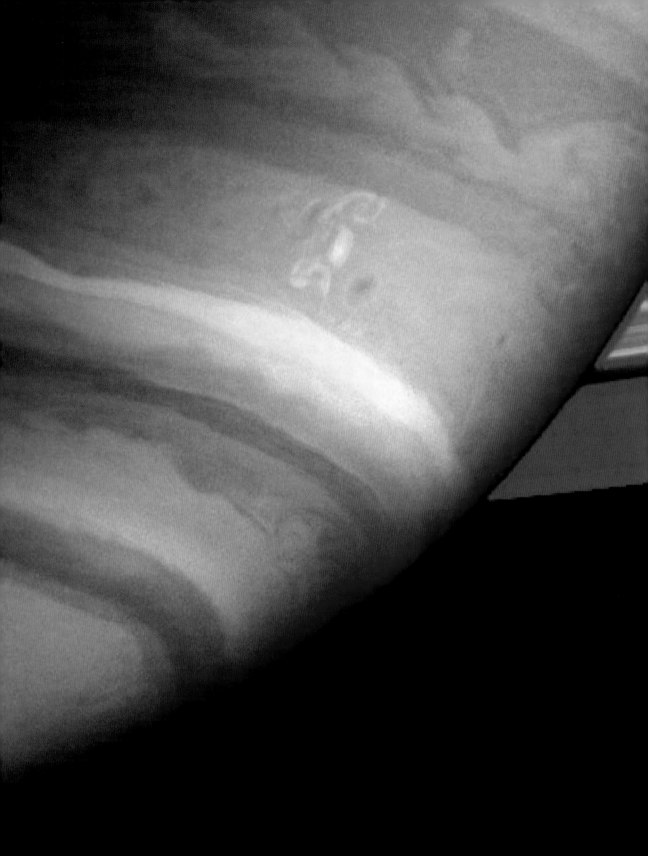

52 Saturn's complex weather

DEFINITION NEWLY DISCOVERED WEATHER FEATURES IN THE DECEPTIVELY CALM-LOOKING ATMOSPHERE OF SATURN.

DISCOVERY THE FIRST 'WHITE SPOT' STORM WAS OBSERVED BY ASAPH HALL IN 1876.

KEY BREAKTHROUGH IN 2010, ASTRONOMERS TRACKED THE DRAMATIC GROWTH OF AN ELECTRICAL STORM INTO A FEATURE THAT WRAPPED ITS WAY AROUND THE PLANET.

IMPORTANCE FUTURE SPACEPROBE MISSIONS WILL NEED TO PLAN FOR INTERFERENCE FROM SATURN'S ELECTRICAL STORMS.

The second largest planet in the solar system, Saturn is renowned for its spectacular ring system and intriguing family of moons. But despite a deceptively placid appearance, the planet itself is a fascinating world wracked with storms and other violent weather systems.

Saturn is the second of the gas giant planets, with a diameter roughly 80 percent of Jupiter's, but less than one third of its weight. Like Jupiter, it is composed mostly of hydrogen and helium with traces of other elements – the main difference between the two worlds is Saturn's lower density (on average less dense than water). This results in weaker gravity and a tendency for the planet to bulge noticeably around the equator. Saturn also receives considerably less heat from the Sun, and as a result its average cloudtop temperature is about 30°C (54°F) cooler, at around –153°C (–243°F).

The lower temperatures allow hazy white ammonia clouds, which only form in cold, high-altitude bands on Jupiter, to create a high layer of sepia haze all over Saturn, and for a long time this haze was all that astronomers could see of Saturn's atmosphere. The first evidence of significant weather features came with the discovery of a large white spot in the atmosphere by American astronomer Asaph Hall in 1876. Similar spots have been seen at regular intervals ever since, but it's only in the past few decades, thanks to improvements in Earth-based telescopes and several spaceprobe missions, that astronomers have been able to study Saturn's weather in detail.

Weather bands and seasons
As with all the giant planets, the overriding structure of Saturn's weather systems is a series of bands wrapped around the planet, parallel to the

OPPOSITE A false-colour Cassini image of Saturn shows the original 'dragon storm' discovered in 2004. Colours indicate the level of clouds in the atmosphere, with reds marking the deepest layers and grey the highest.

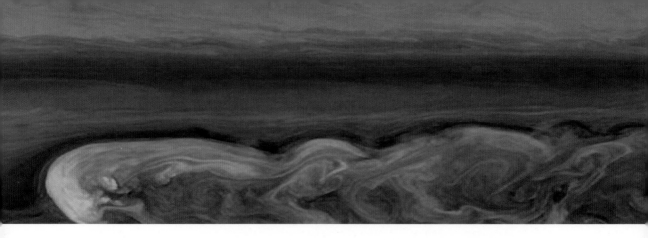

ABOVE This false-colour Cassini image traces the enormous 2011 storm as it wraps its way around the planet's northern hemisphere. High clouds are shown in white and yellow, while deep clouds are shown in red and brown.

equator. Saturn's bands are divided into lighter zones and darker belts, appearing to the naked eye as different creamy tones, rather broader and less defined than those of Jupiter. Although these appear placid, they are in fact blown in opposite directions by prevailing winds of up to 1,800 km/h (1,125 mph). The bands are formed in a similar way to Earth's own circulation cells, through the convection of warm air rising near the equator and sinking down closer to the poles.

Just like our own planet, Saturn's axis of rotation is distinctly tilted, producing a pattern of seasons similar to Earth's. During winter for a particular hemisphere, when its pole is tiled away from the Sun, the effect of low sunlight is complicated by the rings' shadow across the planet. Fine particles in the rings scatter sunlight in a similar way to the air molecules of Earth's atmosphere, giving the winter hemisphere a blue tint.

White spots and dragon storms

While Saturn does not seem to have any semi-permanent storms to rival Jupiter's Great Red Spot, it does produce large white spots on a regular basis. The spots have been observed roughly every 30 years since 1876, with the storm of 1933, discovered by British amateur astronomer and comic actor Will Hay, being the most prominent until recently. They seem to mark high-pressure regions, rather than the familiar low-pressure weather patterns of storms on Earth, and generally coincide with northern midsummer. The white spots follow a complex cycle that sees an intense storm near the equator followed 27 years later by a weaker one in northern temperate latitudes, then a roughly 30-year gap before the next equatorial storm.

The most recent eruption in this cycle was in 1990, but it now seems that Saturn's weather is becoming less predictable. Further outbreaks of bright clouds were seen in 1994 and 2006, while in 2010 Australian amateur Anthony Wesley discovered a spectacular rippling storm that spread rapidly around the planet's mid-northern latitudes. This activity may be linked to low, rather than high-pressure areas, and the swirling electrical storms that have recently been detected in Saturn's atmosphere.

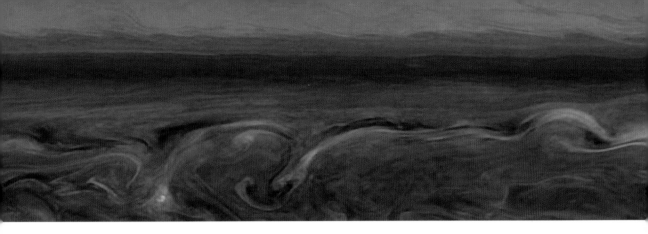

The first of these 'dragon storms' was discovered in 2004. As the Cassini spaceprobe approached Saturn, its Radio and Plasma Wave Science Instrument began to pick up powerful bursts of radio waves from the planet. Cassini's cameras eventually pinpointed their origin to a region of high-altitude white clouds that resembled the top of a thunderhead. Saturn, it seems, like Earth, has thunderstorms driven by rising currents of warm air – though Saturn's lightning bolts carry 10,000 times more energy than Earth's.

The 2004 dragon storm lasted for a month before disappearing, but similar storms recurred in 2006, 2008 and most impressively in 2010. Some astronomers speculate that the outbreaks are all manifestations of a single storm that passes through active and quiet periods.

Polar structures

Cassini has also made intriguing discoveries in the weather systems around Saturn's poles. The north pole is surrounded by an enormous hexagonal pattern, first observed by the Voyager probes, but imaged in detail for the first time by Cassini. Each of its six sides is almost 14,000 km (8,700 miles) long, and the entire structure rotates at the same rate as the planet – that is, at a different speed from Saturn's clouds themselves. One possible explanation is that the structure is a standing wave formed by currents in the atmosphere interfering with one another. Another hypothesis is that it could be linked to the planet's magnetic field, since glowing aurorae seem to concentrate in the upper atmosphere directly above it.

'In 2010, Australian amateur Anthony Wesley discovered a spectacular rippling storm that spread rapidly around the planet's mid-northern latitudes.'

Equally intriguing is an enormous hurricane hanging over the south pole. With a diameter of 8,000 km (5,000 miles), this storm is unique for a hurricane on another planet, since it has a prominent central eye surrounded by a wall of clouds up to 75 km (47 miles) high. Eyes are a familiar feature in hurricanes on Earth, suggesting that this south polar vortex may also be a low-pressure area. This strange feature may be connected to the region's unusually warm temperatures – clouds around the south pole are up to 60°C (108°F) warmer than those close to the equator. If so, it's possible that this huge vortex is a more-or-less permanent feature of Saturn's atmosphere.

53 The secrets of Saturn's rings

DEFINITION SATURN'S COMPLEX RING SYSTEM CONSISTS OF
COUNTLESS ORBITING PARTICLES OF ICE AND DUST.

DISCOVERY THE TRUE SHAPE OF THE RINGS WAS IDENTIFIED BY
CHRISTIAAN HUYGENS IN 1655, WHILE JAMES CLERK MAXWELL
DESCRIBED THEIR COMPOSITION IN 1856.

KEY BREAKTHROUGH THE CASSINI SPACEPROBE HAS REVEALED
PREVIOUSLY UNSEEN FINE STRUCTURE IN THE RINGS.

IMPORTANCE RINGS ARE A COMMON FEATURE OF GIANT PLANETS,
AND SATURN OFFERS OUR BEST OPPORTUNITY TO STUDY THEM.

The rings of Saturn are its most beautiful and instantly recognizable feature, made from countless billions of tiny particles in separate orbits around the planet. But, while they look serene from a distance, recent discoveries have shown that the rings are an evolving system in constant turmoil.

As early as 1610, Italian astronomer Galileo Galilei saw there was something 'wrong' with Saturn: even through his primitive, low-powered telescopes he could tell that its shape was not spherical, and he speculated that the distortion might be due to two huge satellites flanking the planet. In 1655, Dutch astronomer Christiaan Huygens was the first person to correctly explain the cause of Saturn's mysterious shape as a thin, flat ring surrounding the planet.

Structure of the rings

By the late 17th century, improving telescopes allowed astronomers to identify gaps in the rings, raising further questions about their structure. The laws of gravitation and motion identified by Isaac Newton showed that, if such a broad, flat structure were solid, it could not survive in orbit for long – gravitational forces would tend to make its inner edge move much faster than its outer edge, tearing it apart. In 1787, French mathematician and astronomer Pierre-Simon de Laplace suggested that the rings could be made of countless solid ringlets, but it was not until 1856 that Scottish physicist James Clerk Maxwell showed that even such thin structures could not persist for any length of time. Instead, he theorized that the rings were made of huge numbers of separate particles, each in its own flat, circular orbit around the planet. Collisions between the particles would naturally tend to keep these fragments in their orderly orbits, and the gravitational influence of Saturn's large family of satellites could explain the gaps within the rings.

APPOSITE The Cassini spaceprobe captured this spectacular view of Saturn's ring system as it soared high above the planet's northern hemisphere in May 2007. The complex structure of countless ringlets, each differing in brightness and transparency from its neighbours, can clearly be seen, as can Saturn's own shadow cutting across the rings.

Today, Maxwell's model of Saturn's rings has been proven correct, but thanks to giant telescopes and visiting spaceprobes, we know that the ring system is more complex than he could possibly have imagined. The brightest region of the rings lies between 92,000 km (58,000 miles) and 137,000 km (85,000 miles) from Saturn, and is divided into the outer A Ring and the inner B Ring, separated by the relatively empty Cassini Division between 117,600 and 122,200 km (73,000 and 75,900 miles). Despite their extent, the rings are astonishingly thin, on average just 10 metres (33 ft) deep.

Inside the B Ring lies the thin C or Crepe Ring, and the very faint D Ring stretching almost down to Saturn's cloudtops. Outside of the A Ring lies the narrow F Ring, discovered in 1979 by the Pioneer 11 spaceprobe, and the broad, diffuse E Ring extending roughly between the orbits of the icy moons Mimas and Rhea, and apparently formed by ice escaping from geysers on Enceladus (see page 225).

'By studying variations in starlight passing through the ring, they identified spiralling "walls" of ice, roughly 1.6 km (1 mile) tall, on either side of a narrow gap in the ring material.'

The G Ring lies midway between the E and F Rings, while the Cassini spaceprobe has discovered several other rings and fragmented ring arcs associated with the orbits of other small moons. In 2009, infrared images from the Spitzer Space Telescope revealed a disc of dusty material extending more than 200 Saturn radii from the planet and tilted at a 27° angle to the rest of the rings. From Earth, this ring covers an area of sky roughly the size of two full moons, but it is undetectable to optical telescopes. It is thought to be composed of dust blasted off the surface of Saturn's comet-like outer moon Phoebe by tiny micrometeoroid impacts.

Spaceprobe discoveries

While early spaceprobes such as Pioneers 10 and 11 and Voyagers 1 and 2 confirmed a complex structure of countless ringlets, it is only since 2004, thanks to the arrival of the Cassini spacecraft in orbit around Saturn, that the full complexity of the rings has been revealed. Gravitational interactions between small ring particles, 'moonlets' orbiting within the rings, and the planet's more substantial moons create an ever-changing dynamic system. Bright and dark radial spokes occasionally open across huge expanses of the ring plane; rippled waves distort the outer edges of the rings in both radial and vertical directions; and moons drag material out of the rings behind them, opening up dark channels in the rings.

In 2010, a team led by Phil Nicholson of Cornell University highlighted a remarkable example of ring complexity in the form of an ice tsunami within the C Ring. By studying variations in starlight passing through the ring, they identified spiralling 'walls' of ice, roughly 1.6 km (1 mile) tall, on either side of a narrow 0.5-km (0.3-mile) gap in the ring material. This structure, which seems to consist of piled-up ice fragments cleared out from the gap, is

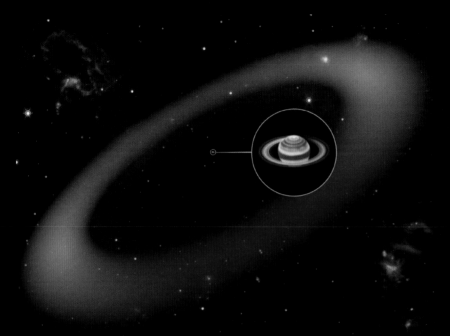

LEFT A composite
artwork reveals
the structure of the
enormous outer ring
discovered in a tilted
orbit around Saturn
in 2009. The infrared
glow of the ring,
between 6 million
and 12 million km
(3.7–12 million miles)
from the planet,
was first detected by
NASA's Spitzer Space
Telescope.

similar to a tsunami and its associated drop in sea level, and ripples through the C Ring every 16 days. This suggests that it is linked to the gravitational influence of Saturn's distant giant moon Titan.

Other discoveries made with Cassini include propellers – clouds of close-packed particles tens of kilometres long. Each of these features is tilted at an angle to the general direction of the ring orbits, and has a gap midway along its length, believed to mark the position of an unseen moonlet that disturbs its surroundings and creates the propeller. Small propellers were first identified in the middle of Saturn's A Ring in 2006, and have since been used to pinpoint more than 150 moonlets of roughly 100-metre (330-ft) diameter in this region. In 2010, a Cornell team led by Matthew Tiscareno identified a new class of giant propellers up to several hundred kilometres long, further out in the A ring, which appear to be linked to rarer, kilometre-scale moonlets. Cassini tracked the propellers and their interactions with the surroundings particles over four years, in a study whose implications reach far beyond ring systems – astronomers believe that the behaviour of these disc-embedded moonlets probably mimics that of planetesimals orbiting within a protoplanetary disc during the formation of a solar system.

But despite Cassini's many breakthroughs, Saturn's rings still hold many secrets. We have not seen the individual particles in detail (and perhaps never will, given the risks to a spacecraft venturing too close), and although they are known to consist of 99.9 percent pure water ice, the impurities that give the particles their individual properties and create the spectacular variations seen across the rings are poorly understood.

The origin of the ring systems

DEFINITION THE FOUR VERY DIFFERENT RING SYSTEMS OF THE SOLAR SYSTEM PRESENT A PUZZLE FOR PLANETARY SCIENTISTS.

DISCOVERY THE RINGS OF URANUS WERE DISCOVERED IN 1977, THOSE OF JUPITER IN 1979, AND THOSE AROUND NEPTUNE WERE CONFIRMED IN 1989.

KEY BREAKTHROUGH IN 2007, THE CASSINI PROBE REVEALED THAT SATURN'S RINGS ARE FAR MORE MASSIVE THAN PREVIOUSLY THOUGHT AND COULD BE BILLIONS OF YEARS OLD.

IMPORTANCE RING SYSTEMS MAY DEMONSTRATE PROCESSES THAT HELPED SHAPE THE EARLY SOLAR SYSTEM.

In recent decades, astronomers have discovered ring systems around Jupiter, Uranus and Neptune, confirming that rings are a common feature of giant planets. But the origin of these systems, and the huge differences between them, are still unresolved questions.

The discovery that a planet other than Saturn had rings came as a complete surprise to airborne astronomers monitoring the predicted occultation of a distant star by Uranus in 1977 (see page 237), but once the initial discovery had been made, it was clear that the Uranian ring system was very different from that around Saturn. While Saturn is orbited by broad, dense planes of material, its outer neighbour has thin, sharply defined ringlets that are mostly just a few kilometres across.

Astronomers immediately began to use a similar technique (looking for telltale dips in the light of stars passing close to the planet) to look for rings around Neptune, but met with mixed and often contradictory results that were only explained when the Voyager 2 spaceprobe photographed three thin and extremely uneven rings during its 1989 flyby. However, the discovery of rings around Jupiter during Voyager 1's 1979 encounter with the giant planet was another unexpected bonus. Jupiter's rings are different again from those of any other planet, consisting of thin but broad planes of dust that can only be spotted when backlit by the Sun.

So it seems that ring systems are a common feature of giant planets – but where do they come from, and is it possible to piece together the four very different examples in our solar system to make a coherent story of ring evolution?

OPPOSITE This stunning Cassini view reveals countless ringlets in orbit around Saturn, with the extended shadow of the satellite Mimas cutting across them. At lower right, the thread-like outer F ring demonstrates the sort of fine structure seen in ring systems throughout the solar system.

RIGHT A Cassini close-up of the outer edge of Saturn's B Ring reveals swirling patterns amid the densely packed ice boulders at lower left. These 'clumps' are thought to be created by slight perturbations in the orbit of Mimas, and may play a key role in recycling material to maintain the B Ring's bright appearance.

Young rings or old?

Understanding the age of ring systems is particularly important to mapping their possible development. Rings exist within a planet's 'Roche limit' – a region where gravitational forces prevent them coalescing into larger bodies – and one consequence of this is that they are slowly but steadily degrading, with ring particles breaking apart and grinding down due to collisions, losing energy thanks to tidal forces, and drifting towards the planet. Because of this, early 20th-century astronomers generally believed that rings were likely to be transitory systems – brief interludes in the life of a giant planet, caused when the disintegration of a moon or infalling comet injected material into the unstable region within the Roche limit. Indeed, the existence of the limit was first calculated in 1850 by French astronomer Édouard Roche as part of his own explanation for Saturn's rings. The volume of a planet's Roche limit is dependent on its mass, which neatly explains why only giant planets are known to have rings. (In 2008, a team analysing magnetic data from the Cassini spaceprobe announced their suspicion that Saturn's second moon Rhea might have a dusty ring system of its own, but a search for visual evidence in 2010 suggested no such rings are present.)

However, the discovery of rings around the other giant planets raised an obvious problem with this prevailing theory – if rings were short-lived, then what were the chances of finding them around all four giant planets at this particular point in the solar system's long history? However, all was not lost, since the bright surface of Saturn's rings (apparently untarnished by infalling meteoritic dust) and the large quantities of material present within them could be seen as a sign of their relative youth. In the 1990s, therefore, scientists developed a neat model in which bright 'young' systems such as Saturn's formed from the disintegration of a parent body, then degraded over time into thinner ringlets like those of Uranus and Neptune, before ultimately being ground down to thin dust planes like those around Jupiter. Despite this, however, the presence of Saturn's brilliant and purportedly short-lived system was still too much of a coincidence for astronomers, so the search for mechanisms capable of resupplying material to the rings, or forming completely new ring systems at relatively frequent intervals continued.

An ancient system

Results from the Saturn-orbiting Cassini spaceprobe have recently overturned the 'young ring' model, replacing it with one in which Saturn's rings are ancient – constantly changing but self-regenerating. The crucial evidence comes from new estimates of the mass of material in the B Ring, based on complex physical simulations and measurements of the flickering light from stars passing behind the rings. In 2007, a team led by Larry Esposito of the University of Colorado published new estimates that the B Ring contains perhaps three times more material than previously thought. They also identified distinctive 'clumpy' structures ranging from tens of metres up to several kilometres across, which they suggest are caused by previously fragmented ring material coalescing back into semi-solid, more robust objects. Esposito and his team proposed that this evidence of recycling would allow the massive B Ring to churn its material, keeping the exposed outer surfaces fresh and relatively free of dust even over billions of years. So it seems that the B Ring, at least, could be quite ancient after all, and the current structure of Saturn's ring system may be just a brief 'snapshot' from its long history.

'If rings were short-lived, then what were the chances of finding them around all four giant planets at this particular point in the solar system's long history?'

Of course, a more accurate age for Saturn's rings still leaves the fundamental question of their origin unanswered. The fact that the rings are still 90–95 percent ice despite the addition of billions of years' worth of dust, suggests that the material which originally formed them was almost pure ice, and thus the rings are unlikely to be simply 'leftovers' from the mix of rock and ice that made the planet's moons. The breakup of a medium-sized moon or even a large comet is unlikely to meet the requirements for similar reasons. However, in 2010 Robin M. Canup of the Southwest Research Institute proposed an ingenious new solution. She suggests that the rings formed from the breakup of a much larger, Titan-sized world, that had differentiated into a rocky core and an icy outer mantle. As this moon's orbit deteriorated and it spiralled towards the planet, tidal forces would have preferentially stripped away the outer layers to form the rings, while the rocky core continued its inward spiral to eventually collide with Saturn. However, this new understanding of Saturn's rings leaves many questions outstanding, not least about how the solar system's other ring systems fit into the picture.

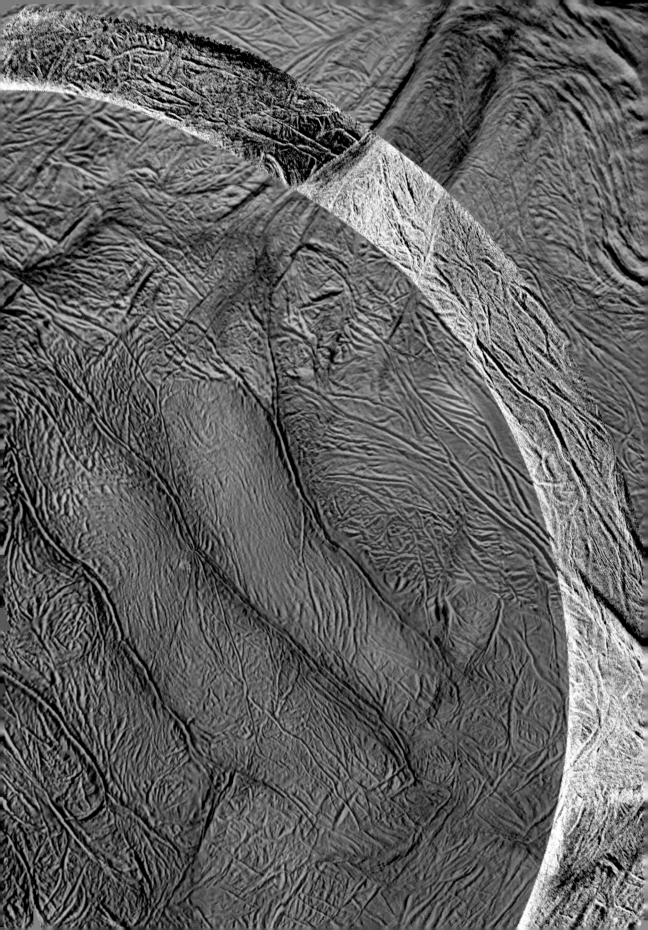

55 The icy plumes of Enceladus

DEFINITION JETS OF LIQUID WATER BURSTING OUT OF TIDAL HOT SPOTS ON THE SMALL SATURNIAN MOON ENCELADUS.

DISCOVERY PHOTOGRAPHS FROM THE 1980s VOYAGER SPACEPROBES SUGGESTED ENCELADUS IS COVERED BY FRESH SNOWFALLS.

KEY BREAKTHROUGH IN 2005, THE CASSINI PROBE FLEW STRAIGHT THROUGH AN ERUPTING PLUME OF WATER ICE.

IMPORTANCE WITH LIQUID WATER JUST BELOW ITS SURFACE, ENCELADUS MAY BE A SUITABLE ENVIRONMENT FOR THE EVOLUTION OF SIMPLE LIFE FORMS.

Enceladus is one of the relatively small inner moons of Saturn and, although icy in composition, is not the sort of place astronomers would normally look for liquid water. But tidal forces created by Saturn and its other moons have resulted in a surprising world where water lurks just below the surface.

From its discovery in 1789 until the Space Age, Enceladus was always assumed to be a near-twin of its inner neighbour Mimas. As with many of Saturn's moons, spectroscopy revealed an icy surface, but it was only in the early 1980s, when the Voyager probes returned the first detailed images, that astronomers realized the 500-km (310-mile) moon might be anything special.

Snowball satellite

At first glance, Enceladus' most striking feature is the sheer brightness of its surface. While many of Saturn's moons are icy, their landscapes are usually somewhat less than pristine – they may be discoloured by chemical contaminants from within, tainted by dust from meteorites and comets that have splattered their surfaces, or chemically transformed by long exposure to solar wind and radiation. Enceladus, in contrast, appears as pure as driven snow – its surface is the brightest in the entire solar system, reflecting a dazzling 99 percent of the light that falls on it.

Voyager 1's initial distant flyby in November 1980 revealed only its surprising brightness and the moon's suggestive position in the densest part of Saturn's tenuous outer E Ring (see page 218). However this was enough for Richard J. Terrile of NASA's Jet Propulsion Laboratory and Allan F. Cook to suggest that liquid water might be escaping through a weak crust, feeding material to the E Ring as well as blanketing the moon's surface with fresh snow. The

OPPOSITE This Cassini image overlays a strip of topographic data, gathered by the spaceprobe's onboard radar, onto a enhanced-colour view of the moon's southern hemisphere. The most prominent features are the blue 'tiger stripes' – warm patches linked to the eruption of icy plumes from beneath the surface.

evidence for their hypothesis grew stronger in August 1981, when Voyager 2 passed closer to Enceladus, returning photographs that revealed features such as craters and canyons beneath the surface. Counts of the crater density on different parts of the surface revealed that some areas were ancient, while others were comparatively young – perhaps as little as 100 million years old. According to models of the time, Enceladus was far too small to have retained much internal heat from its initial formation, so it should have been a heavily cratered, geologically dead world like its neighbour Mimas. Clearly some external force, most likely tidal, had heated the moon and allowed it to become active for at least some of its history.

Enceladus up close

Despite the theories, however, the case for active water geysers on Enceladus remained inconclusive, and so when the Cassini spaceprobe entered orbit around Saturn in 2004, Enceladus was treated as a priority target. Several close flybys, coming within hundreds and sometimes just tens of kilometres of the surface, have been carried out by Cassini, and they have confirmed Enceladus's status as a fascinating world full of unexpected features.

In fact, Cassini struck scientific gold almost immediately, returning images of a plume of material scattering sunlight above the moon's south pole on its first close flyby in February 2005. On its next close encounter in July of that year, the probe's flightpath happened to take it straight through the plume, allowing it to confirm the presence of water vapour.

'The tiger stripes are releasing up to ten times more heat than previously thought possible – equivalent to 20 coal-fired power stations.'

Meanwhile, close-up images revealed the full complexity of the moon's surface. While Voyager 2's pictures had suggested the presence of tectonic features such as troughs and scarps associated with faults, and grooved bands created by stretching of the surface (similar to those found on Jupiter's moon Ganymede, see page 209), Cassini was able to study these in far greater detail. It also discovered a warm, geologically active area around the moon's south pole, centred around four parallel linear trenches that were soon named 'the tiger stripes'. Each of these cracks in the moon's surface is around 130 km (80 miles) long and up to 2 km (1.2 miles) wide, and further observations have linked them directly to the origin of the water plumes. Infrared instruments reveal that the stripes are 45–90°C (81–162°F) warmer than the expected temperature of Enceladus's surface.

So it seems clear that this icy moon is being heated from within – but how? One theory, proposed in 2005 by a team at NASA's Jet Propulsion Laboratory, is that Saturn's moons coalesced quite rapidly after the planet's formation, and as a result benefited from the heating effect of short-lived radioactive materials trapped within them. Enceladus is unusually rocky for a satellite so far out in the solar system, so it would have benefited most

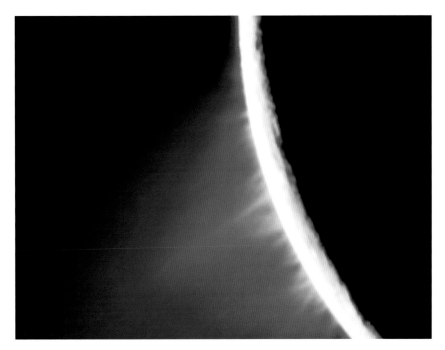

from this heating. As a result, it developed a partially molten interior that separated into a rocky core and icy mantle. Since then, tidal heating tugging at the interior must have done most of the work of keeping Enceladus warm. The tides raised by Saturn alone are far too weak, but the orbit of Enceladus happens to put it in resonance with the larger outer satellite Dione, orbiting Saturn in half the time of its outer sibling. This arrangement raises unusually strong tides that may be enough to keep the moon's core semi-molten.

Surprisingly, a 2011 study of the south polar region, led by Carly Howett of the Southwest Research Institute, suggested that the tiger stripes are releasing up to ten times more heat than previously thought possible – equivalent to 20 coal-fired power stations. This is far beyond the energy that could normally be supplied by the Enceladus–Dione resonance, and one theory is that Dione's relationship to the inner moon changes slowly over time, and we are seeing Enceladus at one of the peaks of its energy output.

In 2007, a team led by Frank Postberg of the Max Planck Institute for Nuclear Physics at Heidelberg, Germany, used Cassini's Cosmic Dust Analyzer instrument to study the composition of the plumes in more detail, revealing that they are salty, alkaline and contain some organic (carbon-based) chemicals. This, together with the more recent discovery of ammonia in the plume material (which helps to lower the freezing point of water considerably) essentially confirms that their source is a reservoir of liquid water just below the surface. This water may be localized in caverns, or perhaps widely distributed in a subterranean ocean, but, wherever it lies, it is now seen as a prime target in the search for life beyond Earth.

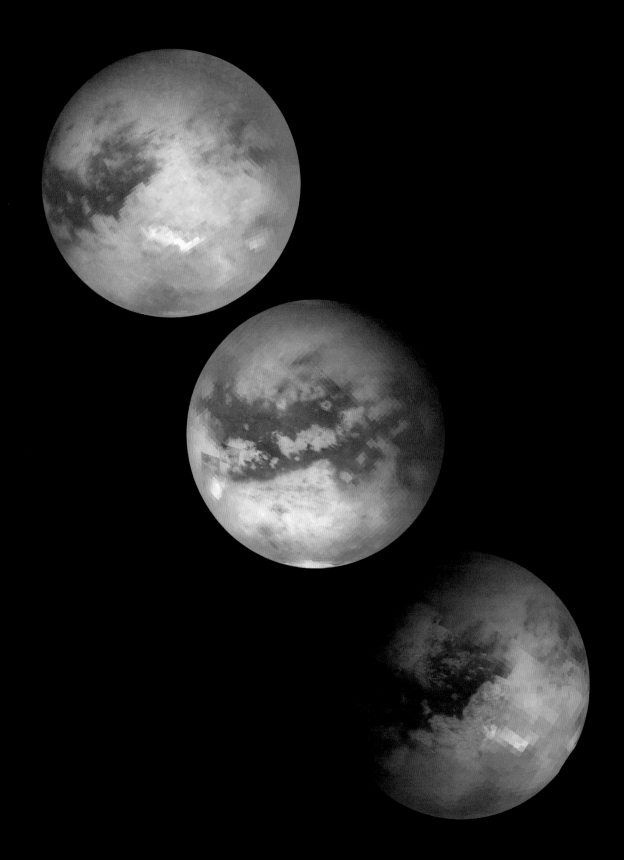

characteristic spectral signature of methane. Kuiper concluded that, thanks to a combination of its substantial gravity and the cold temperatures of the outer solar system, Titan is able to hold onto a thin atmosphere.

Voyager 1 passed close to Titan during its Saturn flyby of 1980, but the pictures it returned only increased the mystery around the moon – Titan was blanketed in a uniform orange haze that blocked any view of the surface. The atmosphere proved far thicker than Kuiper had predicted, and was in fact dominated by nitrogen, with methane accounting for just 1.6 percent (thought even this is enough to form clouds and give the atmosphere its distinctive colour). Despite rampant speculation about conditions beneath Titan's clouds, the scientific community had to wait for more than two decades before they could start to uncover its secrets.

OPPOSITE A series of Cassini images combine infrared and visible light views of Titan to provide the best possible global views of Saturn's giant moon. The mosaics, based on images from October and December 2005, and January 2006, show clear changes in the brightness of various cloud features.

Landing on Titan

Launched in 1997, NASA's Cassini orbiter was equipped with radar and infrared instruments capable of peering through Titan's haze to view the ground beneath. It also carried with it Huygens, a European-built lander that parachuted into Titan's clouds in January 2005. Images sent back as the haze cleared revealed a landscape of smooth eroded highlands, delta-like outflow regions and a plain covered in dark, rippling dunes. The overall appearance was of a coastline with an offshore island, but despite predictions, there were no signs of liquid lakes or seas formed by methane rain or snow.

Huygens returned data from Titan's surface for 90 minutes while the main Cassini spacecraft flew overhead acting as a relay. Its images showed a pebble-strewn landscape shrouded in perpetual twilight. Mission scientists concluded that Huygens had landed in a river delta, amid rock–ice debris that had been swept down from the highlands when the river was last active.

The view from orbit

While Huygens offered only a brief look at Titan from ground level, the Cassini spacecraft has been able to send back images from frequent orbital encounters over several years. Maps produced using special filters to peer through the haze show a world of highland continents and lowland basins that bears more than a passing resemblance to Earth. The landscape appears to be smooth and undulating, indicating that processes of fluvial erosion, linked to flowing rivers and other bodies of water, are at work. Craters on Titan are very rare, suggesting that the landscape is very young, and is resurfaced on relatively short timescales.

RIGHT Cassini's cameras captured this evocative image of sunlight glinting off a lake near Titan's north

Titan's most obvious individual feature is Xanadu, a large, bright area the size of Australia, lying close to the equator. Elsewhere, dark patches mark enormous seas of sand dunes, running east–west parallel to the equator. These dunes are shaped by sluggish but persistent winds, created as Titan's heavy atmosphere is tugged in different directions by tides from Saturn.

As with the detection of methane on Mars (see page 171), its presence on Titan raises interesting questions. The gas tends to break down when exposed to ultraviolet sunlight in the atmosphere, creating a chemical smog, so methane must be constantly replenished – by either impacts of icy comets, volcanic activity or the action of microorganisms.

'Images sent back as the haze cleared revealed a landscape of smooth eroded highlands, delta-like outflow regions, and a plain covered in dark, rippling dunes.'

The lack of other cometary gases in Titan's atmosphere rules out the first option, and the prospects for life on a world where surface temperatures average –180°C (–292°F) seem challenging (although Titan's atmosphere bears a strong resemblance to that of the primordial Earth). But volcanic activity, of a sort, seems a distinct possibility. Cassini's infrared cameras have detected bright hot spots both on Titan's surface and in its atmosphere, alongside structures resembling lava flows. These bright surface spots may mark active low-temperature 'cryovolcanoes', where an icy water/ammonia slush oozes onto the landscape from subterranean reservoirs. The surprising discovery that Titan's crust appears to be slipping, with the locations of some surface features drifting by more than 10 km (6 miles) a year, suggests the presence of a mobile ocean layer, perhaps hundreds of kilometres deep, which may help transfer heat from the moon's interior to its crust.

Shifting climate

Thanks to Cassini, long-cherished theories about Titan's climate have finally been borne out. Titan seems to have a methane cycle analogous to Earth's own water cycle, with chemicals transported around the planet and transferred between solid, liquid and gaseous phases, driving erosion that smooths and shapes the landscape. Huygens' initial discovery of a dry landscape was something of a blow to this theory, but later in 2005 Cassini identified dry lake beds around Titan's south pole, and in 2006, its radar detected basins filled with radar-absorbing liquid at the north pole.

Titan shares Saturn's 29.5-Earth-year cycle of seasons, and it now seems that these affect it far more than was previously suspected. Methane evaporating from warm areas of the moon is transported by prevailing winds and returns to the surface as rain or snow over cooler regions. Since the initial discovery of lakes in the north, Titan's southern pole has moved from summer into fall, and the dry lakebeds of this region have also begun to refill. While many longstanding theories about Titan have now been proven correct, this complex moon surely hides many more secrets.

The contrasting surface of Iapetus

DEFINITION JUPITER'S OUTERMOST LARGE MOON SHOWS A MARKED DISTINCTION BETWEEN LIGHT AND DARK AREAS.

DISCOVERY THE PATTERN OF IAPETUS'S SURFACE WAS IDENTIFIED BY GIAN DOMENICO CASSINI IN THE 1670s.

KEY BREAKTHROUGH IN 2010, ASTRONOMERS EXPLAINED HOW DUST FROM THE OUTER MOON PHOEBE TRIGGERS AN 'ICE MIGRATION' PROCESS THAT CREATES THE STARK DIFFERENCES IN TERRAIN.

IMPORTANCE IAPETUS SHOWS HOW APPARENTLY NEGLIGIBLE EFFECTS SUCH AS A SCATTERING OF DUST CAN HAVE UNEXPECTEDLY POWERFUL CONSEQUENCES.

The outermost of Saturn's regular moons, Iapetus is also one of the strangest worlds in the solar system, with mismatched dark and light hemispheres. Its bizarre surface has been subjected to renewed scrutiny since the arrival of the Cassini spaceprobe in orbit around Saturn.

While in most cases scientists had to wait for the Space Age to discover the intriguing features of the gas giant satellites, Iapetus made its strange appearance clear from the outset. Italian astronomer Gian Domenico Cassini discovered the moon in 1671, while it lay on the western side of Saturn. But when he tried to recover it later on the eastern side of the planet, it was nowhere to be seen, and it was not until 1705 that Cassini finally tracked it down using an improved telescope. Cassini correctly assumed that Iapetus, like our own Moon, spins once on its axis with each orbit, and has a bright 'trailing' hemisphere (which he saw on the western side as the moon moved away from Earth) and a dark 'leading' hemisphere (which was harder to see on the eastern side as the satellite approached Earth).

But while later astronomers confirmed and refined the variations in Iapetus's brightness, the moon remained a mystery until the era of robot spaceprobes. Voyager 2 returned the first close-up images of the moon in 1981, and confirmed a striking difference between a dark, almost sooty, leading hemisphere, and the bright, reflective trailing side. So was Iapetus a light moon with a dark coating, or a dark moon with a light coating?

A coating of alien dust?
In the light of these discoveries, planetary scientists developed a theory that linked the appearance of Iapetus to its outer neighbour Phoebe – a large

OPPOSITE The bright trailing hemisphere of Iapetus was viewed in close-up for the first time by the Cassini spaceprobe in September 2007. This image reveals heavy cratering at high latitudes in the moon's northern and southern hemispheres, including two large overlapping impact basins in the southern hemisphere.

captured comet or centaur (see page 253) that follows a retrograde orbit four times further out than Iapetus. They suggested that dark material chipped off Phoebe by tiny meteorite impacts spiralled towards Saturn, only to be picked up by the leading hemisphere of Iapetus.

But there were complications. Even the relatively distant Voyager images showed that the boundary between the terrains was not straight – bright material overlaps onto the darker hemisphere at the poles, and patches of dark and light both appear on the opposing hemispheres. Images returned by the Cassini probe from 2004 onwards showed that both light and dark materials on the leading hemisphere were redder than their counterparts on the trailing hemisphere, while in places the light and dark terrain lay directly alongside each other with no apparent blurring at the boundaries.

'Cassini correctly assumed that Iapetus spins once on its axis with each orbit, and has a bright "trailing" hemisphere and a dark "leading" hemisphere.'

In 2009, astronomers using the Spitzer Space Telescope discovered Saturn's expansive outer ring, linked to the orbit of Phoebe (see page 218). Together with the Cassini data, this was enough for astronomers Tilmann Denk of the Free University in Berlin and John R. Spencer of the Southwest Research Institute to propose a new explanation for the appearance of Iapetus in 2010.

In this model, reddish dust from the Phoebe ring lands on the icy surface of Iapetus, but does not cover it completely. Instead, it acts as a trigger for a process of 'ice migration': the polluted areas absorb more sunlight and cause ice to sublime (turning directly from solid to vapour), leaving behind the other dust trapped within it as a dark lag. Over time, this process darkens those areas of the leading hemisphere receiving the most sunlight (explaining why the poles and some geographical features such as deep craters remain icy). Meanwhile, ice accumulates from vapour in colder or lighter spots, causing a runaway segregation of the surface into the extremes seen today.

A tough nut to crack

While Cassini's images ultimately resolved an old problem, they also set some new puzzles. Most striking is the equatorial ridge, a 20-km-wide (12.5-mile) plateau running for 1,300 km (800 miles) across the dark terrain, at an average height of 13 km (8 miles) and with individual peaks of up to 20 km (12.5 miles). The ridge, which gives Iapetus a notable resemblance to a walnut, is absent on the brighter face, but isolated peaks mark its path.

The equatorial ridge is unique in the solar system, and planetary scientists have risen to the challenge of explaining it with three rival theories. One suggestion, put forward by a team of Cassini scientists, suggests that it is a frozen remnant from a time when the moon rotated far more rapidly and had a pronounced equatorial bulge. The present shape of Iapetus shows that it almost certainly rotated in about 16 hours early in its history, and has since been slowed to its current 79-day synchronous rotation by tidal forces. However, in order to bulge out even further, Iapetus would need to have been relatively molten early in its history, implying a rapid and hot formation that trapped short-lived radioactive material (as with Enceladus, see page 225). However, explaining how the moon changed its shape while preserving its fossil ridge is still a challenge.

Another idea is that the ridge is made from icy material that welled up from within Iapetus early in its history. If such a ridge formed away from the equator, then tidal forces would have tugged at it and forced the moon onto its current axis of rotation.

Perhaps the most intriguing idea, though, is that the ridge is made of debris dumped from space. In 2006, astronomer W. H. Ip of Taiwan's National Central University pointed out that Iapetus's isolated position in the Saturnian system might have allowed it to trap a ring of orbiting material after its formation. As this ring became unstable, it would have fallen back onto the planet around the equator. A 2010 proposal by William B. McKinnon of Washington University, St Louis, and Andrew Dombard of the University of Illinois, Chicago, took the idea one step further, suggesting that Iapetus actually formed a moon of its own, which assisted with the process of slowing the satellite's rotation before crashing to its doom.

BELOW Iapetus's bizarre equatorial ridge is captured in detail by this Cassini image, taken from a distance of around 62,000 km (38,500 miles).

Unfortunately, all three of these scenarios have problems: none can explain why the ridge only runs across the dark terrain, and the debris hypothesis, in particular, may be undermined by what seem to be tectonic features linking the ridge with its surroundings. The jury is, for the moment, still out.

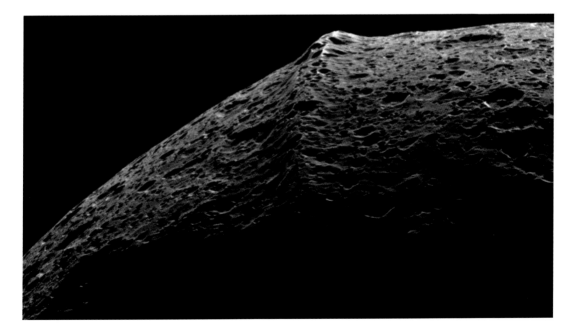

58 The strange tilt of Uranus

DEFINITION THE PLANET URANUS IS TILTED AT A STRIKING $98°$ FROM 'UPRIGHT' – THE BIGGEST TILT OF ANY MAJOR PLANET.

DISCOVERY THE DISCOVERY OF RINGS AROUND URANUS IN 1977 CONFIRMED THE TILT SUSPECTED FROM THE ORBITS OF ITS MOONS.

KEY BREAKTHROUGH IN 2011, SCIENTISTS SHOWED HOW URANUS WAS PROBABLY KNOCKED OFF ITS AXIS BY A SERIES OF IMPACTS.

IMPORTANCE THE EXTREME TILT GIVES URANUS UNIQUE CHARACTERISTICS, INCLUDING EXTREME SEASONS.

The seventh planet from the Sun, Uranus has an extremely tilted axis of rotation that gives it the strangest seasons in the solar system. A quarter of a century after Voyager 2's flyby, astronomers are still trying to understand the planet's remarkably placid weather and the origins of its strange tilt.

At roughly twice the distance of Saturn, Uranus was the first planet to be discovered in the telescopic age, by German-born amateur astronomer William Herschel in 1781. Yet for the next two centuries, Uranus remained mysterious and elusive. Astronomers estimated its diameter at around five times the size of Earth, and in the 1930s succeeded in identifying methane in its atmosphere through spectroscopic analysis (see page 25), but even through the largest telescope the planet remained a pale blue-green blob. The only clue that there was something odd about Uranus came from the behaviour of its moons, the first of which were discovered by Herschel himself in 1787. They appeared to orbit on paths that were sharply tilted to the plane of the planet's orbit around the Sun, and since most moons tend to orbit more or less above their parent's equator, this suggested that Uranus itself was tipped over at a much steeper angle than any other known planet.

Cosmic bulls-eye

This suspicion was finally confirmed in 1977, when astronomers James Elliot, Edward Dunham and Douglas Mink discovered the rings of Uranus. The astronomers were using NASA's Kuiper Airborne Observatory, a converted Lockheed Starlifter cargo aircraft, to observe a predicted occultation, in which Uranus would pass in front of a distant star. To their surprise, however, they also recorded a series of dips in the star's light before and after the main eclipse, as it passed behind the rings. Remarkably, the brightest of the

OPPOSITE This enhanced-colour Voyager image shows the nine brightest rings of Uranus, with the brightest Epsilon Ring on the right. The alignment of the ring system above the planet's tilted equator is an important clue that Uranus was knocked off its axis early in its history.

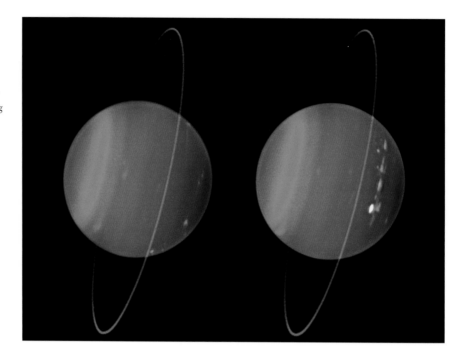

RIGHT A pair of
infrared images
captured by the giant
Keck Telescopes in
July 2004 provide
the most detailed
ground-based view of
Uranus so far, showing
a collar of light
clouds in the planet's
southern hemisphere,
and bright storms
developing in the
northern hemisphere.

13 rings known today matches well with a ring that Herschel himself reported, but no other astronomers were able to confirm. The plane of the rings around the planet revealed that the axis of Uranus was tilted at a remarkable 98°. This tilt has unusual effects on the planet's seasons. The poles experience 42 years of daylight and 42 years of night, while the equatorial regions alternate between long periods of twilight, and a relatively normal day–night cycle driven by the planet's rotation period (now known to be 17 hours).

Despite the discovery of its tilt and rings, the planet itself remained a frustratingly featureless disc, and astronomers were eager to see what the Voyager 2 spacecraft would discover during its 1986 flyby. But after the stunning cloudscapes of Jupiter and Saturn, Uranus turned out to be a surprisingly bland ball of pale turquoise. The most striking features of the planet, whose southern hemisphere was in full sunlight at the time, were a bright patch on the south pole and darker banding around the equator, separated by a bright collar at a latitude of 45–50° S.

Yet the lack of features was itself intriguing. One possibility was that the weather on Uranus was placid simply because the planet did not receive sufficient energy from the Sun – by some measures, it is the coldest planet in the solar system. However, this idea had to be dismissed after Voyager sent back images of active, stormy Neptune in 1989. Instead, perhaps the difference was due to the planet's internal power source – or rather, the lack of it. While Jupiter, Saturn and Neptune all generate substantially more heat from their interiors than they receive from the Sun, Uranus, it appeared, did not – perhaps for reasons connected to its curious tilt.

Fortunately, by the mid-1990s, technological advances began to supplement Voyager's brief view of the planet. Both the Hubble Space Telescope and the new generation of ground-based telescopes were now able to produce detailed images of Uranus from Earth and its immediate neighbourhood. By this time, it seemed that things had changed substantially. Bright clouds had begun to appear in the mid-latitudes of the southern hemisphere, and banding became more pronounced as the northern hemisphere started to move into sunlight at the beginning of spring. By 2006, as the planet approached its equinox, astronomers using the HST identified a dark spot to the north of the equator, similar to those seen on Neptune. It seems that the Uranian climate varies dramatically between solstices and equinoxes, and one theory is that around the equinoxes, the transfer of heat from the summer to the winter pole creates currents that overwhelm the planet's other weather features.

Knocked off axis?

Perhaps the most intriguing question, however, is how Uranus ended up with its extreme tilt. The neat alignment of rings and moons around the present equator suggests that whatever happened must have occurred early in the planet's history, since the entire Uranian system would not have time to recover from a more recent change. In 2009, astronomers Gwenaël Boué and Jacques Lascar of the Paris Observatory in France showed how a giant moon with perhaps 1 percent of the mass of Uranus could have tugged the planet off its axis over around 2 million years. But this raises two important questions – where did this giant moon come from (since it would be unusually large to form from a left-over debris disc), and where did it go to?

'The poles experience 42 years of daylight and 42 years of night, while the equatorial regions alternate between long periods of twilight, and a relatively normal day–night cycle.'

A more generally accepted explanation is an interplanetary impact, similar to those that helped shape both Mercury and Earth early in their histories, but on a much larger scale – perhaps involving an incoming body with the mass of around five Earths. However, even this theory is not without its problems. In 2011, a team of scientists led by Alessandro Morbidelli of France's Cote d'Azur Observatory showed that a young Uranian system could have recovered from an early impact in order to create the rings and moons we see today, but with one difference – in a single-impact scenario, it seems, the moons would probably have ended up orbiting in a retrograde direction, counter to the planet's rotation. However, Morbidelli's team also showed that a series of smaller collisions would be far more likely to end up with prograde moons.

So did a number of impacts knock Uranus off its axis? It seems likely, but this in turn raises awkward questions about the presence of large rogue planets in the outer solar system. Another alternative is that Uranus was tugged off its axis by a series of close encounters with Saturn and Neptune, linked to planetary migrations (see page 101) early in solar system history.

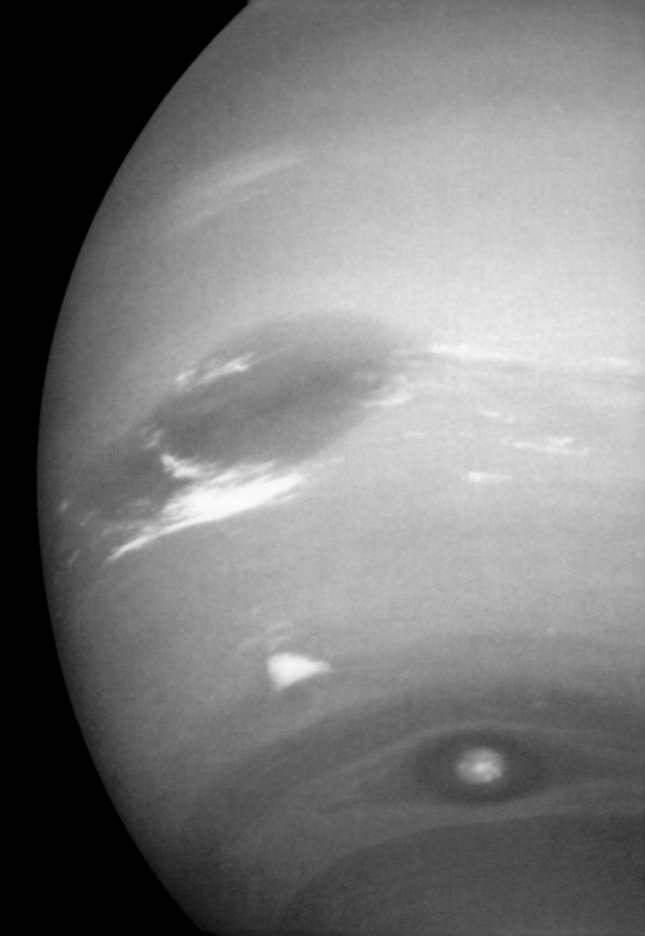

59 Neptune's extreme interior

DEFINITION WITHIN ICE GIANTS SUCH AS NEPTUNE, BIZARRE
CHEMICAL TRANSFORMATIONS FORM HOT ICE AND DIAMOND RAIN.

DISCOVERY IN 1999, SCIENTISTS SHOWED HOW METHANE COULD
DISINTEGRATE UNDER PRESSURE TO CREATE DIAMOND CRYSTALS.

KEY BREAKTHROUGH IN 2005, A STUDY REVEALED HOW WATER CAN
FORM A STEEL-HARD 'SUPERIONIC' FORM UNDER HIGH PRESSURES.

IMPORTANCE SUPERIONIC WATER ICE MAY FINALLY EXPLAIN THE
PUZZLING MAGNETIC FIELDS OF THE OUTER ICE GIANTS.

According to the latest research, the outermost giant planet Neptune may contain layers deep beneath its stormy surface in which diamond forms in tiny droplets, and where a strange form of water ice sets as hard as iron and glows yellow.

A surprising oasis of ocean-blue in the cold depths of the solar system, Neptune, like Uranus, was only discovered in the telescopic age. In this case the find was the result of a deliberate search in 1846 for a massive object disturbing the orbits of its inner neighbours, but, again like Uranus, we knew very little about it before the Voyager 2 spaceprobe flew past in 1989.

A dynamic planet

Despite its almost identical size, Neptune proved to be a very different world from placid Uranus. When Voyager arrived, the planet was dominated by an enormous storm dubbed the Great Dark Spot (though unlike Jupiter's Great Red Spot, it now seems that storms on Neptune are comparatively short-lived, lasting only a few years). There were pronounced weather bands and high-altitude white clouds whose motions revealed that Neptune has the highest winds in the entire solar system, up to 2,100 km/h (1,300 mph).

At an average of 30 times Earth's distance from the Sun, Neptune receives far too little sunlight to power such active weather systems, yet measurements showed that its surface temperatures were similar to those of Uranus (which receives twice as much solar energy). Calculations show that Neptune emits 2.6 times as much energy as it receives from the Sun, indicating that it has a powerful internal energy source. The quest to explain the structure of Neptune's interior, and the powerful magnetic fields found at both Uranus

OPPOSITE At the time of Voyager 2's 1989 flyby, the blue orb of Neptune was dominated by an enormous storm called the Great Dark Spot – just one manifestation of the powerful weather systems driven by the planet's internal energy.

and Neptune (which are strongly tilted to each planet's axis of rotation, and offset so that they do not pass through the planet's centre) has led to some surprising discoveries about conditions inside these outer giant worlds.

Given their marked differences from the inner gas giants Jupiter and Saturn, Uranus and Neptune are often referred to as the 'ice giant' planets. While their inner neighbours are dominated by enormous envelopes of hydrogen that take on different forms at different depths and pressures, Uranus and Neptune have very little of this material (probably due to the time they took to coalesce in the early days of the solar system – see page 98). Instead, they are dominated by heavier compounds with low melting points, known in chemical parlance as ices. These include familiar water ice (chemical formula H_2O), as well as methane (CH_4) and ammonia (NH_3). A small proportion of methane (around 2 percent) in the atmospheres of the ice giants is thought to be responsible for their distinctive bluish colours – it absorbs the red component of incoming sunlight so that the planets only reflect back other, shorter wavelengths.

Under pressure

As with the gas giants, temperature and pressure increase with depth, and the general result of this is that, despite rising temperatures, the ices do not melt in the way that we would understand. Instead, they form a hot chemical slush that makes up the planet's mantle, at temperatures of around 2,000–5,000°C (3,600–9,000°F). At the centre of each planet lies a rocky core, probably about the size of Mars.

While the internal power sources of Jupiter and Saturn are believed to be linked to their gradual cooling and gravitational compression (see page 191), this 'Kelvin–Helmholtz contraction' is not enough to explain the energy generated inside Neptune. Instead, astronomers believe there must be chemical transitions happening at certain depths within the planet. In 1999, a team of scientists led by Laura Robin Benedetti of the University of California at Berkeley discovered a remarkable process that may happen around 7,000 km (4,400 miles) beneath the surface of Neptune, at pressures of around 250,000 Earth atmospheres. Using a laser-heated diamond anvil, which compresses a sample of material between two facets of diamond and then energizes it using a laser beam, they applied extreme temperatures and pressures to small samples of methane. This revealed that methane decomposes into its component elements more easily than previously suspected, releasing carbon and hydrogen atoms that react with one another to form other hydrocarbon molecules, as well as pure hydrogen, and carbon in the form of crystalline diamond. If the interior of Neptune behaves as the experiments suggest, then deep beneath the surface, microscopic diamonds are precipitating out of their surroundings and sinking downwards in a

'As the pressure rose, the molecules split apart, with oxygen atoms remaining fixed within the lattice structure, and the hydrogen atoms moving around freely.'

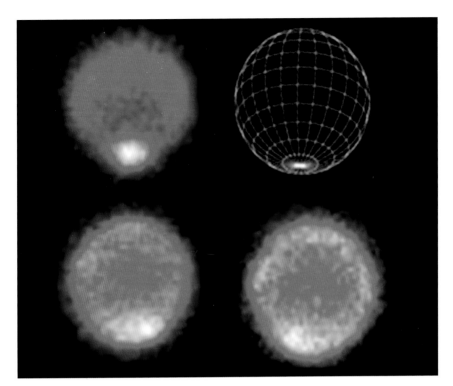

diamond rain. Benedetti's team suggested that heat released by this process, coupled with a boost to the gravitational contraction created as the diamond and hydrocarbons sink downwards and the lightweight hydrogen rises upwards, helps fuel Neptune's internal power planet.

Hard as steel

In 2005, a team led by Alex Goncharov of Lawrence Livermore National Laboratory in California used similar equipment to study the behaviour of water under similar extreme pressures. While the ice giant interiors are assumed to be a strange mix of slushy chemicals heated to well above their melting point, but kept solid by the intense pressure from above, the Livermore experiments were some of the first detailed investigations into what happens under such conditions.

Analysing the spectrum of the water under pressures of 470,000 Earth atmospheres, heated to temperatures of around 1,300°C (2,400°F), revealed that it had taken on a strange superionic state. Initially, the water molecules froze into a crystalline lattice as expected, but as the pressure rose, the molecules split apart, with oxygen atoms remaining fixed within the lattice structure, and the hydrogen atoms moving around freely. The Livermore tests tracked the behaviour of just a few dozen water molecules but, in bulk, superionic water would be as hard as steel and would glow yellow. It's possible that hydrogen ions moving through this strange ice might be crucial to generating the strange magnetic fields of the ice giants.

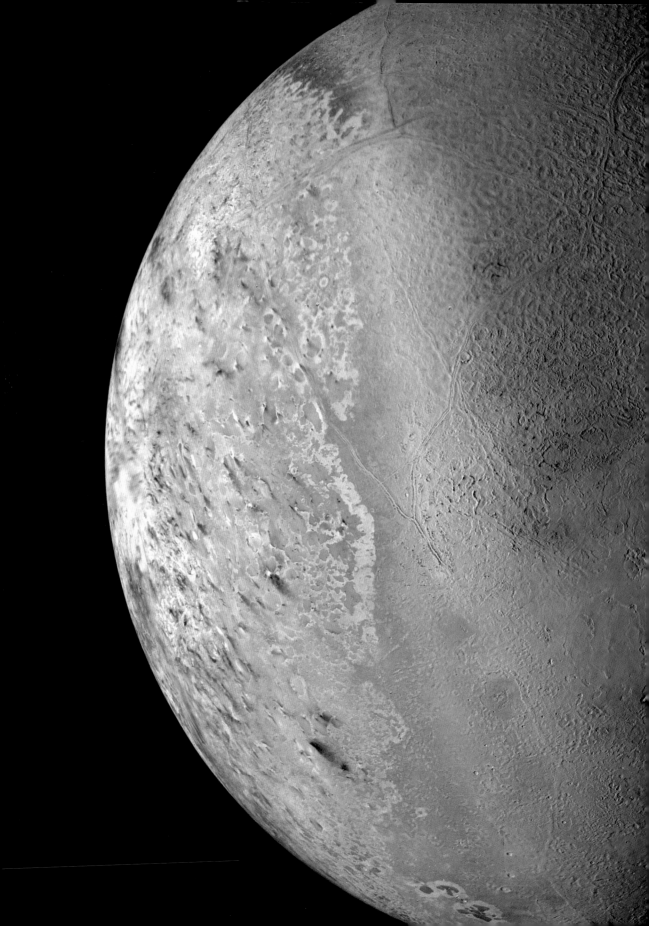

60

Triton's orbit and activity

DEFINITION NEPTUNE'S STRANGE GIANT MOON SEEMS TO BE A
CAPTURED ICE-DWARF WORLD FROM THE KUIPER BELT.

DISCOVERY TRITON'S UNUSUAL ORBIT, DISCOVERED IN THE EARLY
1980S, WAS THE FIRST HINT THAT IT MIGHT HAVE BEEN CAPTURED
INTO ORBIT AROUND NEPTUNE.

KEY BREAKTHROUGH IN 1989, VOYAGER 2 DISCOVERED ACTIVE
GEYSERS ON THE SURFACE OF TRITON.

IMPORTANCE TRITON OFFERS OUR FIRST GLIMPSE OF AN IMPORTANT
CLASS OF SMALL WORLDS IN THE OUTER SOLAR SYSTEM.

The Voyager 2 spaceprobe revealed Neptune's giant moon Triton as a
remarkably complex world that seemed out of place even among the varied
satellites of the outer solar system. Today, astronomers suspect that it may be
an ice-dwarf world, captured from the Kuiper Belt by Neptune's gravity.

Triton was discovered by British amateur astronomer William Lassell in
October 1846, just weeks after Neptune itself had been identified. For a
long time, it was the only known satellite of Neptune, and it was not even
officially named until a second moon, Nereid, was discovered a century
later. From the outset, Triton's orbit marked it out as something peculiar.
The moon was clearly large (at 2,700 km or 1,700 miles across, it is the
seventh largest satellite in the solar system), and it orbited at a sharply tilted
angle to the plane of Neptune's orbit. But while the similarly tilted orbits of
the satellites of Uranus provided evidence that the planet itself was tipped
over, in Triton's case there was another factor to take into account – the
moon orbits in a retrograde direction, orbiting in the opposite direction to
the planet's spin.

Intruder moon

Following the chance discovery of rings around Uranus (see page 237) in
1977, astronomers attempted to use the same technique (detecting dips in the
light from occulted stars), to find rings around Neptune. These observations
suggested that the rings were tenuous and clumpy, but they also showed that
Neptune itself is tilted at a relatively modest angle of 28° to the plane of its
orbit. So Triton not only orbits the wrong way around Neptune, but it also
does so at a sharp angle to the planet's equator. This was strong evidence that
Triton did not originate in orbit around Neptune, but is instead a captured

OPPOSITE A Voyager
2 close-up of Triton
reveals the moon's
complex landscape,
ranging from relatively
smooth grey regions
peppered with the
dark trails from gas
plumes, to the lumpy
and distinctly bluish
cantaloupe terrain.

body – a wandering world caught up by the planet's gravity at some time in the past. This theory also neatly explains the lack of other large moons that we would expect to find around Neptune – Triton's arrival disrupted their orbits and scattered them into the depths of the solar system. Neptune's outer moon Nereid, which takes almost a year to orbit the planet, may be a rare survivor from the original satellite system.

Astronomers got their first close-up look at Triton in 1989, during Voyager 2's brief, high-speed Neptune flyby, and the moon proved as intriguing as its possible origins suggested. The geometry of Sun, satellite and spacecraft during the flyby meant that only 40 percent of the surface could be imaged, but this still revealed many fascinating features, including a broad dichotomy between lumpy or pitted regions (soon nicknamed 'cantaloupe terrain') in the western hemisphere, and more varied landscapes in the east, with a wide range of features such as ridges, furrows and broad, flat plateaus. The entire surface showed remarkably little cratering, suggesting that it was resurfaced in the relatively recent past.

Unexpected activity

Perhaps most surprising of all, however, were the dark streaks that Voyager photographed on the flat planes around Triton's south pole. Close analysis revealed that they were formed by geysers of invisible gas (most likely nitrogen) erupting from beneath the surface and being carried northwards by prevailing winds. While the gas itself is invisible, it carries dark dust particles within it, that slowly fall back to the ground in Triton's weak gravity, marking the trail of the geyser. Some Voyager photographs even showed the tenuous geysers in profile, revealing that the columns of dusty gas rise up to 8 km (5 miles) into the thin atmosphere before being caught up in the prevailing winds.

'One hundred suspected craters were neatly clustered on Triton's leading hemisphere, suggesting that they formed as the incoming ice dwarf ploughed through other material in orbit around Neptune.'

Triton's surface proved to be a blend of ices, dominated by frozen nitrogen, water ice and carbon dioxide. Its tenuous atmosphere is believed to be predominantly nitrogen, with traces of carbon monoxide and methane. The Voyager scientists soon noted that the geyser eruptions were concentrated beneath Triton's antisolar point, suggesting that, even in the chill depths of the outer solar system, the effect of heat from the Sun is able to raise the temperature of subsurface nitrogen pockets above melting point.

The various unusual features of Triton were irresistibly reminiscent of the little that is known about Pluto, still classified at the time as the ninth planet of the solar system. The two worlds are roughly the same size, and have similar surface and atmospheric chemistry. Astronomers had long suspected that Pluto was just the most conspicuous member of a ring of small icy worlds orbiting beyond Neptune, known as the Kuiper Belt – so did this explain the mystery of Triton's origin? Was

Neptune's giant moon actually offering us a first glimpse of what we would today call an 'ice dwarf'?

A lost world

In the decade following Voyager's encounter, the evidence for this connection grew ever stronger, as numerous other Kuiper Belt Objects (KBOs) both large and small were discovered by a new generation of telescopes. Today, the ice-dwarf nature of Triton is widely accepted, and its unusually active surface is largely attributed to the enormous amounts of tidal energy that were dissipated in the form of heat as the rogue world was forced into its present orbit around Neptune. Heating of the mantle beneath Triton's western hemisphere caused it to become partially molten, and rising 'bubbles' of less dense ice forcing their way to the surface created the cantaloupe terrain.

In 2007, astronomers Paul M. Schenk of the Lunar and Planetary Institute and Kevin Zahnle of NASA's Ames Research Center produced further evidence to back up the capture theory in the form of an analysis of the moon's rare impact craters. Mapping the positions of 100 suspected craters, they discovered they were neatly clustered on Triton's leading hemisphere, suggesting that they formed as the incoming ice dwarf ploughed through other material in orbit around Neptune. What's more, models of the cratering process suggested that Triton's surface is remarkably young – even if the cratering was a result of chance encounters with infalling comets, the most heavily cratered parts of Triton should be no more than 50 million years old, and the youngest cantaloupe terrain around 6 million years old. If the cratering is due to debris orbiting Triton, then it suggests an even younger surface, and an interior that might remain warm enough to sustain a subsurface ocean of liquid water even today.

61

Distant Pluto

DEFINITION A SMALL WORLD THAT ORBITS JUST BEYOND NEPTUNE, AND WAS THE FIRST KUIPER BELT OBJECT TO BE DISCOVERED.

DISCOVERY PLUTO WAS FOUND AS THE RESULT OF A DELIBERATE SEARCH BY CLYDE TOMBAUGH IN 1930.

KEY BREAKTHROUGH IN 1978, ASTRONOMERS DISCOVERED PLUTO'S GIANT MOON CHARON, WHICH ALLOWED ITS SURFACE TO BE MAPPED FOR THE FIRST TIME.

IMPORTANCE PLUTO IS THE CLOSEST LARGE KUIPER BELT OBJECT, AND PRIME TARGET FOR THE NEW HORIZONS SPACEPROBE.

Once classified as a planet in its own right, since 2006 Pluto has been relegated to the status of 'dwarf planet'. Nevertheless, it is still one of the largest objects in the Kuiper Belt beyond Neptune, and a fascinating and mysterious world in its own right.

While Uranus was found by chance, and Neptune as the result of precise mathematical calculations, Pluto's discovery, some 60 years before any of the other worlds in the Kuiper Belt, was due largely to hard work and perseverance. In 1929, astronomer Clyde Tombaugh, working at the Lowell Observatory in Flagstaff, Arizona, began a painstaking survey of the sky in search of a trans-Neptunian planet whose existence was suspected at that time. Through meticulous comparison of photographic plates taken several nights apart, Tombaugh hoped to discover objects that were moving against the background stars, and within months, his strategy proved successful – Pluto was hailed as the ninth planet of the solar system.

However, Pluto was a problem almost as soon as it was found. Based on its brightness, it was clearly too small to affect the inner planets and cause the disturbances that had led to predictions of its existence. Indeed, it eventually became clear that these disturbances could be explained without the need for a ninth planet at all, and that Pluto's discovery was a fortunate accident.

The out-of-place planet

But what was this strange little world doing so far from the Sun? For a while, astronomers wondered if it could be a lost satellite of Neptune (Pluto's orbit comes closer to the Sun than Neptune for 20 of its 248 Earth years), but the smaller world's orbit is tilted sharply to the plane of the solar system,

OPPOSITE From its orbit high above Earth, the Hubble Space Telescope was able to separate Pluto and its giant moon Charon in this 2006 image. The telescope also confirmed the presence of two new moons around the dwarf planet, later named as Nix and Hydra.

so the two never come close to each other. Shortly after Pluto's discovery, astronomer Frederick C. Leonard suggested that it might be the first of a new class of objects orbiting beyond Neptune – what eventually became known as the Kuiper Belt (see page 253). However, the second 'Kuiper Belt Object' was not discovered until 1992, and Pluto was only demoted from its special status as a planet in 2006, after it became clear that it was not even the largest member of the Kuiper Belt.

Despite its diminished status, Pluto remains an intriguing world, and is the initial target for the New Horizons probe, currently on its way to the Kuiper Belt with a Pluto flyby planned for 2015. Its small size meant that it was little more than a star-like point of light for decades, and it was only in 1976 that a team from the University of Hawaii obtained a spectrum showing that its surface is largely covered in ice. This had important implications since it meant that Pluto was far more reflective than Earth, and therefore even smaller and less massive than previously suspected.

Multiple moons

In 1978, James Christy and Robert Harrington of the US Naval Observatory in Washington, DC, discovered a slight distortion in the image of Pluto that appeared to change its position over time. This was the first sighting of Charon, a moon that proved to have remarkable properties. With a diameter of 1,207 km (750 miles) Charon is more than half the size of Pluto's own 2,306 km (1,432 miles), and orbits in 6.4 Earth days just 19,600 km (12,200 miles) from the centre of Pluto itself. Just as Charon orbits with one face permanently towards Pluto, Pluto also rotates in the same 6.4-day period, and thus has one face permanently towards Charon.

'In 1985, astronomers viewing Pluto's occultation of a star discovered signs that Pluto has a thin atmosphere, now known to have a similar chemical composition to its surface ice.'

Charon's movement also reveals that Pluto, rather like Uranus, is tipped over on its side in relation to its orbit around the Sun, with an axial tilt of 119.5°, and this gave astronomers a unique opportunity to map the surfaces of the two worlds. Between 1985 and 1990, the plane of Charon's orbit lined up with Earth, and the two worlds eclipsed each other, twice in each 6.4-day orbit. The eclipses altered the combined brightness of the two worlds as seen from Earth, and careful measurements allowed Marc Buie of Lowell Observatory and David J. Tholen of the University of Hawaii to make surface maps for both Pluto and Charon. These initial maps were only superseded using the Hubble Space Telescope (HST) in 2003, and two years later, Hubble also discovered the presence of two small new moons, Nix and Hydra, orbiting Pluto. The discovery of an as-yet-unnamed satellite in 2011 brought the known total to four. In 2005, Robin Canup of the Southwest Research Institute published the results of modelling that suggests Pluto's satellite probably formed as the result of a giant impact similar to that which is thought to have created Earth's own Moon (see page 121).

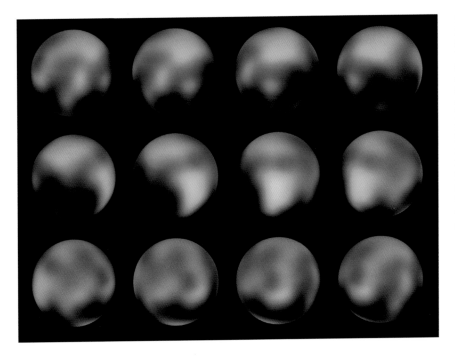

An icy surface

Pluto proved to have a distinctly varied surface, with an orange pallor and dark and bright patches. In 2010, Buie published a new comparison of HST images taken in 1994 and 2003, showing that the patterns across the surface have changed considerably, and that Pluto has brightened overall.

Spectroscopic measurements show that the surface is dominated by nitrogen ice with traces of methane, and carbon monoxide concentrated in one particularly bright spot. In 1985, astronomers on NASA's Kuiper Airborne Observatory, viewing Pluto's occultation of a star, discovered signs that Pluto has a thin atmosphere, now known to have a similar chemical composition to the surface ice. In 1989, Pluto was at its closest to the Sun, and astronomers believe solar heating has caused the surface ice to evaporate and form gases.

However, this neat idea is complicated by the fact that Pluto's atmosphere appears to be thickening and changing its composition as it retreats from the Sun. In 2011, a team led by Jane Greaves of the University of St Andrews in Scotland presented evidence that the size of the atmosphere and the amount of carbon monoxide within it have shot up in recent years, and that the atmosphere may form a comet-like tail as it is blown away from the Sun on the solar wind. One possible explanation for the changing nature of Pluto's atmosphere and surface is that the planet's south pole is emerging into sunlight for the first time in 120 years – if a volatile frost cap is present here, then its evaporation could pump gas into the atmosphere quicker than condensation at the cooling north pole could remove it. Hopefully, things will become clearer during New Horizons' forthcoming Pluto encounter.

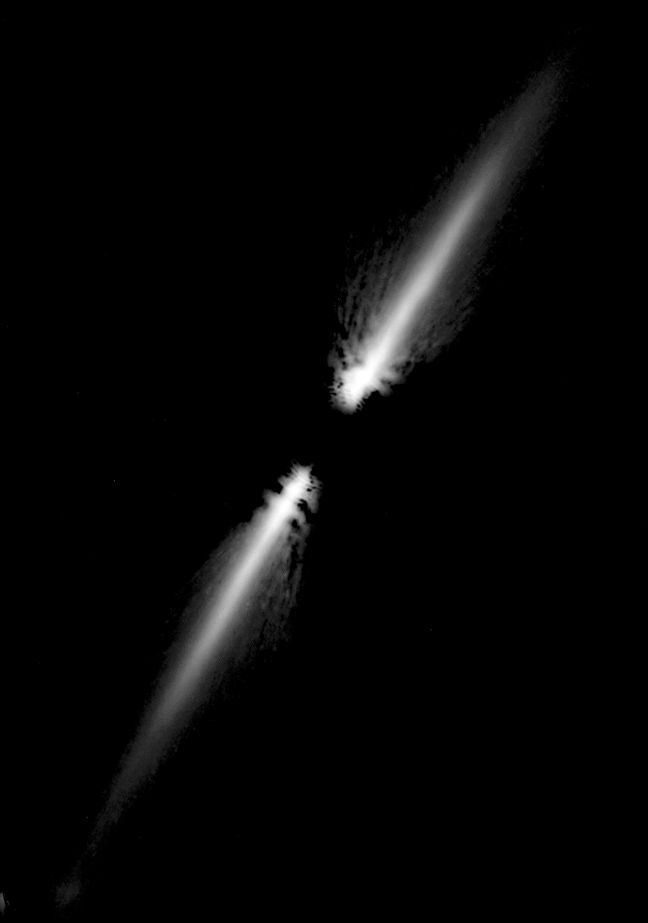

62

The Kuiper Belt and Oort Cloud

DEFINITION HUGE CLOUDS OF SMALL, ICY OBJECTS THAT SURROUND OUR SOLAR SYSTEM.

DISCOVERY THE KUIPER BELT WAS HYPOTHESIZED IN 1930, AND THE FIRST KUIPER BELT OBJECT OTHER THAN PLUTO WAS FOUND IN 1992.

KEY BREAKTHROUGH IN 2003, ASTRONOMERS DISCOVERED SEDNA, THE MOST DISTANT KNOWN OBJECT IN THE SOLAR SYSTEM.

IMPORTANCE THE KUIPER BELT AND OORT CLOUD ARE IMPORTANT SOURCES OF COMETS THAT BOMBARD THE INNER SOLAR SYSTEM.

Beyond the orbit of Neptune, the solar system is surrounded by the Kuiper Belt, a broad ring of frozen ice-dwarf worlds such as Pluto. At its outer limits, this region merges with the innermost parts of the Oort Cloud, a spherical halo of frozen comets up to one light year from the Sun.

The existence of a belt of small worlds beyond Neptune was first proposed by American astronomer Frederick C. Leonard in 1930, within months of the discovery of Pluto (see page 249). However, the lack of direct evidence for any companions for Pluto meant that Leonard's idea was largely ignored. Irish astronomer Kenneth Edgeworth and Dutch-American Gerard Kuiper proposed the existence of similar belts based on models of the solar system's formation in 1943 and 1951. Ironically, the belt is now named after Kuiper despite his belief that the outer belt of icy bodies was a long-vanished feature of the early solar system, dissipated by the influence of Pluto (which at the time was still considered to be an Earth-sized world).

But evidence for the belt remained elusive until 1977, when American astronomer Charles T. Kowal discovered Chiron, the first of a new class of small icy worlds called centaurs, with elliptical orbits that typically cross the orbits of the outer planets and reach their aphelion (furthest point from the Sun) beyond the orbit of Neptune. Various comets, including the famous Comet Halley, had orbits that also reached aphelion in this region – was it possible that all these objects had origins in the Kuiper Belt?

Among the ice dwarfs

In 1992, after a five-year search, David Jewitt and Jane Luu of the University of Hawaii finally announced the discovery of a new object orbiting within the

OPPOSITE While our own solar system's Kuiper Belt is impossible to image from within, similar belts around other stars reveal its likely structure. The 'debris disk' shown here surrounds the young red dwarf star AU Microscopii, some 32 light years from Earth.

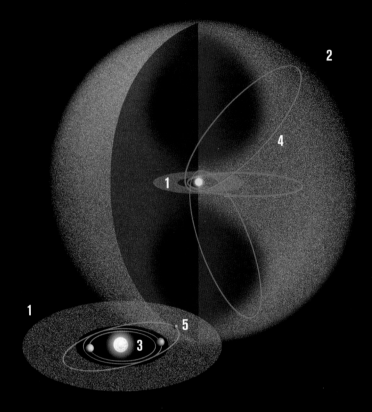

hypothetical Kuiper Belt region. Catalogued as 1992 QB1, this new object followed a near-circular orbit more than 40 astronomical units (AU) from the Sun, far beyond the orbit of Neptune. The discovery opened the way for a torrent of further discoveries using both Earth- and space-based telescopes, and today more than a thousand are known. According to Jewitt's estimates, there are probably at least 70,000 Kuiper-Belt Objects (KBOs) with diameters greater than 100 km (60 miles), and millions of smaller ones. The largest of these approach the size of Pluto, and at least one, Eris, is slightly larger: its discovery in 2005 forced astronomers to reassess their definition of a planet. After much controversy, they created a new dwarf planet category for objects that have enough gravity to pull themselves into a spherical shape, but are not massive enough to clear other objects away from their orbit.

While the Kuiper Belt shares some similarities with the asteroid belt between Mars and Jupiter, its structure is somewhat more complex. Most KBOs have average orbits between 39.5 and 48 AU, where they are shepherded by the effects of Neptune's gravity. Their orbits are inclined at a variety of angles, and objects that stray into certain regions are ultimately ejected by Neptune, either falling Sunwards to become centaurs, or moving outwards into a region called the Scattered Disc. Some astronomers classify the Scattered Disc as a separate region from the classical Kuiper Belt, and consider Eris to be a Scattered Disc Object (SDO) rather than a true KBO.

At the time of writing, the most distant known solar system object is Sedna, officially listed as an SDO and discovered in 2003 near the inner edge of its 11,400-year orbit. Sedna follows a highly elliptical path between 76 and 937 AU from the Sun, and has a remarkably red surface. Its discoverers, Michael Brown of Caltech, Chad Trujillo of the Gemini Observatory on Mauna Kea and David Rabinowitz of Yale University, have argued that it should be considered not as a remote member of the Scattered Disc, but as an inner member of the most distant family of solar system objects – the Oort Cloud.

Distant comets

The existence of a huge halo of comets surrounding the solar system at distances of almost a light year from the Sun was first suggested in 1932 by the Estonian Ernst Öpik, and developed independently by Dutch radio-astronomer Jan Hendrik Oort in 1950. Despite the impossibility of observing the Oort Cloud directly, the evidence for its existence was initially stronger than that for the Kuiper Belt. Long-period comets which occasionally pass through the inner solar system clearly have aphelion points far from the Sun, and Oort identified that they tended to cluster beyond 20,000 AU. Moreover, these comets approach from all parts of the sky, with no tendency to hug the ecliptic plane in which the planets orbit. Since short-period comets have a natural tendency to degrade, losing ice with each passage round the Sun (see page 258), there must be a reservoir of fresh comets somewhere in the depths of the solar system.

'According to Jewitt's estimates, there are probably at least 70,000 Kuiper-Belt Objects with diameters greater than 100 km (60 miles), and millions of smaller ones.'

In the past few decades, deeper analysis of long-period comet orbits has revealed further structure within the Oort Cloud. It is thought to contain several trillion cometary nuclei greater than 1 kilometre (0.6 miles) across, with a combined mass several times that of Earth. The Oort Cloud is divided into a spherical outer cloud and a disc-shaped inner cloud (sometimes called the Hills Cloud).

The comets of the Oort Cloud cannot possibly have formed so far from the Sun, so astronomers agree they must have come from elsewhere. The most popular theory is that they formed in the region where the outer planets now reside and were ejected into long elliptical orbits by early planetary migrations (see page 101). Galactic tides and close encounters with passing stars then acted to circularize the orbits. Supporting evidence for this idea came from the discovery of an object called 1996 PW: this apparently rocky body follows a comet-like orbit, suggesting that some asteroids were caught up in the turmoil and ejected alongside comets into the Oort Cloud. However, there are some problems with the migration theory, and other possible origins have been proposed. For example, in 2010, Hal Levison of the Southwest Research Institute published research showing how the Sun could have captured large numbers of comets from the protoplanetary discs of other stars as they formed alongside our own solar system.

63 Complex comets

DEFINITION SMALL BODIES MADE FROM A MIX OF ROCK AND ICE, FOLLOWING ELLIPTICAL ORBITS AROUND THE SUN.

DISCOVERY EDMOND HALLEY IDENTIFIED THE FIRST RETURNING, PERIODIC COMET IN 1705.

KEY BREAKTHROUGH FLYBYS OF COMET HALLEY IN 1986 CONFIRMED THAT ITS NUCLEUS CONTAINS A MIX OF ROCK AND ICE.

IMPORTANCE UNDERSTANDING THE HISTORIES OF COMETS OFFERS VITAL CLUES TO CONDITIONS IN THE EARLY SOLAR SYSTEM.

Since the 1980s, comets have generally been described as 'dirty snowballs' – loose clumps of rock and ice that evaporate during their passage around the Sun. However, recent spaceprobe investigations of dormant comets have revealed a surprising variety among cometary nuclei.

Bright comets have been seen and recorded throughout history. Often taken as omens of disaster, they were for a long time considered to be phenomena of the upper atmosphere rather than more distant celestial realms. Indeed, Tycho Brahe's proof that the Great Comet of 1577 lay beyond the Moon made a great contribution to the Copernican Revolution (see page 11).

The first person to calculate the orbit of a comet was English astronomer Edmond Halley in 1705. He showed that bright comets seen in 1531, 1607 and 1682 were in fact the same object, following a 76-year elliptical orbit around the Sun. He correctly predicted the comet would return in 1758, and so it is named in his honour. Today, Comet Halley is considered the brightest and most reliable of the short-period comets, with orbits of less than 200 years and aphelia (furthest points from the Sun) in the Kuiper Belt. Most really bright comets follow orbits that take centuries or even millennia to return, and originate in the far more distant Oort Cloud.

The nature of the nucleus

Until quite recently, the physical composition of comets was a matter of debate; Isaac Newton and German philosopher Immanuel Kant speculated in the 18th century that they were largely icy in nature, but the mid-19th century discovery that Earth's passage across cometary orbits can produce regular meteor showers led to an assumption that they were more like flying

OPPOSITE Comet Lulin of 2009 displayed several impressive features including a distinctly greenish coma, probably indicating carbon-rich gases around the nucleus. In this image, the yellowish dust tail (below) streams out behind the moving comet, while the bluish ion tail (above) consists of charged gas particles blown away from the comet on the solar wind.

gravel banks, containing relatively little ice. In 1950, however, Harvard astronomer Fred Whipple produced a new model that explained many aspects of comet behaviour. His 'dirty snowball' theory described comets as a mix of rock and ice debris with dark surfaces that absorb heat as they approach from the Sun. The evaporation this triggers produces a halo or coma of gases around the comet's solid nucleus. Gas blown away from the comet on the solar wind is ionized through interaction with solar radiation, creating a blue-white gas tail that always points directly away from the Sun, while the yellowish tail of ejected dust and rubble is less affected, and tends to curve back along the comet's path.

'Deep Impact produced a spectacular explosion that ejected some 20 kilotons of material from the comet's surface and formed a new crater some 150 metres (500 ft) across.'

The 1986 return of Comet Halley saw the reliable comet visited by an international armada of spaceprobes that measured the composition of its tail and coma. The European Space Agency's Giotto probe flew to within 600 km (370 miles) of the nucleus and returned close-up images of a peanut-shaped body some 16 km (10 miles) long, with jets of ice emerging from a surface so dark that it only reflects 3 percent of all the sunlight that strikes it.

The Halley missions appeared to prove Whipple's model correct in spectacular style, but the story has since turned out to be rather more complex. Recent comet missions have shown that comets are extremely varied in appearance, behaviour and composition.

Stardust, Deep Impact and beyond

NASA's Stardust probe targeted Comet Wild 2 for a close flyby in 2004, collecting particles from the comet's tail on a lightweight aerogel surface for return to Earth during a 2006 flyby. These have since been subjected to exhaustive study in the laboratory, revealing a wide range of carbon-based organic molecules and silicate minerals. In 2008, researchers led by Tomoki Nakamura of Japan's Kyushu University announced evidence, based on oxygen isotope ratios, that Wild 2 originated beyond the orbit of Pluto but later accumulated tiny crystals of material that had formed much closer to the Sun. Even more intriguingly, in 2011 a team from the University of Arizona announced their discovery of hydrated minerals that must have formed in the presence of liquid water, suggesting that cometary interiors sometimes get warm enough to melt.

In 2005, NASA's Deep Impact mission sent an oil-drum-sized projectile hurtling towards Comet Tempel 1. Watched by its parent spaceprobe, as well as an array of Earth-based telescopes, it produced a spectacular explosion that ejected some 20 kilotons of material from the comet's surface and formed a new crater some 150 metres (500 ft) across. Analysis of the comet's debris showed a mix of carbon dioxide and water ices that was surprisingly similar to those detected in the comet's tail, suggesting that, in this comet

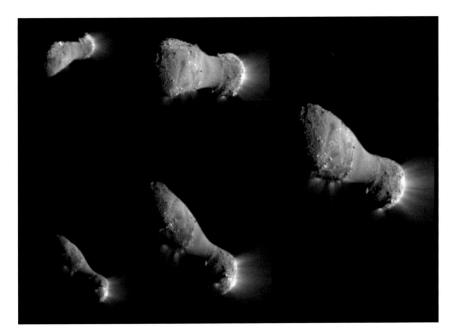

LEFT This sequence of images of Comet Hartley 2 was captured by the Deep Impact mission during its 2010 flyby. The comet's distinctive double-lobed structure is obvious, as is the smooth material around its 'waist'.

at least, material evaporates without a noticeable bias towards the more volatile carbon dioxide ice. In 2011, the Stardust probe flew past Tempel 1 to measure changes to its surface since the Deep Impact encounter – roughly an entire orbital cycle later. Stardust's images suggest that an average 50 cm (20 in) of material was eroded from the comet's surface during a single trip around the Sun, with some areas unaffected but others losing tens of metres of crust, presumably due to dramatic fragmentation.

The strangest of all the recently visited comets, however, must be Hartley 2. This small but unusually active comet in a 6.5-year orbit around the Sun was visited by Deep Impact in 2010, and shown to emit different materials from various parts of its surface. Carbon dioxide vapour and solid water ice emerge from one of its twin lobes, while water vapour is released from a smooth area around its 'waist'. Furthermore, the comet is surrounded by a halo of football-sized ice fragments. Astronomers think that these chunks are blown out by the pressure of escaping carbon dioxide from beneath the active lobe, and fall back around the waist, creating the smoother terrain which slowly releases water vapour. In fact, it's possible that the comet's two lobes have substantially different compositions, indicating that they formed in different parts of the solar system and only later fused together.

As a result of these missions and others, it now seems the origin of comets is more complex than once thought. While they clearly must have formed beyond the frost line of the solar system (see page 97), they often incorporate material from much closer to the Sun, suggesting that they may have migrated both inwards and outwards before settling into their current preferred locations in the Oort Cloud (see page 255).

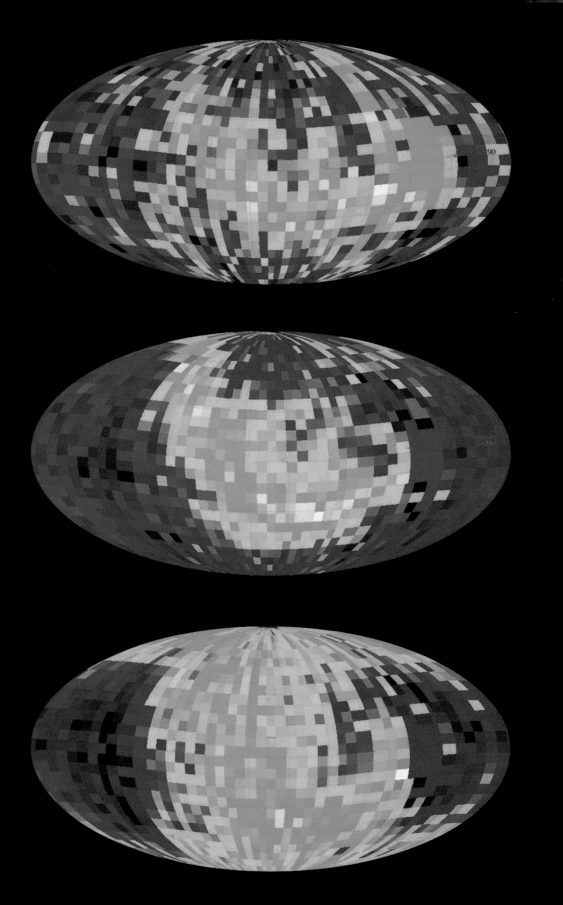

64 The edge of the solar system

DEFINITION THE COMPLEX BOUNDARY WHERE INTERPLANETARY SPACE, DOMINATED BY THE SOLAR WIND, GIVES WAY TO THE INTERSTELLAR MEDIUM.

DISCOVERY THE EXISTENCE OF THE SOLAR WIND WAS CONFIRMED BY SOVIET LUNA SPACEPROBES IN 1959.

KEY BREAKTHROUGH IN 2009, NASA LAUNCHED IBEX, THE FIRST SATELLITE DEVOTED TO EXPLORING THE BOUNDARY REGION.

IMPORTANCE THE STRENGTH OF THE SOLAR WIND CAN HAVE A MAJOR EFFECT ON SPACECRAFT AND SATELLITES.

Between the Kuiper Belt and the Oort Cloud, the Sun's influence begins to falter, as the solar wind of material flowing out from the Sun encounters the interstellar medium around a turbulent region known as the heliopause.

While the Sun's gravitational influence over its surroundings extends to the very edges of the Kuiper Belt, perhaps more than a light year away, its other effects on surrounding space begin to wane far sooner. The realm of the planets is strongly influenced by the solar wind, a steady stream of particles that leaves the surface of the Sun with a speed of some 3 million km/h (1.9 million mph). It bombards each object it passes with particles, creating aurorae and sky glows through its interactions with magnetic fields and the upper atmosphere. Where a planet has a weak or non-existent magnetic field, solar wind particles can strip gas from its atmosphere or chemically transform its surface.

Astronomers first became aware of the solar wind in spectacular fashion, when the most powerful solar storm ever recorded sent a torrent of particles past Earth in 1859, sending early electrical systems such as the telegraph haywire, and creating spectacular aurorae. However, it was not until 1958 that American astrophysicist Eugene Parker produced the first thorough explanation of the wind. Parker traced the wind's origin to the multi-million-degree gases of the Sun's outer atmosphere or corona, and showed how interaction with the solar wind could explain phenomena such as the way that comet tails always stream away from the Sun. Within a year, Parker's ideas were confirmed, with the first direct detection of the solar wind by Soviet Luna spaceprobes on their way to the Moon.

OPPOSITE Three IBEX maps chart energetic emissions from the edge of the solar system, including a surprising ribbon of emission (shown in green and yellow) that is thought to indicate the shape of our galaxy's magnetic field.

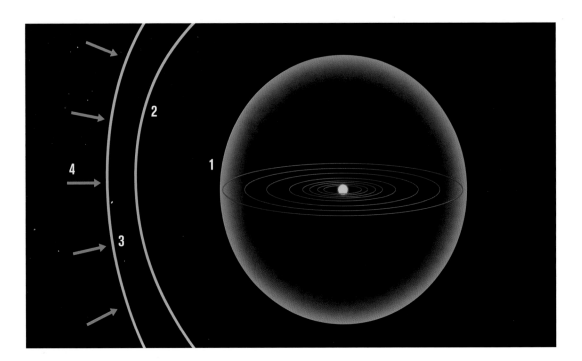

Leaving the solar system

As the solar wind spreads across the solar system, it inevitably loses momentum, and at some point beyond Neptune it reaches a significant threshold where it drops below the speed of sound in the interplanetary medium (about 360,000 km/h or 225,000 mph). The transition generates an enormous sonic boom, a shock wave known as the termination shock at which the smooth supersonic flow transforms into a slower subsonic flow that loses its sense of direction and dissolves into swirling eddies, drifting far more slowly outwards.

From here on out, the solar wind is disturbed by the interstellar medium (ISM) – a stream of particles from the stellar winds of a billion other stars. The contest between this steady inward pressure and the decreasing outward pressure of the solar wind creates a complex boundary zone known as the heliosheath, with an outer edge called the heliopause marking the point at which the solar wind's speed effectively drops to zero. The entire region within the heliopause, dominated by the solar wind, is known as the heliosphere.

Scientists monitoring data from the Voyager spaceprobes currently on their way out of the solar system believe that Voyager 1 crossed the termination shock in late 2004, while Voyager 2 crossed into the heliosheath in mid-2007. Voyager 2 seems to have encountered this boundary about 1.6 billion kilometres (1 billion miles) closer to the Sun than Voyager 1, seeming to confirm long-held assumptions that the entire heliosphere is squashed by the solar system's motion through the Milky Way, so that it resembles a bullet with a long tail trailing behind it. In 2010, NASA announced that Voyager 1 was no longer detecting the motion of the solar wind, indicating that it had reached the heliopause, far sooner than expected, and is now entering the ISM. Further analysis of the Voyager data in 2011 revealed that the two intrepid probes are passing through a foamy region in which the Sun's magnetic field is breaking down into a series of huge bubbles.

Mapping the boundary zone

While the heliopause marks one common definition of the edge of the solar system, the Sun's influence on nearby space extends beyond it. Not only does its gravitational field reach much further out, but the solar system's orbit around the galaxy produces an equivalent of the termination shock where the speed of the ISM itself drops below supersonic. The resulting curved pressure wave is known as the bow shock, and is analogous to the wave that forms in front of a fast-moving ship.

'The contest between this steady inward pressure and the decreasing outward pressure of the solar wind creates a complex boundary zone known as the heliosheath.'

Most astronomers believe that the bow shock is accompanied by a region of hot gas known as the hydrogen wall, formed as gas atoms in the ISM collide with particles from the heliosphere. This process produces Energetic Neutral Atoms (ENAs) that can pass through the solar system at high speeds, and be recorded using various detection methods. Since ENAs are often generated by planetary magnetic fields, detectors have been carried on several spacecraft, including NASA's Cassini probe to Saturn. In 2009, scientists from Johns Hopkins University led by Stamatios Krimigis announced that they had used Cassini to map the pattern of ENAs coming from around the sky for the first time. Their most striking result was the discovery that the bow shock is surprisingly close even on the solar system's trailing edge – it seems that the heliosphere is actually shaped more like a bubble and less like a bullet after all.

In October 2008, NASA launched the first satellite dedicated to charting the boundaries of the heliosphere. IBEX, the Interstellar Boundary Explorer, was fitted with two detectors to measure ENAs of different energies, and scientists expected it to find a pattern of high-energy ENAs coming from the direction of the Sun's motion through space. However first results revealed a very different image of the boundary – a bright 'ribbon' wrapped around the solar system. In 2010, Jacob Heerikhuisen of the University of Alabama in Huntsville explained this as a reflection of solar wind particles, bounced back into the solar system by interactions with a powerful band of the galactic magnetic field. Together, these Cassini and IBEX results are suggesting that the solar system's motion through the galaxy affects the heliosphere far less than previously thought – instead, the governing forces seem to be the changing pressure of particles and interactions between the solar and galactic magnetic fields.

65 Stellar evolution

DEFINITION THE WAY IN WHICH STARS CHANGE AND EVOLVE AS THEY GENERATE POWER BY DIFFERENT MEANS THROUGH THEIR LIVES.

DISCOVERY AROUND 1910, HERTZSPRUNG AND RUSSELL DISCOVERED THAT STARS TENDED TO FOLLOW CERTAIN RELATIONSHIPS BETWEEN THEIR SPECTRAL TYPE AND LUMINOSITY.

KEY BREAKTHROUGH ARTHUR EDDINGTON'S DISCOVERY OF THE MASS–LUMINOSITY RELATIONSHIP SHOWED THAT STARS DID NOT EVOLVE UP OR DOWN THE MAIN SEQUENCE OF THE H–R DIAGRAM.

IMPORTANCE THE PATTERNS OF STELLAR EVOLUTION ARE VITAL TO UNDERSTANDING THE PROPERTIES OF INDIVIDUAL STARS.

Most of the changes stars experience throughout their lives take place on timescales of millions, even billions of years. Fortunately, a series of observational breakthroughs and conceptual leaps have allowed astronomers to turn our present-day view of the galaxy into a model of stellar evolution.

The variety of stars in the night sky is obvious even to the most casual observer – a glance at the night sky with the naked eye will reveal that stars vary widely in colour and brightness. Ancient astronomers interpreted the brightness differences as inherent, since they believed the stars were pinned to the surface of a celestial sphere at a fixed distance from Earth. From the Renaissance onwards, astronomers began to realize that stars were in fact scattered across vast gulfs of space, but it was not until the mid-19th century that the first accurate stellar distances could be measured (see page 18), confirming that the brightness of stars seen from Earth (their apparent magnitudes) are created by a combination of varying distances and real variations in their luminosity (or absolute magnitude).

The Harvard Computers

By late in the century, photography and telescope technology had advanced to the point where it was possible to capture the spectra of individual stars for the first time. From 1888, Edward C. Pickering, head of the Harvard College Observatory, launched an ambitious project to catalogue stars according to their spectra, recruiting a team of female astronomers (known as the Harvard Computers, led by his former maid Williamina Fleming (see pages 318 and 337), and including Annie Jump Cannon and Henrietta Swan Leavitt (see page 31). The resulting Henry Draper (HD) Catalog, named in honour of the amateur astronomer whose legacy financed its completion,

OPPOSITE This Hubble Space Telescope image of a region 20,000 light years away in the constellation of Carina showcases various stages in stellar evolution. At its centre lies the open cluster NGC 3603, still surrounded by remnants of the gas from which it formed, and dominated by hot young white stars. The bright red stars are red giants that are already nearing the end of their lives.

provided a wealth of data that allows astronomers to compare the properties of stars on a large scale for the first time. In particular, Cannon's work on the classification of stellar spectra led to the development of the Harvard Classification Scheme, the basis for the modern system of spectral types.

Around 1910, Swedish physicist Ejnar Hertzsprung and American astronomer Henry Norris Russell independently had the idea of comparing the spectral types of stars (and by extension their colours and surface temperatures) with their brightness using a graph – what is today known as a Hertzsprung–Russell (H–R) diagram, Hertzsprung used the apparent magnitudes of stars within particular star clusters as a substitute for their true luminosities – since the cluster stars are all at about the same distance from Earth, variations in their appearance reflect real variations in their properties. Russell, working slightly later, plotted stars with known parallaxes, from which he could find their distance and therefore their true luminosity.

Understanding the H–R diagram

The resulting diagrams revealed an important pattern – the vast majority of stars lie somewhere on a diagonal band linking cool, red and faint stars with hot, blue and bright ones. Hertzsprung named stars that were significantly brighter than the Sun 'giants', significantly fainter ones 'dwarfs', and the band linking the two the 'main sequence'. Stars away from this region also seemed to fall into distinctive groups – there were faint blue and white ones (white dwarfs), bright orange and red ones (red giants), and rare brilliant 'supergiants' of all colours.

'Stars condense from nebulae, joining the main sequence at a location determined by their mass, and remaining in more or less the same place through most of their lives.'

Russell presented his version of the diagram to London's Royal Astronomical Society in 1912, and it was rapidly adopted as a powerful new tool for analysing the stars. Looking at the patterns revealed by the diagram, many astronomers immediately suspected they were looking at an evolutionary path of some sort. Applying the principle that the stars we see today represent a snapshot of stellar evolution, it was clear that the vast majority of stars spend the vast majority of their lives on the main sequence. Since the most obvious track seemed to lead down this diagonal from hot and blue to cool and red, astronomers developed a model in which stars started out life as red and orange giants, contracting to join the main sequence and then sliding down it as they aged. This tied in relatively well with the gravitational contraction mechanism that most astronomers of the time believed must power the stars.

Eddington and after

The diagram also inspired Cambridge astronomer Arthur Eddington (see page 47) to consider what it said about the properties of stars. Since the temperature and colour of a star are governed by the energy heating a given area of its surface, it was clear that, if a blue and a red star have the same luminosity, the red star with the cooler surface must be significantly

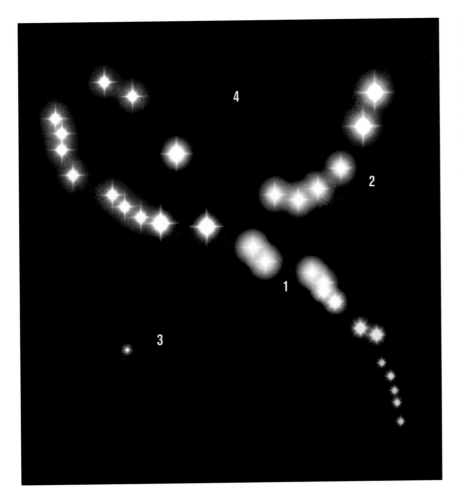

LEFT The Hertzsprung–Russell diagram plots the colour and surface temperature of stars (along the horizontal axis) against their luminosity (on the vertical axis). Most stars lie along the diagonal line of the main sequence (1), but others distinct groups include the red and orange giants (2), white dwarfs (3) and supergiants (4).

larger in order to spread out the escaping energy. Insights such as this led to Eddington's groundbreaking work on the internal structure of stars (see page 85). By 1924, he had also proved that stars on the main sequence showed a mass–luminosity relation – the heavier a star is, the brighter it shines and the higher its location on the sequence. This discovery made it clear that gravitational contraction could not be the true power source of the stars (since it relied on the star retaining its mass but becoming denser with time). Instead, Eddington's suggestion of nuclear fusion reactions (allowing stars to retain their mass through their lifetime) was now taken more seriously.

By the late 1920s, the modern interpretation of the H–R diagram was largely in place. The diagram does indeed show an evolutionary sequence, but one in which stars condense from nebulae, joining the main sequence at a location determined by their mass, and remaining in more or less the same place through most of their lives, before evolving off the main sequence to become red giants as they start to exhaust their nuclear fuel (see page 318). The mystery of white dwarfs and other extreme stars, however, would only be resolved through breakthroughs in theoretical physics (see page 337).

66 The Eagle Nebula

DEFINITION A HUGE CLOUD OF INTERSTELLAR GAS AND DUST THAT
HAS REVEALED MANY OF THE SECRETS OF STAR FORMATION.

DISCOVERY THE EAGLE NEBULA WAS DISCOVERED INDEPENDENTLY
BY TWO FRENCH ASTRONOMERS IN 1745 AND 1764.

KEY BREAKTHROUGH IN 1995, THE HUBBLE SPACE TELESCOPE
RETURNED THE FIRST DETAILED IMAGES OF STAR-FORMING GAS
COLUMNS WITHIN THE NEBULA.

IMPORTANCE THE EAGLE NEBULA HAS GIVEN ASTRONOMERS MANY
NEW INSIGHTS INTO THE EARLY STAGES OF STAR FORMATION.

Star-forming nebulae are scattered widely throughout the Milky Way, but a particular cloud of gas, dust and young stars in the constellation of Serpens Cauda has provided astronomers with some of their best views of the processes and forces involved.

Hovering just below naked-eye visibility and lying at a distance of some 7,000 light years from Earth, the Eagle Nebula is a beautiful cloud of glowing gas with a similar rosette-shape to Orion's Great Nebula (see page 377), distinguished from it by the central dust clouds whose silhouette provides the region with its name. The nebula's central star cluster was noted by French astronomer Philippe Loys de Chéseaux around 1745, and in 1764 was rediscovered by another Frenchman, Charles Messier. This famous comet hunter recorded the faint nebulosity surrounding the stars for the first time: anxious to avoid confusion with any comets passing through the region, he added it to his famous Messier Catalogue as object M16.

Nevertheless, for the next two centuries the Eagle Nebula (later catalogued as IC 4703 to distinguish it from the star cluster M16) was seen as a distinctly second-rank object compared to such wonders as the Orion and Carina nebulae and the great star-forming clouds of Sagittarius. It was only in 1995, when astronomers Jeff Hester and Paul Scowen of Arizona State University turned the Hubble Space Telescope towards it with stunning results, that the Eagle finally took flight. Hester and Scowen's 1995 photograph was published around the world as headline news. It offered our most detailed view yet of the processes involved in star formation, and its finger-like dust columns, from which infant stars could clearly be seen emerging, were soon named the 'Pillars of Creation'.

OPPOSITE This Hubble Space Telescope view of the 'spire' feature in the Eagle Nebula shows an enormous column of gas being steadily eroded by radiation from newborn stars off the top of the picture. Ultraviolet excitation causes oxygen near the top of the column to glow blue, while hydrogen near the base glows red.

In the years since that first image, the Eagle has been scrutinized repeatedly by both Earth- and space-based telescopes at a variety of wavelengths, transforming it into a unique laboratory for studying the early stages of starbirth.

Pillars and spires

With lengths of around four light years, the famous pillars are believed to surround regions in which dozens of stars are being born. Within them, knots of gas have grown dense enough to exert substantial gravity, and have begun to pull in material from their surroundings, just as our own Sun did billions of years ago (see page 77).

In 2005, the Hubble team returned to the nebula and photographed a longer tendril of gas, named 'the Spire' in more detail. This structure is around 9.5 light years long, and is being rapidly eroded by the radiation from the nearby young stars of the M16 cluster. Believed to be the first generation of stars formed by the nebula, M16's members are blue-white stellar heavyweights that emit fierce radiation and stellar winds. Where their ultraviolet radiation interacts with gas in the outer nebula, it energizes and excites it, creating an eerie glow. As the radiation penetrates further into the nebula, it seems to have two contrary effects, creating waves of compression that trigger further starbirth, but at the same time blowing away much of the gas that will provide new generations with their raw material. As a result, stars currently forming within the nebula will probably not grow much larger than our own Sun. Despite this, the Spire seems to contain denser clouds of hydrogen than its surroundings, allowing it to withstand the torrents of radiation for longer. But this is not the only way in which early generations of stars conspire to stunt the growth of their successors. In 2007, French astronomer Nicholas Flagey used NASA's Spitzer Space Telescope to study the nebula in the infrared, identifying a tower of hot dust next to the original pillars. This dust seems to have been heated and sculpted by the expanding shock wave from a supernova – the spectacular death of a heavyweight first-generation star – and the shock wave appears to be on a collision course for the pillars. In fact, it may already have reached them long ago, but thanks to the nebula's great distance, it will be another thousand years before we see it tear the pillars apart, bringing any ongoing starbirth to an abrupt halt.

Mysterious EGGs

For the moment, however, astronomers can continue to learn about the processes at work in these cauldrons of star formation. One particular focus of interest has been the small, tendril-like extrusions that are spread across the surface of all the major pillars, but most prominent around the top of the tallest. Known as evaporating gaseous globules or EGGs, these structures appear to be growing out of the pillars, but the reality is rather different. In fact they mark regions of denser gas and dust that are better able to weather the pressure of radiation eroding the top of the pillar around them. Each dark globule has roughly the diameter of our solar system and remains connected to the bulk of the pillar by a thin river of gas that is protected from erosion by the EGG's own shadow.

'Thanks to the nebula's great distance, it will be another thousand years before we see the supernova shock wave tear the pillars apart, bringing any ongoing starbirth to an abrupt halt.'

Because EGGs protect the material within them from the corrosive effects of radiation, they are thought to be ideal incubators for the formation of star systems – either single stars or binaries and multiple groups. In a handful of EGGs observed by Hubble in both the Eagle and other nebulae, these stars have just emerged from their cocoons, and sit on top of cones of dark material.

However, a near-infrared survey carried out in 2001 using the European Southern Observatory's Very Large Telescope revealed a rather more complex story. Astronomers Mark McCaughrean and Moren Anderson from Germany's University of Potsdam found infrared signatures of star formation from only 11 out of 73 EGGs, while 57 appeared to be empty. Furthermore, those stars that do form inside the EGGs seem to be relatively small and faint (perhaps due to the limited amounts of material available to them). The main centres of starbirth, containing both more and brighter stars, it seems, lie at the tops of the main pillars.

In 2007, a team led by Jeffrey Linsky of the University of Colorado used NASA's Chandra satellite to image the nebula's X-ray sources. They found little relationship between the region's hottest, X-ray emitting stars and the pillars or EGGs, confirming the view that the nebula may already be past its star-forming prime.

67

Infant stars

DEFINITION THE TURBULENT EARLY YEARS OF A STAR'S LIFE, WHERE IT SIMULTANEOUSLY SHEDS AND ACCUMULATES MASS.

DISCOVERY THE UNPREDICTABLE VARIABLE STAR T TAURI WAS FIRST SEEN BY JOHN RUSSELL HIND IN 1852.

KEY BREAKTHROUGH GEORGE HERBIG REALIZED THAT T TAURI STARS WERE VERY YOUNG. RICHARD D. SCHWARZ EXPLAINED NEBULAE SEEN NEARBY AS A PRODUCT OF JETS FROM THE CENTRAL STARS.

IMPORTANCE THE PROCESSES OF MASS ACCRETION AND EJECTION DETERMINE THE EVENTUAL PROPERTIES A STAR WILL DISPLAY THROUGH THE REST OF ITS LIFE.

From the initial collapse of an interstellar gas cloud, stars travel a rocky road before they finally settle down onto the main sequence of stellar evolution. The effects of infalling gas and dust, sudden eruptions on the star's surface and huge outflows of material from its poles can produce spectacular results.

One night in October 1852, British astronomer and asteroid hunter John Russell Hind came across a faint star in the constellation Taurus that was not recorded on earlier charts. The object proved to be a new variable star, eventually designated as T Tauri. Hind noticed a nearby reflection nebula that was also variable due to the changing intensity of T Tauri itself. When the star's brightness dropped considerably around 1890, Sherburne Wesley Burnham of the University of California's Lick Observatory discovered that it was also embedded in a compact nebula of its own. Burnham also noticed an oddly shaped emission nebula nearby, although the significance of this object was not recognized at the time.

In the early 1940s, American astronomer Alfred Joy carried out a systematic study of these faint variables, and discovered shared characteristics such as the presence of nebulae, low overall luminosity, variations in brightness by a factor of around 10–20 and distinctive Sun-like spectra. In 1945, he suggested they formed a distinctive class of T Tauri variables.

OPPOSITE This spectacular Hubble Space Telescope view of the Carina Nebula shows a starbirth region nicknamed 'Mystic Mountain'. At the top of the image, a young star embedded within the dust and gas is ejecting jets of excess material from its poles.

Understanding infant stars

Joy's work was followed up by George Herbig of the Lick Observatory, who determined that T Tauri variables were most likely young stars still surrounded by the nebulosity in which they had formed. Today, astronomers believe that T Tauri itself is one of the youngest stars in the sky, with an age of just a million years. Measurements of the mass of these stars suggests that they are generally Sun-like, with less than twice the Sun's mass, and are at various stages along a journey of roughly 100 million years that will take them onto the main sequence.

Since T Tauri stars are not yet burning hydrogen in their cores, they must shine in other ways. For the youngest, this power source is probably gravitational contraction. The lower luminosity of these stars means that the major method of energy transport within them is convection, and this, coupled with rapid rotation, allows them to behave in a similar way to low-mass flare stars (see page 281). They form powerful but tangled magnetic fields that create large starspots on their surfaces and generate powerful stellar flares and explosions.

Many T Tauri-like stars, however, are invisible, concealed within the dust clouds from which they formed. Fortunately their low temperatures mean they generate large amounts of infrared radiation and even radio waves, which shine through the opaque dust – since 1981, two infrared companions have been found alongside T Tauri. As the material around the unseen stars begins to thin out and the stars themselves intensify, we will eventually be able to see them in visible light.

'Low-level fusion in the core cause the star's outer layers to swell rapidly, from about the size of Jupiter to several times the size of the Sun, before gravity takes control once again.'

About half of all T Tauri stars are surrounded by discs of gas and dust. Much of the material from these discs is still falling in onto the central star, and the concentration of mass at the centre of the system causes the star to spin up, rotating more and more rapidly (thanks to the same law of conservation of angular momentum that causes an ice skater to pirouette more rapidly as they pull in their arms). Two forces eventually slow the growth of the central star – strong stellar winds blowing away from its surface, and the so-called 'centrifugal force' experienced as gas piles onto the fast-moving equator. This latter effect, in particular, has dramatic consequences.

Herbig–Haro objects

While looking at a range of T Tauri objects and other suspected young stars, George Herbig found that they were often associated with distinctive nebulae on either one or both sides – including the nebula recognized by Burnham close to T Tauri itself. Herbig's spectral analysis showed that these nebulae emitted characteristic wavelengths associated with hydrogen, oxygen and sulphur. Mexican astronomer Guillermo Haro, who worked independently on the same objects in the late 1940s, identified other distinctive characteristics such as a lack of infrared emissions, which indicated they were extremely hot. Early speculations on these Herbig–Haro (H–H) objects suggested that they might be heated by faint but hot young stars embedded within them. However, in the mid-1970s Richard D. Schwartz of the University of Missouri-St Louis suggested that they might be heated by shock waves as

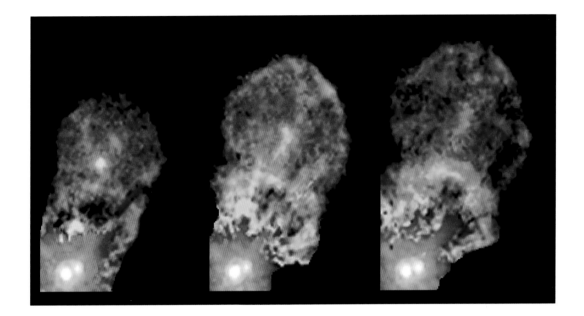

material ejected from the star itself slams into interstellar gas. Images in the 1980s revealed the presence of extremely narrow, jet-like structures linking H–H objects to their central stars.

So how do these jets form? Astronomers believe that if a young star spins rapidly enough, material falling onto its equator can move so fast that it overcomes the pull of gravity and is flung back out into space. As it encounters the ring of infalling material that still surrounds the star, this escaping matter is channelled into two jets, roughly parallel to the star's poles. As this high-speed bipolar outflow interacts with clouds of gas in nearby space, it injects them with energy, creating spectacular glowing displays.

Bipolar jets last for just a brief instant in a stellar lifetime, faltering and dying after just a few thousand years. The balancing act between infalling and ejected material causes conditions within the star itself to vary considerably, so depending on the sensitivity of the processes generating the star's light at a particular stage in its infancy, its brightness can fluctuate wildly.

Meanwhile, the star's interior is still changing. As it approaches the main sequence, less demanding forms of fusion that do not require such extreme conditions begin to take hold. Low-level fusion in the core cause the star's outer layers to swell rapidly, from about the size of Jupiter to several times the size of the Sun, before gravity takes control once again. The result is a slow shrinking of the star's outer layers, as the core steadily grows hotter and denser. The fluctuations only cease when the core finally becomes hot enough to ignite true hydrogen fusion, at which point the star's dimensions and brightness stabilize, and it settles down into a location on the main sequence, determined by its mass, where it will spend the majority of its life.

The smallest stars

68

DEFINITION DWARF STARS THAT LIE JUST ABOVE OR EVEN BELOW
THE LIMIT WHERE THEY ARE ABLE TO SHINE THROUGH NUCLEAR
FUSION OF HYDROGEN.

DISCOVERY PROXIMA CENTAURI, THE MOST FAMOUS RED DWARF
STAR AND THE CLOSEST STAR TO EARTH, WAS DISCOVERED IN 1915.

KEY BREAKTHROUGH IN 1994, ASTRONOMERS IDENTIFIED THE FIRST
BROWN DWARF STAR, GLIESE 229B.

IMPORTANCE RED AND BROWN DWARFS FORM THE VAST MAJORITY OF
STARS, AND YET ARE STILL POORLY UNDERSTOOD.

Just what is the lower limit of stellar size? Recent discoveries
from both visible-light and infrared telescopes have pushed the
definition of a star to its limit, revealing a strange borderland
between stars and planets.

Tracking down the smallest main-sequence stars presents a huge challenge
to even the most powerful modern telescopes. While stellar remnants such
as white dwarfs and neutron stars (see page 337) may be tiny, they are also
superheated and emit large amounts of radiation. In contrast, even the
closest of small main-sequence dwarfs are invisible to the naked eye.

A dwarf on the doorstep

Take, for instance, the closest star to Earth, Proxima Centauri. It lies just
4.2 light years from the solar system, and is the third member of the Alpha
Centauri system, whose other two stars form a close-orbiting binary pair.
Alpha Centauri A and B have masses of 1.1 and 0.9 Suns respectively, and
their combined light makes them the third brightest naked-eye star in the
sky. Proxima, in contrast, has a mass of just 0.12 Suns, and shines with just
1/500th of the Sun's luminosity, glowing red thanks to a surface temperature
just half that of our Sun. Despite its closeness to Earth, Proxima is visible
only though telescopes, and it was the least luminous star known for some
time after its discovery in 1915. It is the prototypical red dwarf star.

Red dwarfs are faint because the nuclear fusion reactions that power main-
sequence stars are critically dependent on the density and pressure of a star's
core. The lighter a star is, the less mass there is in the outer layers to push
down on the core, heating and compressing it. As a result, the luminosity

OPPOSITE This
image from the
European Southern
Observatory's New
Technology Telescope
at La Silla, Chile,
reveals the famous
Orion Nebula in
the near-infrared.
Alongside the bright
newborn stars of the
Trapezium Cluster, a
variety of other objects
become visible,
including faint red
dwarfs (shown here
in white), and brown
dwarfs (shown
in yellow).

of a star rises almost exponentially as its mass increases, rather than just following a linear relationship.

In the century or so since Proxima's discovery, many more red dwarfs have been found, but they still present some unique puzzles for astronomers. Of the 30 closest stars to Earth, 19 are dwarfs, either moving alone through space, or orbiting within multiple systems. Models suggest that red dwarfs are the most widespread and numerous stars in our galaxy and others, but they are difficult to detect away from our cosmic doorstep.

They also present a problem of definition. By convention, red dwarfs are stars with less than 40 percent of the Sun's mass, but what is the bottom limit? How small can a star be, yet still shine? Once the pathways involved in stellar fusion were established in the 1950s (see page 83), it became clear that there must be a threshold, of roughly 8 percent of the Sun's mass (or about 80 times the mass of Jupiter) below which a Sun would be unable to shine by conventional nuclear fusion of hydrogen nuclei into helium.

Stars below the limit

However, even once this limit was established, there was no reason why smaller star-like objects could not form within the same nebulae as brighter stars. Initially, it was assumed that the material within these objects would simply collapse under its own weight to become a dense black dwarf, but in 1975, American astronomer Jill Tarter pointed out that this term was also used for cooled-down white dwarfs (see page 337), which are very different objects. What was more, there were a variety of other mechanisms by which these stars could still emit radiation, so these failed stars might more accurately be named brown dwarfs.

'Far from being inactive balls of gas, some brown dwarfs have shown extraordinary activity, including variable brightness ... and X-ray outbursts caused by surprisingly powerful magnetic fields.'

Theoretical work carried out in the 1980s showed that brown dwarfs could still glow faintly in visible light, and would emit substantial amounts of infrared radiation, thanks to a combination of processes. These include gravitational contraction (similar to that found in giant planets – see page 191), and in the case of heavier brown dwarfs, some less demanding nuclear fusion processes. For example deuterium fusion, which involves heavy hydrogen isotopes that fuse more readily than normal nuclei, can be triggered at comparatively moderate temperatures and pressures. In general, though, brown dwarfs are mostly powered by the residual heat left over from their own formation, so they get fainter with age and are most easily spotted when they are young.

Searching for brown dwarfs

Despite these conceptual breakthroughs, observational evidence for brown dwarfs remained elusive until the 1990s. Hunting for brown dwarfs in empty space seemed akin to looking for a needle in a haystack, so when a team of astronomers from the California Institute of Technology and Johns Hopkins University began a methodical search, they concentrated on potential binary systems in which the brighter star was itself a faint red dwarf. This reduced the risk of starlight swamping the much fainter object, and the technique paid off in 1994 when a candidate brown dwarf was spotted using the infrared spectroscope on the 5-metre (200-inch) Hale Telescope at Mount Palomar, California. Confirmed with NASA's Hubble Space Telescope the following year, the brown dwarf orbits a feeble star called Gliese 229, 19 light years from Earth, and is designated as Gliese 229B. With a mass equivalent to 20–50 Jupiters, it is far too large to have formed in a protoplanetary disc around the brighter star. Instead, it must have formed in a star-like way as an independent knot within a collapsing starbirth nebula. The stars are separated by roughly the distance from Pluto to the Sun, and infrared measurements indicate that Gliese 229B has a surface temperature of around 700°C (1,300°F).

Since this discovery, astronomers have begun to find large numbers of brown dwarfs hidden within star-forming nebulae and young star clusters, as well as in orbit around red dwarfs and in open space. With surface temperatures lower than the coolest M-type red dwarf stars, they have been allocated spectral classes L, T and Y (in decreasing order of temperature). Furthermore, far from being inactive balls of gas, some brown dwarfs have shown extraordinary activity, including variable brightness that may be produced by fast-moving clouds, and X-ray outbursts caused by surprisingly powerful magnetic fields. Planets have been detected in orbit around a handful of brown dwarfs, and there remains the intriguing prospect that a brown dwarf might still lurk unseen in nearby space, closer to Earth than even Proxima Centauri.

BELOW A pair of false-colour images show the first brown dwarf star to be discovered, known as Gliese 229B. The left-hand image, taken at Palomar Observatory in 1994, allowed the first identification of the suspected object, orbiting a faint red dwarf star some 18 light years away in Lepus. The right-hand image from the Hubble Space Telescope confirmed the discovery.

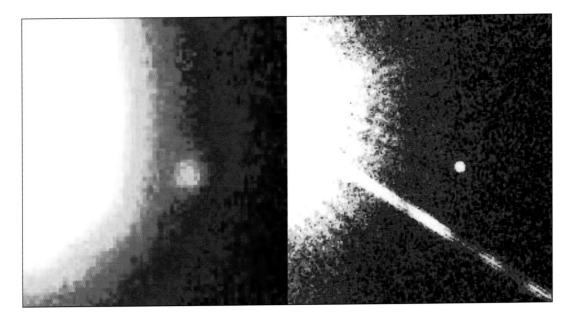

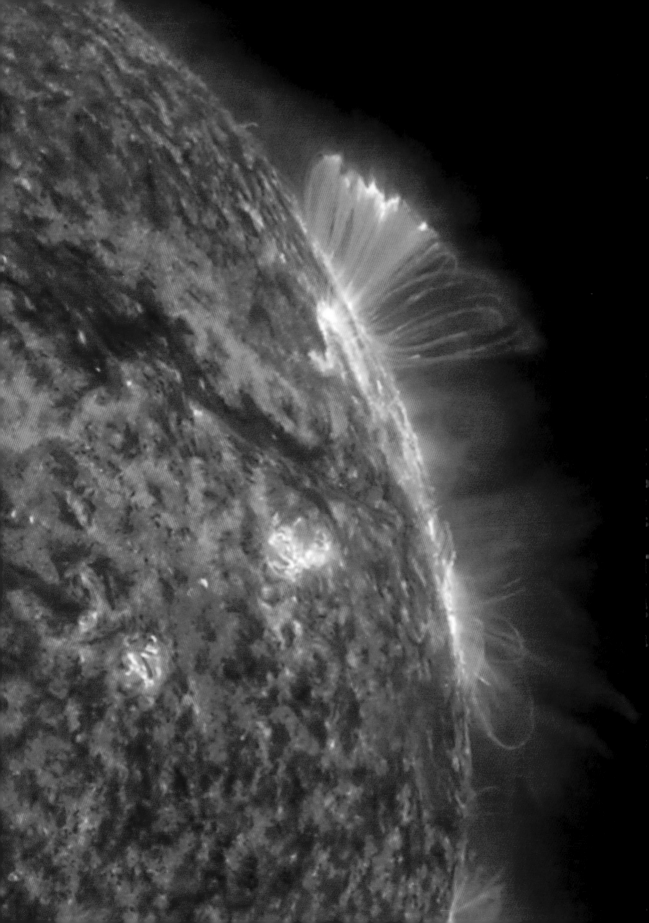

69

Flare stars

DEFINITION FAINT, LOW-MASS DWARF STARS THAT NEVERTHELESS PRODUCE POWERFUL ERUPTIONS.

DISCOVERY WILLEM J. LUYTEN DISCOVERED UNEXPECTED VARIABILITY WHILE CATALOGUING DWARF STARS IN THE 1940s.

KEY BREAKTHROUGH STUDIES OF THE 2008 EV LACERTAE SUPERFLARE SUGGEST THESE STARS OWE THEIR ACTIVITY TO A COMBINATION OF TURBULENT CONVECTION AND RAPID ROTATION.

IMPORTANCE FLARES ARE A USEFUL TOOL FOR UNDERSTANDING THE STRUCTURE OF VERY SMALL DWARF STARS.

While the smallest stars can generate a mere fraction of the energy of our Sun, they can also show surprising activity, with huge starspots in their atmosphere and unpredictable high-energy outbursts. This behaviour seems to be linked to unusually powerful stellar magnetic fields.

The first trace of dramatic activity in dwarf stars was found by Dutch-American Willem J. Luyten. He identified unexpected changes in the stars V1396 Cygni and AT Microscopii: rapid brightening of their hydrogen emission lines seemed similar to behaviour associated with solar flares.

Luyten's survey of stars with high proper motions (see page 18) revealed large numbers of faint nearby stars, and one of these, Luyten 726-8, proved to be among the closest stars to Earth at a distance of just 8.7 light years. Discovered in 1948, it proved to be a binary pair of closely matched stars, each with about 10 percent of the Sun's mass. However, shortly after its discovery, the star designated Luyten 726-8B underwent a sudden outburst, brightening hugely in a matter of seconds before fading away more slowly. Working from California's Mount Wilson Observatory, Alfred Joy and Milton Humason were able to record the star's spectrum during the outburst: analysis showed the star had brightened by a factor of 40, while its temperature had soared from 3,000°C (5,400°F) to 10,000°C (18,000°F). Assigned the designation UV Ceti, the star became the prototype for a new class of variables, the flare stars.

Many other stars of this kind came rapidly to light, revealing that flare stars are common in our galaxy (or at least in the relatively limited region where we can see faint dwarf stars at all).

OPPOSITE Flares on the surface of our Sun can have spectacular effects, but the Sun is so brilliant that they do little to alter its overall brightness. Flares of similar magnitude on the surface of much smaller and fainter stars seem far more dramatic in comparison.

Activity beyond the visible

It soon became clear that the stars were not just active in visible light. In 1966, Bernard Lovell of the University of Manchester's Jodrell Bank Radio Observatory, and Leonard H. Solomon of the Smithsonian Astrophysical Observatory collaborated to measure UV Ceti's activity simultaneously at optical and radio wavelengths, revealing that the flares coincided with bursts of radio emission. A decade later in 1975, Dutch astronomers led by John Heise used the recently launched Astronomical Netherlands Satellite (ANS) X-ray and ultraviolet telescope to identify X-ray emissions coinciding with the flares of both UV Ceti and another red dwarf star, YZ Canis Majoris.

Astronomers immediately suspected that the activity taking place in flare stars was very similar to that seen in the flares of our own Sun. In particular, analysis of the spectra of flare stars revealed the telltale signs of their magnetic fields at work.

Magnetic origins

Based on studies of the Sun, astronomers believe that stellar magnetic fields are generated in the radiative zone immediately surrounding the core, but modified by the upper layers, where churning convection currents transfer heat from the deep interior to the visible surface, the photosphere. Within the

Sun, the field starts out in a similar configuration to Earth's own magnetic field, with lines of magnetic force running beneath the surface from pole to pole. However, thanks to the differential rotation that causes equatorial regions to spin faster than polar ones (with periods of around 25 and 35 days respectively), the field becomes stretched, and ultimately tangled. Where loops of magnetic field are pushed out of the photosphere, they suppress convection on a local scale, creating sunspots – relatively cool and therefore dark areas of the solar surface. And when the tangled magnetic field above a sunspot short-circuits or 'reconnects' closer to the surface, enormous amounts of energy are liberated, heating the surrounding gas to temperatures of millions of degrees and creating a spectacular flare that explodes away from the Sun's surface.

'The star had brightened by a factor of 40, while its temperature had soared from 3,000°C (5,400°F) to 10,000°C (18,000°F). Assigned the designation UV Ceti the star became the prototype for a new class of variable "flare stars".'

With less radiation to support their outer layers against their own weight, dwarf stars generally have interiors that are denser and more opaque than those of stars like the Sun. The opacity prevents energy transport by radiation beneath the surface (see page 86), and means that dwarfs are convective all the way from the core to the photosphere. This turns the entire star into a seething cauldron of hot gas, and by supplying fresh hydrogen fuel to the core, helps dwarf stars to shine on the main sequence for far longer than larger stars.

Superflares

Lack of an apparent radiative zone within such stars should, in theory, rob them of their internal magnetism, but the presence of flares shows this is clearly not the case. In fact, while red dwarfs are so faint that a Sun-like solar flare alone would be enough to massively increase their brightness, it seems that flares on many red dwarfs are actually far more powerful than those on the Sun.

In 2008, NASA's Swift Gamma-Ray Burst Mission produced some valuable new insights when it observed the most powerful flare star ever recorded. EV Lacertae, a young red dwarf some 16.5 light years from Earth, was already known to have a rapidly changing magnetic field, but astronomers were caught by surprise when it produced an eruption of light and X-rays carrying several thousand times more energy than the largest known solar flare.

Previous studies of EV Lac had also revealed that it rotates rapidly, in around four days, and astronomers now suspect that this rapid rotation may be key to explaining the most violent flare stars. The turbulent convection and rapid rotation of their gases may turn the entire star into a dynamo, generating a complex magnetic field that produces huge and unpredictable reconnection events and flares. Certainly there is some evidence that the most violent flare stars are also the fastest rotators.

70

Extrasolar planets

DEFINITION RECENTLY DISCOVERED PLANETS IN ORBIT AROUND
LARGE NUMBERS OF OTHER STARS.

DISCOVERY THE FIRST PLANETS WERE FOUND IN ORBIT AROUND A
PULSAR IN 1992.

KEY BREAKTHROUGH IN 1995, MICHEL MAYOR AND DIDIER QUELOZ
USED THE RADIAL VELOCITY METHOD TO DETECT THE FIRST
PLANETS AROUND A SUN-LIKE STAR, 51 PEGASI.

IMPORTANCE THE EXISTENCE OF SUBSTANTIAL NUMBERS OF
EXTRASOLAR PLANETS INCREASES THE CHANCE OF LIFE BEING
WIDESPREAD IN OUR GALAXY.

Astronomers have long hoped to discover planets in orbit around other stars, but it was only in the mid-1990s that a combination of improving technology and an array of new approaches led to a breakthrough. Since that time, hundreds of alien solar systems have been found.

The detection of planets orbiting other stars is one of the greatest challenges of modern astronomy. Shining only through reflected starlight, they are, almost without exception, too faint and too close to their stars to observe directly with current instruments. As a result, astronomers must use indirect methods of detection, and it is these that have finally come into their own in the last two decades.

Wobbling planets

Inspired by the discovery of Neptune, the earliest attempts to identify planets orbiting other stars looked for perturbations in the paths of stars moving through space. Just as binary stars orbit around a common centre of mass, so a star with a planetary system will be pulled in different directions as the planets complete their orbits around it. As early as 1855, Captain W.S. Jacob of the Madras Observatory claimed to have detected anomalies in the movement of the binary star 70 Ophiuchi that pointed to the existence of a planet. This claim persisted until the 1890s, before a new model of the binary's motion did away with the need for an unseen influence.

Similar claims emerged in the 1960s for wobbles in the motion of the famous Barnard's Star, a faint but nearby red dwarf that is the fastest-moving star in the sky. However the sad reality is that, even for a star that is just six light years from Earth, the scale of any wobbles caused by planetary influence

OPPOSITE In late 2011, NASA's Kepler mission discovered a planetary system containing three rocky planets in orbit around a red dwarf star called KOI-961, some 130 light years from Earth. The planets range in size from 0.57 to 0.78 Earth radii, and have orbital periods between half a day and two days. Proximity to their feeble star means their surfaces are scorching hot.

would be so small as to make measurement impossible. Or rather, such wobbles would be impossible to see visually, and measure astrometrically. In the 1980s, a different technique began to look more promising.

Radial velocity

The new approach involved measuring small stellar motions not laterally in the sky, but radially – back and forth along the line of sight to Earth. Using the well-established techniques of spectroscopy, it was now becoming possible to measure the Doppler shifts in starlight caused by relatively small radial motions, while advances in computer technology were making it possible to measure and analyse large numbers of spectra within a single telescopic field of view simultaneously.

'The vast majority of planets discovered so far have been giants of Jupiter-mass or greater, in relatively close, fast orbits around their stars.'

In the late 1980s, Canadian astronomers Bruce Campbell, G.A.H. Walker and S. Yang made one of the first concerted attempts to use this technique, collecting spectra for sixteen stars using the Canada–France–Hawaii Telescope on Mauna Kea, Hawaii. They identified seven stars that seemed to be oscillating in the predicted way (as well as two with larger wobbles probably due to undiscovered stellar companions). Ironically, it was one of this latter pair, a star called Gamma Cephei, that ultimately proved to be the earliest detection of evidence for an extrasolar planet.

As it turned out, though, the first confirmed discovery of extrasolar planets used a very different technique, and revealed a planetary system orbiting a very different kind of star. By measuring tiny changes in the rapid signals from a pulsar called PSR 1257+12, roughly 2,000 light years from Earth, Polish radio-astronomer Alexander Wolszczan and his Canadian colleague Dale Frail found evidence in 1992 of a system of three planets and one tiny 'comet' in orbit around the superdense stellar lighthouse.

While the very existence of planets orbiting close to a pulsar raised interesting questions (see page 291), astronomers were still eager to locate planets around more mainstream stars. In the early 1990s, Swiss astronomers Michel Mayor and Didier Queloz began to collect stellar spectra using the advanced ELODIE spectrograph at the Observatory of Haute-Provence in France. By 1995, they had conclusive evidence that the Sun-like star 51 Pegasi, some 51 light years from Earth, wobbles under the influence of a companion with at least half the mass of Jupiter, orbiting the star every 4.23 days. Mayor and Queloz's discovery opened the floodgates for many more – as of late 2011 more than 700 extrasolar planets have been identified (including confirmation of Campbell, Walker and Yang's planet around Gamma Cephei), the vast majority using the same technique.

But the radial velocity method is not flawless. The orbiting planet must be massive enough to pull its star off balance by a considerable amount in order

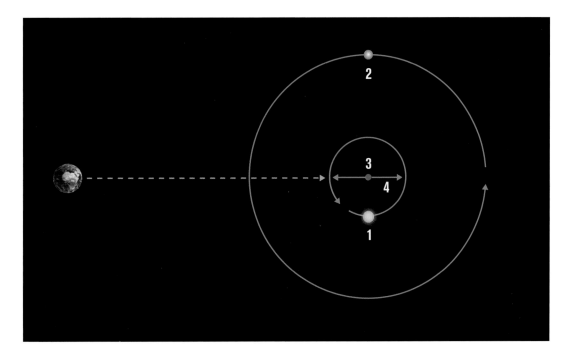

to be detectable (although the sensitivity of the technique has improved over time), and the system must be observed over several orbital cycles in order to confirm that the wobble really is periodic in nature. As a result, the vast majority of planets discovered so far have been giants of Jupiter-mass or greater, in relatively close, fast orbits around their stars. In addition, the technique only shows us the radial component of a star's motion, directly towards and away from Earth. We currently have no way of knowing how much of the star's motion may be in a lateral direction, and so can only put a lower limit on the mass of any planet.

New techniques

In an effort to overcome these limitations, various other planet-hunting techniques have been developed. The most intuitive is the transit method, which simply involves a precisely aimed telescope pointed at a group of stars and looking for telltale variations in brightness caused by a planet passing across the face of a star. This is the approach used by NASA's Kepler mission, and ESA's COROT (see page 297).

Gravitational microlensing is almost a mirror-image of the transit method, since it involves looking for unusual brightening in the appearance of stars. Microlensing is a form of gravitational lensing (see page 393) that occurs when two stars line up precisely as seen from Earth, and the foreground star focuses and amplifies light from the background star. If the foreground star has a planet in orbit around it, then this can modify the strength of the lensing effect. As of 2010, four extrasolar planets have been detected using the microlensing technique.

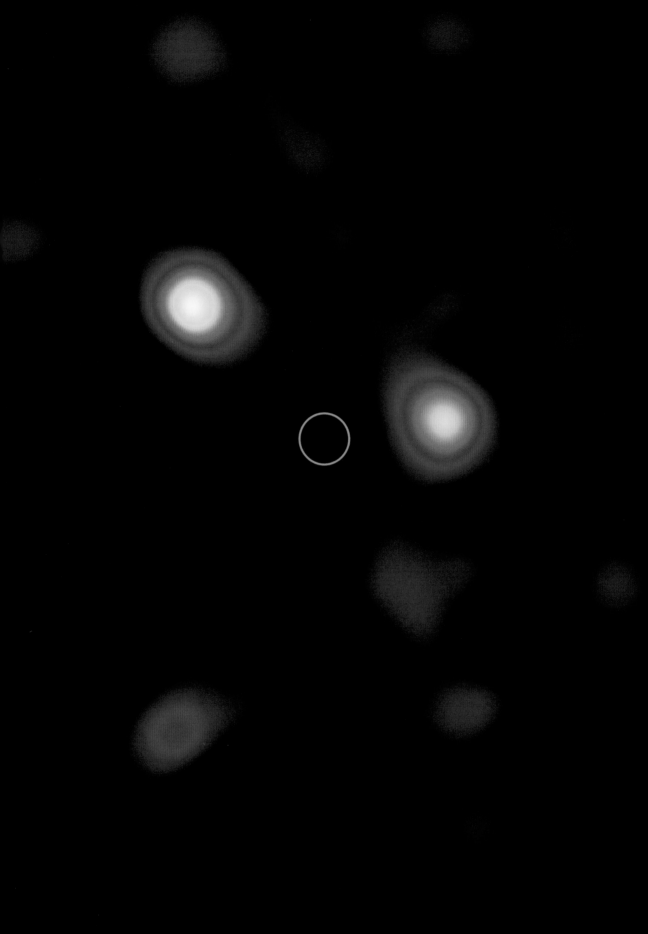

71

The variety of extrasolar planets

DEFINITION ANALYSIS OF EXTRASOLAR PLANETS REVEALS A RANGE OF BIZARRE WORLDS IN STRANGE ORBITS.

DISCOVERY 51 PEGASI, THE FIRST PLANET FOUND AROUND A SUN-LIKE STAR IN 1992, PROVED TO BE A 'HOT JUPITER' – A GAS GIANT IN A TIGHT ORBIT AROUND ITS STAR.

KEY BREAKTHROUGH IN 2011, ASTRONOMERS DISCOVERED A PLANET THAT APPEARS TO BE THE STRIPPED-DOWN CORE OF A STAR.

IMPORTANCE THE STRANGE VARIETY OF EXTRASOLAR PLANETS SUGGESTS THAT OUR NEATLY ORDERED SOLAR SYSTEM MAY BE A RARITY IN THE GALAXY.

The recent discovery of hundreds of extrasolar planets around other stars is revealing new types of planets that were never previously imagined. These include gas giants skimming the surface of their suns, huge rocky worlds far larger than Earth, and planets orbiting dead stars.

Until the 1990s, astronomers tended to think that our solar system was an average one. They assumed that others, when they were eventually found, would follow similar rules, with small rocky worlds and larger gas giants following near-circular orbits around their parent stars. The discoveries of the past two decades have shown the reality is rather different – the current orderly state of our own solar system seems to be the lucky result of complex processes early in its history (see page 101), and the planetary systems of other stars show no inclination to obey the rules of our own.

Hot Jupiters

The signs were there from the beginning – 51 Pegasi b, the first extrasolar planet to be discovered around a normal star (see page 286) proved to be the prototype for a new class of planet unlike anything previously suspected. It has a mass at least half that of Jupiter (more than 150 times that of Earth), but orbits the Sun-like star 51 Pegasi in just 101 hours, at a distance of just 7 million km (4.3 million miles), or 0.045 astronomical units. At first, astronomers assumed that such a massive body so close to its star would have to be a ball of solid rock, but of course there are theoretical problems in forming any large planet so close to its parent star. Once it became clear that such planets must have migrated into their current positions, astronomers concluded that these massive bodies were more likely to be gas giants (so-called 'hot Jupiters') – and this has been borne out by further discoveries.

OPPOSITE This false-colour image is a rare photograph of another solar system. It shows three gas giant planets in orbit around the young star HR8799, some 120 light years from Earth. In order to capture the faint light reflecting off these remote worlds, the central star itself has been hidden by a device called a coronograph – its position is marked by the green circle.

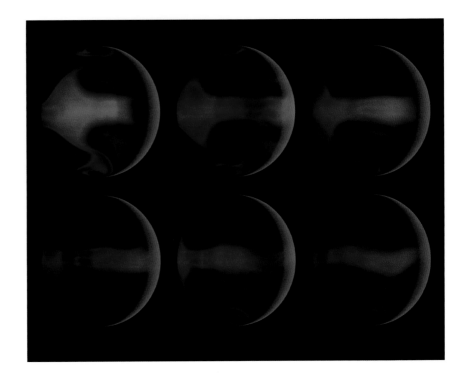

The idea of a gas giant surviving so close to its planet seems unlikely –
surely the intense heat would cause its atmosphere to evaporate? Indeed,
comet-like tails of gas being blasted away from such worlds have since been
detected. However, it seems that most giants have enough mass to hold
themselves together even when heated to thousands of degrees. Hot Jupiters
all have extremely low-eccentricity circular orbits as a result of the powerful
tidal forces they experience, and these same forces have slowed their rotation
so that they have one face permanently turned towards their star, resulting
in bizarre climates.

So how did these strange worlds get so close to their stars? The models of
planetary migration that have proved so useful for understanding our own
solar system do not seem to apply here. Instead, hot Jupiters are thought
to have migrated very early in the development of their solar systems,
before their stars even begin to shine properly. According to this model, the
formation of a giant planet generates waves in the protoplanetary nebula,
causing the planet to lose angular momentum and spiral inwards. The
migration comes to an end as fusion processes ignite within the star and its
radiation and stellar wind blow away the remains of the nebula.

Stranger worlds, stranger orbits

Hot Jupiters are just one of the new classes of planets. There are also 'hot
Neptunes', with Neptune-like masses and orbits smaller than Earth's, and
'Chthonian planets' – the stripped-down cores of hot Jupiters that have lost
their gas layers. 'Super-Earths' are planets with masses up to 10 times that of

Earth. Despite their name, these worlds are not necessarily Earth-like, and some of them may in fact be 'gas dwarfs'.

The strangeness of these planets does not stop with their physical structure. Near-circular orbits such as those followed by hot Jupiters and the planets of our solar system have turned out to be the exception rather than the rule, and most planets move on distinctly elliptical paths. Some have even been found in apparently stable orbits around one or both stars of binary systems.

Challenging pulsar planets

Perhaps the most surprising group, however, are the pulsar planets, which include the first extrasolar planets to be discovered in 1992 (see page 286). Several pulsars are now known to have planetary systems, and the very existence of these planets presents a big challenge to astronomers. Pulsars are the remnants left behind by devastating supernovae that should have had enough force to destroy any planets in orbit around them – especially considering several of these planets orbit closer to the pulsar than Earth does to the Sun. Even if planets somehow make it through the explosion, they will be subjected to high-energy radiation from the newly formed pulsar that may be powerful enough to strip their surfaces away, ultimately causing them to evaporate into space.

'The current orderly state of our own solar system seems to be the lucky result of complex processes early in its history and the planetary systems of other stars show no inclination to obey the rules of our own.'

Some astronomers speculated that the planets could be interstellar wanderers captured into orbit after the supernova, or more distant worlds that have spiralled towards the pulsar quite recently. However in 2006, astronomers using the infrared Spitzer Space Telescope discovered a debris disc surrounding the pulsar 4U 0142+61, around 13,000 light years from Earth. According to investigator Deepto Chakrabarty of the Massachusetts Institute of Technology, this disc is probably composed of metal-rich material produced in the supernova around 100,000 years ago. Based on comparisons with the protoplanetary discs around normal stars, it seems likely that it could ultimately coalesce into a system of small, dense planets.

In 2011, researchers from Germany's Max Planck Institute for Radio Astronomy announced evidence for an even more bizarre way to make a planet. A team led by Australian astronomer Matthew Bailes found a Jupiter-mass planet orbiting the pulsar PSR J1719–1438 in just 130 minutes. For the planet to survive in such extreme conditions, it must be very dense, and the researchers believe it might in fact be the surviving core of a companion star whose outer layers were stripped away by the pulsar. As pressure from the star's outer layers was removed, fusion in the star's core ultimately shut down and it transformed into a premature white dwarf (see page 337). Based on its likely carbon-rich composition, this strange new world has been nicknamed the 'diamond planet'. It seems certain that astronomers will find even weirder new planets in future.

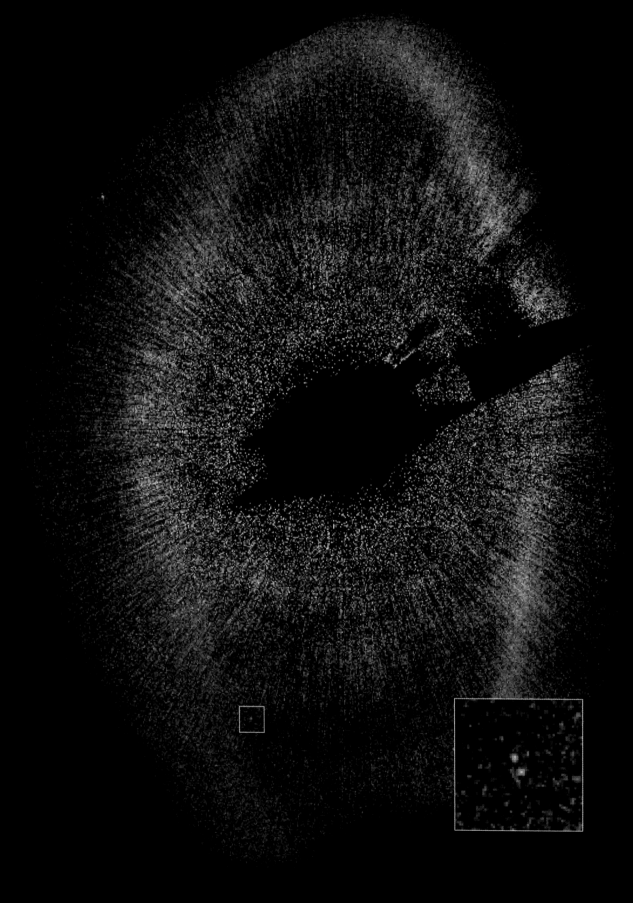

72

The Fomalhaut system

DEFINITION A RELATIVELY NEARBY STAR THAT HAS A PROMINENT
DISC OF DUSTY MATERIAL IN ORBIT AROUND IT.

DISCOVERY THE DISC AROUND FOMALHAUT WAS FIRST MAPPED WITH
RADIO WAVES IN 1998 AND IMAGED WITH THE HUBBLE SPACE
TELESCOPE IN 2004.

KEY BREAKTHROUGH IN 2008, ASTRONOMERS ANNOUNCED THE
DISCOVERY OF A PLANET MOVING WITHIN THE DISC.

IMPORTANCE FOMALHAUT GIVES US A RARE CHANCE TO OBSERVE
THE PROCESSES OF PLANET FORMATION IN ACTION.

The nearby bright star Fomalhaut is surrounded by a huge disc of dust that is thought to be its equivalent of our own solar system's Kuiper Belt. Within this cloud, astronomers believe they have traced the motions of a newly formed planet.

With a name that means 'mouth of the fish', the star Fomalhaut is the brightest member of the constellation Piscis Austrinus, and one of the brightest stars in Earth's entire sky. At a distance of some 25 light years, it is about 18 times as luminous as our Sun and has about twice its mass. According to standard models of stellar evolution (see page 267), it is probably about 100–300 million years old, with an expected lifespan of about a billion years.

A dusty disc

In 1983, IRAS, the Infrared Astronomical Satellite, detected an unexpected excess of infrared radiation coming from Fomalhaut. Since the star's surface glows at a white-hot 8,500°C (15,300°F), it should produce even less infrared radiation than the Sun, so astronomers suspected the star was surrounded by a cloud of cooler dust that was actually responsible for the infrared excess. IRAS successfully imaged a similar disc around the star Beta Pictoris, but was not able to resolve a disc around Fomalhaut. However, in 1998 a team of British and American astronomers viewed the disc for the first time in submillimetre radio waves. Further radio observations in 2002, together with infrared images obtained by the Spitzer Space Telescope in 2003, confirmed that the disc lies at a shallow angle as seen from Earth, and identified an empty gap some 20 astronomical units (AU) wide at its centre. While Fomalhaut's disc bears a passing resemblance to the dust produced by collisions in the Kuiper Belt of our own solar system, it is roughly four times the size. Strangely,

OPPOSITE This Hubble Space Telescope view shows the turbulent disc of planet-forming material around Fomalhaut (the direct light of the central star is blocked out by a coronagraph). The inset shows the movement of a suspected planet orbiting within the debris.

however, the centre of the disc seemed to be offset from the star itself. Based on the radio images, astronomers also identified warps within the disc that they believed were caused by one or more planets orbiting some 60 to 100 AU from the star.

However it took the sharp vision of the Hubble Space Telescope, and specifically the Advanced Camera for Surveys (ACS), installed during a servicing mission in 2002, to transform our view of Fomalhaut. Using a movable disc called a coronagraph to block out the light of the star itself, the ACS was able to photograph the disc in visible light for the first time, at far higher resolution than previously available.

The debris in detail

Hubble's image revealed that Fomalhaut's disc is strangely eye-like in appearance, with most of its matter concentrated in a relatively well-defined ring between 133 and 158 AUs from the star. Inside and outside of this region, the dust is far less dense, but still present. The dark area in the middle of the disc, created by the coronagraph, obscures the fact that the star is actually located about 15 AU from the geometric centre of the disc.

'Based on radio images, astronomers identified warps within the disc that they believed were caused by one or more planets orbiting the star.'

Despite its flat appearance, the disc has a significant thickness, especially in the region of the dense ring. This presents something of a puzzle, since, in theory, the processes of accretion should cause protoplanetary discs to flatten out over time. In 2007, a team led by Alice Quillen of Rochester University, New York, suggested that the puffiness of the dust ring was due to disturbance and heating as planetesimals collide and coalesce within it. According to their calculations, these bodies have probably grown to around the size of Pluto and are entering a runaway growth phase as their gravity becomes strong enough to drain dust out of the ring.

Further analysis of the ring's relatively sharp inner boundary leads Quillen to propose the existence of a Neptune-sized planet orbiting just inside the ring. Such a planet would clear material from the dust disc that ventured into its path, causing it to pile up in the ring beyond its orbit. If the planet's orbit is noticeably elliptical, with a perihelion significantly closer to the star than its aphelion, it could also explain the offset distribution of material in the disc. Explaining the presence of a planet with such an elliptical orbit in such a young solar system, however, is problematic in itself, since infant planets are believed to inherit near-circular orbits from the protoplanetary disc that gives birth to them. Notably elliptical orbits are generally thought to evolve over longer periods of time through interactions between the planets in a solar system, but, in this case, it seems to have happened at an unusually early stage. It may be that Quillen's proposed planet has suffered some rare cataclysm that propelled it into a different orbit, or that existing theories of planet formation are missing something that applies more generally.

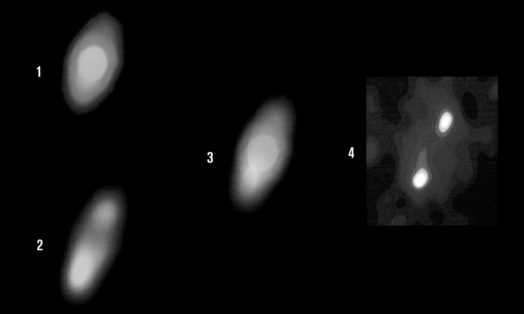

A planet in sight?

In 2008, a team of astronomers led by Paul Kalas of the University of California at Berkeley announced dramatic confirmation of the theory that a planet helps shape Fomalhaut's ring. Comparing Hubble ACS images of the dust disc taken in 2004 and 2006, they noticed a bright spot just inside the inner edge of the ring had changed positions slightly. Careful calculations appeared to confirm that the object was in orbit around the star.

Fomalhaut b, as the object is known, was the first extrasolar planet to be directly imaged in visible light. It lies about 115 AU from its parent star (almost four times the distance of Neptune from the Sun), and has a mass less than three times that of Jupiter. With an age of less than 100 million years, Fomalhaut b's surface temperature is still above boiling point – changes to its brightness between the two observations have been blamed on the action of a hot atmosphere, or the presence of a ring around the planet.

But, as with many tentative observations of extrasolar planets, there are still doubts. When Kalas's team used Hubble to image Fomalhaut in 2010, they were shocked to find Fomalhaut b some way from its predicted position. What's more, calculations of the object's revised orbit showed that it cuts straight across the dust ring – given the size inferred from its brightness, this should cause obvious disturbances within the ring. One possible explanation requires the presence of a second, unseen planet to hold the ring steady against these disturbances, but there are others – Fomalhaut b might turn out to be nothing more than a transient concentration of material within the disc, or even a background star with a deceptive path across the sky.

ABOVE Infrared images from the Spitzer Space Telescope reveal unseen details of the Fomalhaut system. A short-wavelength image (1) shows warm dust in the apparently empty centre of the ring. Longer-wavelength radiation (2) shows obvious differences in the dust distribution between one side of the star and the other. The centre image (3) combines the two Spitzer views, while a radio map from the James Clerk Maxwell Telescope (4) confirms the ring's inclination with respect to Earth.

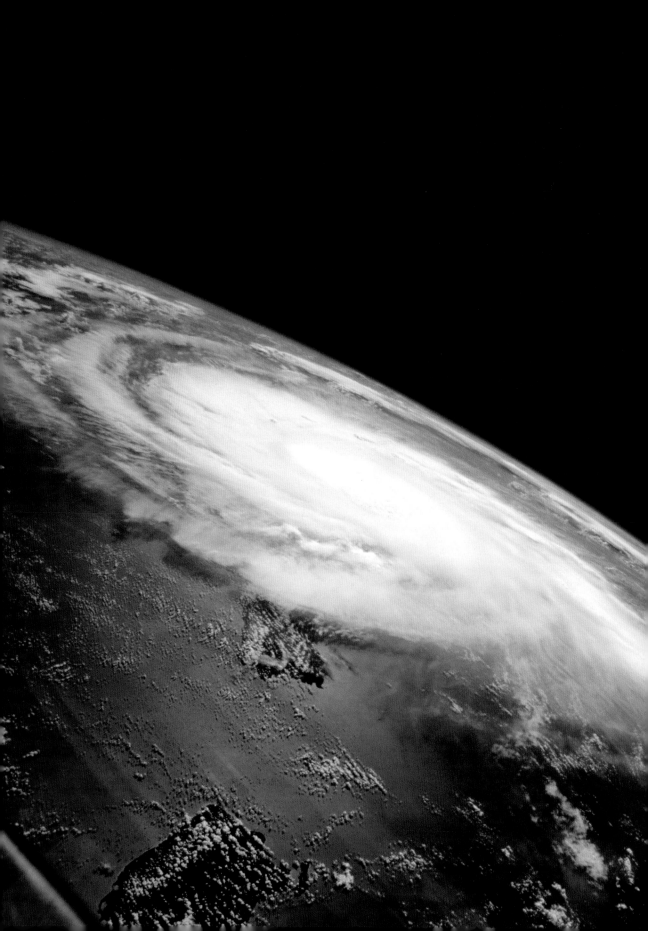

73

Earth-like worlds

DEFINITION SMALL WORLDS IN THE HABITABLE ZONES AROUND THEIR STARS, WHOSE DETECTION PRESENTS UNIQUE CHALLENGES.

DISCOVERY THE FIRST SATELLITES TO USE THE TRANSIT TECHNIQUE FOR FINDING SMALL EXTRASOLAR PLANETS WERE COROT, LAUNCHED IN 2006, AND KEPLER, LAUNCHED IN 2009.

KEY BREAKTHROUGH IN 2011, ASTRONOMERS ANNOUNCED THE DISCOVERY OF KEPLER-22B, A PLANET ROUGHLY TWICE THE SIZE OF EARTH, AT A HABITABLE DISTANCE FROM ITS STAR.

IMPORTANCE IT IS PROBABLE THAT EARTH-LIKE WORLDS PRESENT THE BEST OPPORTUNITIES FOR LIFE ELSEWHERE IN OUR GALAXY.

The quest for Earth-like planets capable of supporting life presents unique challenges that push modern technology to the limits. Nevertheless, in late 2011, it met with its first major success – the discovery of a relatively small planet at a comfortable distance from a Sun-like star.

While the radial velocity method of planet hunting has proved extremely successful for locating giant planets in orbit around other stars (see page 285), locating less massive, Earth-like worlds still presents enormous problems, and demands unique and ingenious solutions. Fortunately, technological advances undreamt of even in the 1990s have now made a more direct method of detection a reality. Thanks to new generations of ultrasensitive electronic light detectors (advanced versions of the CCDs found in cameras), they can measure the amount of light coming from individual stars with such accuracy that they can detect the minute change caused when a planet passes across or 'transits' the face of the star.

Although some transiting planets have been detected using ground-based telescopes, the constant twinkling of starlight caused by Earth's turbulent atmosphere makes small transits in particular almost impossible to detect. Instead, large-scale searches for transiting planets rely on space-based observatories orbiting far above the atmosphere. Here, a telescope can focus on the stars in the same field of view for months, even years at a time, looking for telltale variations in their brightness. Transits can offer new information about the properties of extrasolar planets, such as a direct indication of their diameter, but they cannot directly reveal a planet's mass. However if a planet can be confirmed by the radial velocity method (which does produce an estimate of mass), its density and possible composition can be discovered.

OPPOSITE Planet Earth is the largest rocky world in the solar system, and offers a hospitable environment for abundant life. Astronomers hope to soon discover similar worlds in orbit around other stars.

COROT and Kepler

The first mission to put the transit method into effect was the French-led European COROT satellite (COnvection, ROtation et Transits planétaires). Launched in late 2006, it began operations in February 2007 with twin objectives of planet-hunting and asteroseismology (measuring oscillations in stellar surfaces similar to those used in helioseismology – see page 86). COROT is equipped with a modest 27-cm (10.6-inch) telescope and four 2,048 x 2,048 pixel CCDs, which it uses to monitor two starfields on opposite sides of the sky in the constellations Serpens Cauda and Monoceros.

In March 2009, NASA launched its own transit-hunting mission, named Kepler. Equipped with 42 CCDs each of 2,200 x 1,024 pixel resolution and a 1.4-metre telescope, it has a larger field of view and a different observing technique. Unlike COROT, which orbits Earth, Kepler was placed in its own orbit around the Sun, allowing it to stare at a single area of the sky, straddling the borders of Cygnus, Lyra and Draco, without the danger of Earth getting in the way. Kepler will monitor a field of view containing some 145,000 measurable main-sequence stars for at least three and a half years.

RIGHT Kepler's view of the sky comprises 42 neighbouring rectangular regions covering 100 square degrees among the dense star clouds of the northern Milky Way.

Both satellites have had to face their share of problems. COROT's planned mission involved studying each target region for 150 days at a time, alternating between them with short observation runs in between for asteroseismology observations. However the loss of a data processing unit in March 2009 crippled two of the four CCDs, and the satellite's long observations were reduced to 90 days in order to maximize the number of stars it could study. Kepler, meanwhile, produced unexpected noise in its measurements, which in some cases could increase the number of separate transit events that will have to occur before a planet can be confirmed.

A promising start

Nevertheless, the two missions have proved a resounding success, demonstrating the transit method's huge potential. COROT's first two planets, hot Jupiters called COROT-1b and COROT-2b, were detected within weeks of its launch, and COROT-1b subsequently became the first extrasolar system to reveal its secondary eclipse (the minute dip in light when a planet passes behind its star). Detection of secondary eclipses has huge scientific potential, since it may allow astronomers to isolate light from the planet alone, revealing properties such as temperature and even atmospheric chemistry. Later discoveries include some of the smallest planets yet found, and numerous Jupiter-sized worlds.

'Kepler will monitor a field of view containing some 145,000 measurable main-sequence stars for at least three and a half years.'

Kepler also began to find planets within a few weeks of deployment – mostly hot Jupiters and hot Neptunes in very small orbits. This is not surprising given the nature of the transit method – it can only detect planets whose orbits happen to pass directly in front of their stars as seen from Earth, and the chances of this rare event happening get far smaller as the size of a planet's orbit increases. However, Kepler's enormous sample of stars means that even rare events are likely to be seen, and sophisticated statistical techniques based on more than 2,000 currently unconfirmed 'candidate' planets have allowed astronomers to reach some extraordinary conclusions. Small Earth-like planets seem to be more common than was expected, as are multiple-planet systems. The existence of 'Tatooine' planets in orbit around both members of a tight binary star system has also been confirmed. Most excitingly, rough calculations suggest that as many as 3 percent of all stars could have planets orbiting in the habitable zone where liquid water could exist on their surface (see page 118).

In December 2011, the Kepler team announced a discovery that added a concrete example to the statistics. Kepler-22b is a planet with roughly 2.4 times the radius of Earth, orbiting in the middle of the habitable zone around a Sun-like star some 600 light years from Earth. Although some experts believe the planet is more likely to be Neptunian in nature than a large rocky world, it is still a major breakthrough, and was followed within days by the discovery of the first genuinely Earth-sized worlds (albeit in very short orbits that make them far too hot for life).

74 Epsilon Aurigae

DEFINITION A STAR SYSTEM THAT UNDERGOES LONG ECLIPSES IN A 27-YEAR CYCLE CREATED BY A MYSTERIOUS ORBITING OBJECT.

DISCOVERY THE FIRST ECLIPSING BINARY WAS IDENTIFIED BY JOHN GOODRICKE IN 1783. EPSILON AURIGAE'S OWN CHANGES WERE DISCOVERED BY JOHANN FRITSCH IN 1821.

KEY BREAKTHROUGH IN 2010, ASTRONOMERS IMAGED EPSILON AURIGAE'S ECLIPSE, CONFIRMING A LONG-STANDING THEORY THAT IT IS CAUSED BY AN ORBITING DISC OF OPAQUE MATERIAL.

IMPORTANCE THE BEHAVIOUR OF EPSILON AURIGAE HAS BEEN ONE OF THE LONGEST-RUNNING MYSTERIES IN ASTRONOMY.

Once every 27 years, an apparently normal star in the constellation of Auriga undergoes a remarkable change – a drop in brightness that lasts for almost two years. The star's behaviour puts it in a class known as 'eclipsing binaries' – but, in this case, the eclipsing object is like no other.

In 1783, a young astronomer named John Goodricke presented a paper to London's Royal Society, outlining his investigations of Beta Persei, a bright star in the constellation Perseus. He showed that the star, known since ancient times as Algol, the Demon, underwent significant drops in brightness in a repeating cycle of a little under three days, and he suggested the pattern was caused by a small object in orbit around the star blocking out part of its light.

Binary systems

Goodricke's discovery gave astronomy a new class of object – the 'eclipsing variable'. But it was not until 1881 that Edward C. Pickering of the Harvard Observatory investigated Algol in detail and concluded that the eclipsing object was in fact another star. German astronomer H.C. Vogel confirmed Pickering's theory in 1889 with the discovery of complex absorption lines in Algol's spectrum, caused by the two stars orbiting each other. Algol was therefore the earliest 'eclipsing binary' and the first 'spectroscopic binary', paving the way for the discovery that double and multiple stars are far more common than previously thought. Today, astronomers believe that lone stars like our own Sun are probably in a minority in the Milky Way.

Algol's secondary star proved to be a relatively faint orange subgiant, making little contribution to the system's overall light compared to the bright blue-white primary. As a result, the much smaller dips in brightness caused when

OPPOSITE This artist's impression depicts the most likely solution to the puzzle of Epsilon Aurigae, in which the primary star is orbited by a hotter secondary star that is embedded within a semi-opaque disc of dusty, potentially planet-forming, material.

the bright primary eclipses the fainter secondary were not detected until after the star's nature had been confirmed by other methods.

Once astronomers had identified the true nature of Algol, they tried to apply its example to many other variable stars. While some did indeed turn out to be eclipsing binaries, others turned out to be single stars undergoing regular or irregular pulsations, or even more complex systems.

Mystery star

Amongst them all, however, Epsilon Aurigae stood out. Thanks to its position at one corner of a compact triangle of stars known as 'the Kids', its brightness is fairly easy to estimate, and its variability was first noted by German astronomer Johann Fritsch in 1821. Several others observed the occasional dips in its brightness throughout the 19th century, but it was only in 1904 that another German, Hans Ludendorff, identified the 27.1-year cycle in its variations and suggested it was an eclipsing binary.

As methods for studying these stars improved, it became clear that little about the system made sense. With eclipses lasting between 640 and 730 days out of every 27 years, the object obscuring the primary star must clearly be huge, and calculations showed that it must have roughly the same mass as the primary. So why did the secondary object apparently not make its own contribution to the light of the system? Analysis of Epsilon's light showed no spectroscopic trace of light from a second object, except during eclipses when some peculiar dark absorption lines appeared, shifting their wavelengths through the eclipse in a way that suggested a rotating object.

'Observations from the infrared Spitzer Space Telescope have suggested that there may be just a single star at the centre of the disc after all, and that material in the disc is gravel-like in consistency.'

Small variations in the brightness of the primary white supergiant added further complexity to the system, but something else didn't add up. The eclipses were clearly partial (blocking out 50 percent of the primary's light at most), but the 'light curve' of the system's brightness during each event 'flatlines' in the middle, suggesting a long period in which the proportion of the primary that is blocked remains constant (behaviour that suggests a considerably smaller eclipsing object).

An eclipsing disc?

In order to explain all these characteristics, astronomers suggested a variety of exotic theories through the 20th century. Ludendorff suggested the eclipses were caused by a swarm of meteorites, while Dutch-American astronomer Gerard Kuiper and others proposed that the bright star was in fact in orbit around a huge and semi-transparent 'infrared star', through which its light could shine during eclipses. In 1954, Czech astronomer Zdenek Kopal showed how many of Epsilon's strange features could be accounted for if the eclipsing object was a semi-transparent disc of dust, inclined at an angle to both its orbit around the primary star and to our point of view on Earth.

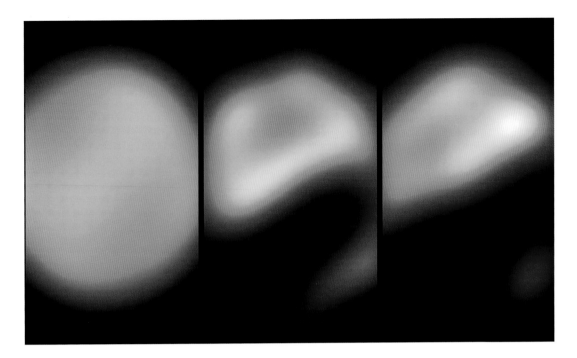

ABOVE A sequence of synthesized infrared images captured by an international team offered astronomers their first view of the Epsilon Aurigae eclipse in progress.

While the semi-transparent disc model resolved many problems with Epsilon's peculiar light curve, explaining its presence and long-term stability was another challenge. So was understanding how the disc could apparently have the same mass as the primary star, and how it could remain tilted relative to its orbit for a sustained period. In 1971, Canadian astronomer Alastair G. W. Cameron suggested the disc might surround a black hole, but the lack of distinctive high-energy emissions has since shown this cannot be the case. Following the eclipse of 1982–84, Peter Eggleton and Jim Pringle of Cambridge University proposed that the disc itself was opaque, with a pair of hot blue-white stars spinning around each other at its centre. Their rotation would help to stabilize the disc's plane of rotation, and the gap they created in the centre of the disc could also help explain the slight brightening of the system seen around the middle of each eclipse.

The eclipse of 2009–11 became the subject of an international observing campaign on an unprecedented scale, and has led to new discoveries and suggestions that are still being assessed. Interferometric imaging from Georgia State University's CHARA telescope array has directly shown the disc moving across the face of the primary for the first time. Observations from the infrared Spitzer Space Telescope have suggested that there may be just a single star at the centre of the disc after all, and that material in the disc is gravel-like in consistency. In this case, the primary star may be a relatively low-mass evolved giant rather than a young supergiant. Finally, there are various new theories that extrasolar planets may also play a role in the system – perhaps helping to clear the gap at the centre of the disc, or generating the primary's still unexplained short-scale oscillations.

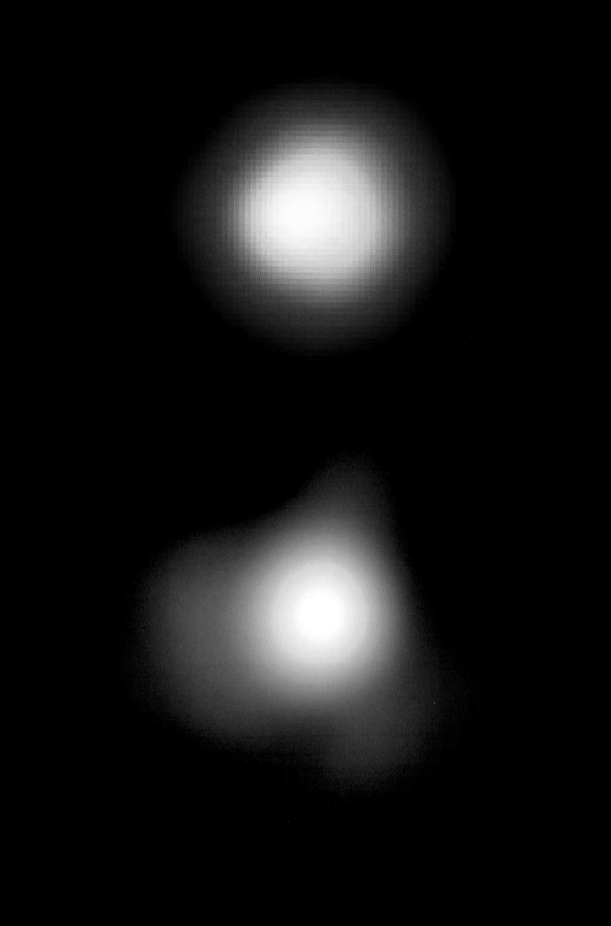

75 Betelgeuse

DEFINITION THE CLOSEST SUPERGIANT STAR TO EARTH, AND
THEREFORE THE STAR WITH THE LARGEST VISIBLE DIAMETER.

DISCOVERY THE FIRST ATTEMPTS TO MEASURE THE SIZE OF
BETELGEUSE WERE MADE IN 1920.

KEY BREAKTHROUGH IN 1995, THE HUBBLE SPACE TELESCOPE
IMAGED THE STAR'S DISC FOR THE FIRST TIME.

IMPORTANCE THE EVOLUTION OF MASSIVE STARS IS STILL POORLY
UNDERSTOOD, AND BETELGEUSE IS A VALUABLE NEARBY EXAMPLE.

Brilliant red Betelgeuse is one of the most prominent stars in Earth's skies, and also one of the most intensely studied. As the closest example of a supergiant star, it is one of a handful of stars for which astronomers, pushing the limits of technology, can detect surface features.

Marking the shoulder of the constellation of Orion, the hunter, Betelgeuse is normally the eighth brightest star in the night sky, and especially noticeable because of its distinctive red colour. However, this giant star varies somewhat in magnitude, and, at its most brilliant, can overtake its near neighbour Rigel to become the constellation's brightest star.

Betelgeuse's brightness made it an early target for parallax measurement (see page 17), and by the early 20th century it was believed to lie about 180 light years from Earth, suggesting it was extremely luminous and likely to be extremely large. As a result, it was a prime target for the earliest attempts to measure the diameter of a star, carried out in 1920 by Francis Pease and Albert Michelson at California's Mount Wilson Observatory.

Pease and Michelson used an interferometer, which relies on measuring interference patterns between light waves travelling on slightly different paths, to estimate Betelgeuse's angular diameter at 1/20th of a second of arc (1/52,000 degree). This corresponded to a physical diameter of 390 million km (240 million miles) or 2.6 astronomical units (AU).

However, measuring the diameter of Betelgeuse was, and remains, a particular challenge. Due in part to its enormous size, the outer edge of its atmosphere is particularly hazy, making it difficult even to track its position

OPPOSITE A pair of cutting-edge images highlight different aspects of the nearest supergiant star. Above, an ultraviolet image from the Hubble Space Telescope shows Betelgeuse's diffuse photosphere, including a prominent 'hot spot'. Below, a visible-light image from the Very Large Telescope reveals the clouds of expelled gas surrounding the star.

RIGHT An infrared image of the surface of Betelgeuse, produced by a team of French astronomers, shows both dark and light spots in the star's atmosphere. The spots are probably linked to deep-rooted convection cells.

for parallax measurements. Nevertheless, current estimates suggest the star's true parallax is far smaller than Pease and Michelson believed, at around 5 milliarcseconds, giving Betelgeuse a distance of around 640 light years and a diameter of 1.65 billion km (1.02 billion km) or 11 AU. This means that if Betelgeuse were to replace the Sun at the middle of our solar system, its outer layers would engulf the orbit of Jupiter.

An evolving monster

Betelgeuse is a supergiant – a star that weighs as much as 18 Suns and produces perhaps as much as 100,000 times its energy. Depending on their mass, supergiants can have various colours, but as they near the end of their lives, they tend to cool and redden due to the same changes in their internal fuel sources that transform Sun-like stars into red giants (see page 318). Spectroscopic evidence from the chemistry of its atmosphere suggests that Betelgeuse is currently fusing helium into carbon, oxygen and neon within its core, while continuing to burn hydrogen in a spherical shell around the core. Ultimately when this fuel supply is exhausted, the star's mass will allow it to continue fusing heavier elements, developing a series of fusion shells before destroying itself in a supernova explosion.

For the moment, however, this enormous star has a tenuous, distended atmosphere whose upper reaches are equal to the best vacuums achieved on Earth. With a surface temperature of around 3,300°C (6,000°F), it is so cool that it emits roughly 90 percent of its energy in the infrared, so that in visible light, the star is a mere 9,400 times brighter than the Sun.

The star's slow variations in brightness show that it is pulsating in size, with a complex cycle that appears to involve a main period of 5.7 years and several shorter cycles that seem to specifically affect certain wavelengths of radiation. Its appearance is also complicated by the expulsion of gas and dust from its upper atmosphere.

A complex envelope

In 1995, Ronald Gillilan of the Space Telescope Science Institute and A.K. Dupree of the Harvard-Smithsonian Center for Astrophysics used the Hubble Space Telescope's Faint Object Camera to view Betelgeuse, producing the first direct picture of the surface of another star. The image confirmed the fuzzy nature of Betelgeuse's outer surface, and also revealed the presence of an enormous starspot – a bright area more than 200°C (360°F) hotter than its surroundings. Astronomers speculated that this was caused by a rising plume of hot material from deep inside the star. In 1998, radio images obtained using the Very Large Array in New Mexico confirmed the presence of these plumes, and showed that they inject low-temperature gas into the high-temperature environment of Betelgeuse's atmosphere. (As with the Sun, the tenuous gases of the supergiant's outer layers are mostly considerably hotter than the visible surface.)

'If Betelgeuse were to replace the Sun at the middle of our solar system, its outer layers would engulf the orbit of Jupiter.'

Infrared images obtained in 2009 by Pierre Kervela and colleagues at the Paris Observatory revealed the presence of a gas plume extending to an extraordinary six times the star's radius (equivalent in our solar system to reaching the orbit of Pluto) on one side. Two years later, Kervela and an international team succeeded in imaging the nebula in further detail using the European Southern Observatory's Very Large Telescope. Based on the new images, Kervela's team suggest that this nebula's irregular appearance is due to enormous bubbles rising through the star's atmosphere and transferring enough energy for the outer layers to escape completely. The dust clouds are thought to be mostly silica and alumina – the raw materials of the crusts of Earth-like planets.

The complex structure of Betelgeuse's outer layers may also be responsible for surprising observations reported by Charles Townes and Edward Wishnow of the University of California at Berkeley in 2009. Comparing interferometric measurements of the star made at regular intervals since 1993, they found strong evidence that Betelgeuse's angular diameter has shrunk by more than 15 percent in the past two decades. It's possible that this shrinkage is an illusion caused by measuring the star's asymmetric envelope at different points in its slow rotation. However another, more intriguing suggestion is that the contraction is a genuine and global effect caused by internal changes to Betelgeuse's power source as this dying giant moves into the next phase of its life.

Runaway stars

DEFINITION STARS THAT MOVE THROUGH OUR GALAXY WITH
UNUSUALLY HIGH SPEEDS.

DISCOVERY THE FIRST STELLAR RUNAWAYS WERE IDENTIFIED IN
THE 1950S. IN 1961, ADRIAN BLAAUW SUGGESTED THEY MIGHT BE
A RESULT OF SUPERNOVA EXPLOSIONS.

KEY BREAKTHROUGH IN 1967, ARCADIO POVEDA SUGGESTED CLOSE
INTERACTIONS OF MULTIPLE STARS MIGHT CREATE RUNAWAYS.
RECENT EVIDENCE SHOWS BOTH MECHANISMS ARE AT WORK.

IMPORTANCE RUNAWAY STARS PRESENT A LESSON THAT SIMILAR
OBJECTS CAN SOMETIMES BE CREATED IN VERY DIFFERENT WAYS.

The discovery of stars that move through interstellar space at abnormally high speeds created a long-standing puzzle for astronomers, triggering a fierce debate over which of two possible mechanisms was at work. Recent discoveries have shown that the answer is: 'probably both'.

Even after the old idea of the stars as fixed points of light on a celestial sphere was dismissed (see page 9), the idea that stars might be moving independently from one another through space took some time to take hold. The reality of this so-called 'proper motion' was finally confirmed in 1718 by English astronomer Edmond Halley, through comparison of the 18th-century positions of the bright stars Sirius, Arcturus and Aldebaran with those recorded by the ancient Greek astronomer Hipparchus in the second century BC.

Moving targets

Proper motions have since been measured for countless stars and, as might be expected, they tend to be greatest for stars close to Earth: the greatest proper motion of all belongs to Barnard's Star, a red dwarf six light years away that traverses the diameter of the full moon every 175 years. What is more, proper motion is only a measurement of 'transverse' motion *across* the sky. Fortunately, analysis of spectra can reveal blue- and redshifts in starlight caused by the Doppler effect (see page 51), allowing the star's 'radial velocity', its motion towards or away from Earth to be calculated. By combining transverse motion, radial velocity, distances obtained from parallax or other techniques (see page 17) and a knowledge of the contribution made by the orbit of Earth and the motion of the solar system, astronomers can calculate the true speed and direction of stars through space.

OPPOSITE An infrared image from NASA's WISE satellite shows the bow shock produced as the supergiant star Zeta Ophiuchi ploughs through the interstellar medium at a speed of about 24 km/s (15 miles per second).

These individual measurements of stellar motion reveal general patterns of motion linked to the rotation of our galaxy and the large-scale distribution of stars within it (see page 345). They also allow astronomers to track stars that originated in the same place, for instance confirming the way in which open clusters of new-born stars dissolve steadily over time.

However, among these general trends, a small number of stars stand out. These stellar runaways move at speeds of more than 100 km/s (60 miles per second) relative to the general motion of the galaxy in our neighbourhood – around 10 times faster than the individual drifts of the majority of stars. Some of them, such as Zeta Ophiuchi, generate spectacular bow shocks (see page 262) as they plough through the interstellar medium. In addition, a few 'hypervelocity stars' (HVSs) move at even greater speeds of around 1,000 km/s (600 miles per second) – fast enough that they can overcome the Milky Way's gravitational pull and will ultimately escape to become wanderers in intergalactic space.

One of the most intriguing aspects of these fast-moving refugees is that they all tend to be hot, blue-white stars of a type normally found in bright star clusters known as OB associations. The problem is that these clusters are bound together tightly by gravity, and their brightest stars are normally short-lived, dying before they can drift out of the cluster. So what kind of event could cause a cluster to eject stars at such great speed?

Ejection mechanisms

Runaway stars were first identified in the 1950s, and in 1961, Dutch astronomer Adrian Blaauw proposed that they might be ejected by the supernova explosion of their companions within binary systems. Because they are home to the heaviest stars, open clusters are also the most common site for supernovae, and if such an explosion dramatically altered the balance of mass in a binary system, then the other star could be flung out of its orbit at high speed. Blaauw traced two runaway stars on the fringes of Orion, AE Aurigae and Mu Columbae, back to an origin in the famous Trapezium star cluster in the Orion Nebula, and argued that they could have originated in a similar multiple star system in which one member had gone supernova.

'A few "hypervelocity stars" move at even greater speeds of around 1,000 km/s (600 miles per second) – fast enough that they can overcome the Milky Way's gravitational pull.'

In 1967, meanwhile, Mexican astronomer Arcadio Poveda and others put forward an alternative mechanism for ejection, in which the stars were kicked out simply by gravitational interaction with their neighbours in the heart of an open cluster.

The debate appeared to be settled in 1997, when astronomers at the European Southern Observatory photographed a spectacular bow shock around the distant OB star HD77581, confirming its runaway status. Crucially,

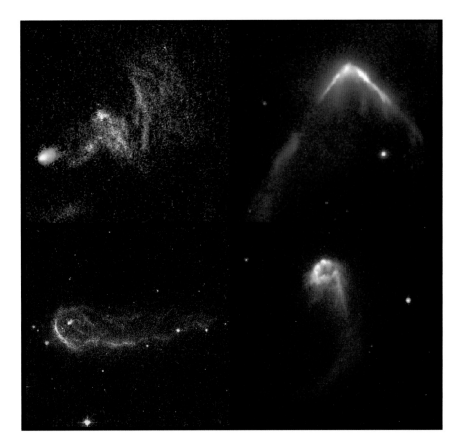

LEFT Hubble Space Telescope images capture comet-like patterns produced by four runaway stars discovered during a 2005 survey using the telescope's Advanced Camera for Surveys.

HD77581 is orbited by an X-ray pulsar supernova remnant (see page 315), the compact remnant of its once-massive companion, now carried with it on an epic journey through space.

However in 2000, University of Leiden astronomer Ronnie Hoogerwerf and colleagues produced evidence that both mechanisms were possible Using data from the Hipparcos satellite (see page 19), they confirmed the origin of AE Aurigae and Mu Columbae in Orion, but that the binary star Iota Orionis appeared to have been ejected from the Trapezium at the same time, most likely in a close interaction. Hoogerwerf's team also linked the trajectory of Zeta Ophiuchi to that of another pulsar, suggesting that they escaped from each other when the pulsar formed around a million years ago.

In 2011, astronomers from Leiden produced another ejection mechanism – a variant on Povoda's model. Simon Portegies Zwart and Michiko Fujii modelled encounters between single stars and massive binaries in the centre of young star clusters with several thousand solar masses of material. They showed how these 'bully binaries' have the ability to snatch up smaller stars, swing them round, and fling them out of the cluster altogether. On balance, it seems that a variety of processes are probably at work to create the current population of runaway stars.

Contact binaries

Although the standard theory of stellar life cycles explains the properties of the vast majority of stars, close study reveals numerous examples where it seems to fail. Fortunately, these problem stars can usually be explained by the transfer of matter between binary stars.

The model of stellar structure and evolution begun by the Hertzsprung–Russell (H–R) diagram around 1910 (see page 266) and largely completed by the work of Arthur Eddington and Hans Bethe (see pages 82 and 85) does a remarkable job of explaining the properties of the vast majority of stars. Stars that are shining by hydrogen fusion within their cores range between hot, blue and brilliant at one extreme and cool, red and dim at the other. Where exactly they sit along this spectrum is determined by their initial mass, and they retain more or less the same position on the H–R diagram throughout their main-sequence lifetimes. It is only as stars begin to exhaust the hydrogen fuel in their cores that they move off the main sequence, becoming brighter, larger and cooler giants (see page 318). What's more, because more massive stars can burn hydrogen by the CNO cycle (see page 83), they squander their fuel at a tremendous rate, leaving the main sequence much sooner than their more sedate siblings.

Binary and multiple stars normally offer a useful confirmation of this model: by measuring the orbits of the stars involved (either directly or through spectroscopy), astronomers can work out their relative masses – a calculation first made by French astronomer Félix Savary as early as 1827. Furthermore, since we can usually be confident that the stars within a system formed at the same time, we can see that more massive stars do indeed shine brighter and hotter, and evolve more rapidly.

OPPOSITE Shortly after its 2009 refit, the Hubble Space Telescope imaged the heart of Omega Centauri, the largest and brightest globular cluster in the sky. The field is filled with stars tracing the range of stellar evolution, including average yellow stars, evolved red giants, and faint white dwarfs. The brighter blue-white stars, known as 'blue stragglers', are a result of interactions between stars in this crowded region.

But some stars still refuse to fit in. For instance, the famous eclipsing binary Algol (see page 301) consists of a blue main sequence star with 3.7 times the mass of the Sun, and an evolved yellow subgiant with just 0.8 solar masses of material. How can the lower-mass star be the more evolved?

The solution to this mystery lies in a model first proposed by Dutch American astronomer Gerard Kuiper in 1941. Kuiper was keen to explain a complex star called Beta Lyrae, which combines the features of an eclipsing binary with those of a pulsating variable (see page 318) with unique properties such as an eclipse period that grows 19 seconds longer each year. He suggested that the star is actually a contact binary – a system in which one star (initially the heavier of the two) has overflowed beyond the Roche lobe, where material is gravitationally bound to the star. As a result, gas from the star's atmosphere has spiralled onto the surface of the other star, allowing it to gain mass to a point where it is now the more massive member of the system. Kuiper coined the term 'contact binary' to describe the system.

Although Beta Lyrae offers a rare chance to see a contact binary in action, Algol and other similar systems show that the phenomenon is far from rare. Some astronomers have even speculated that Sirius, the brightest star in the sky, benefited from mass transfer when its companion (now the white dwarf Sirius B) passed through its red giant phase millions of years ago.

Riddle of the blue stragglers

Mass transfer also seems to solve the long-standing puzzle concerning globular clusters – densely packed balls containing many thousands of stars, found in orbit around our galaxy and others (see page 345). Most globular

BELOW One theory to explain blue stragglers suggests that they arise from close encounters between stars in the crowded cores of globular clusters (1). The stars swing into orbit around each other (2), and may pass through a contact binary phase (3) before merging completely to produce an offspring (4) that burns brighter and hotter thanks to its increased mass.

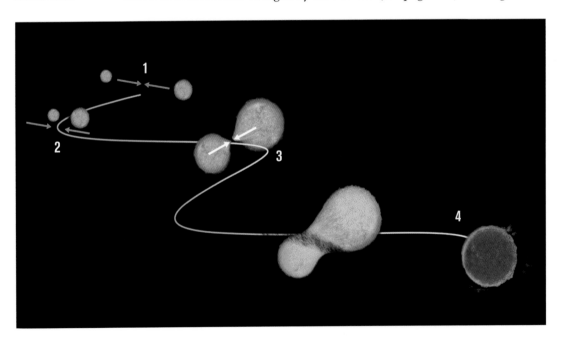

cluster members are ancient but sedate, yellow-red stars of Population II (see page 69). They formed billions of years before our own Sun, and contain few of the heavy elements that encourage younger Population I stars to burn fuel at a faster rate. In addition, globular clusters lack the raw materials to create new stars – they are in effect cosmic fossils.

In 1953, however, astronomer Allan Sandage discovered a number of luminous blue stars near the centre of globular cluster M3. If all the stars in a globular cluster formed at around the same time, and there has been no further star formation since, then how could such massive stars, which Sandage named 'blue stragglers', have survived for so long? In 1964, British astronomers Fred Hoyle and William McCrea suggested their location in the core of globular clusters might indicate they were created during close encounters between stars that stirred up their interiors, injecting new hydrogen fuel into the cores and rejuvenating them.

'Stragglers form when stars in the crowded cores of globular clusters fall into close orbit around each other. Such a system can pass through a contact binary phase, or culminate in the stars merging completely.'

Hubble Space Telescope surveys of globular clusters in the 1990s revealed that blue stragglers are far more common than previously imagined. They also confirmed that the stragglers are significantly heavier than their neighbours, and that at least some of them rotate unusually quickly. These clues allowed astronomers to improve on Hoyle and McCrea's theory, suggesting that stragglers form when stars in the crowded cores of globular clusters fall into close orbit around each other. Such a system can pass through a contact binary phase, or culminate in the stars merging completely. Either situation produces a star with significantly increased mass, which would ramp up the rate of fusion in the core, increasing both its brightness and its surface temperature. Further Hubble observations have since revealed that both mechanisms probably have a role to play in creating these out-of-place stars.

Cataclysmic variables

Perhaps the most spectacular contact binaries, however, involve systems where one component is already a dense stellar remnant – a white dwarf, neutron star or even a black hole (see page 337). In these conditions, the intense gravity of the burnt-out star strips material from its companion at an increased rate. In a system with a white dwarf, this can produce a hot, dense layer of captured gas on the remnant's surface. Conditions may become so extreme that this atmosphere ignites in a burst of nuclear fusion to create a nova outburst. If the white dwarf is close to 1.4 solar masses, the accumulated material may ultimately push it over the Chandrasekhar limit (see page 338), triggering its collapse into a neutron star in a spectacular Type 1a supernova explosion. If the remnant is already a neutron star or black hole, the stripped material can form an accretion disc around it. This disc is heated to tremendous temperatures by tidal forces, so that it emits high-energy radiation, producing a so-called X-ray binary system.

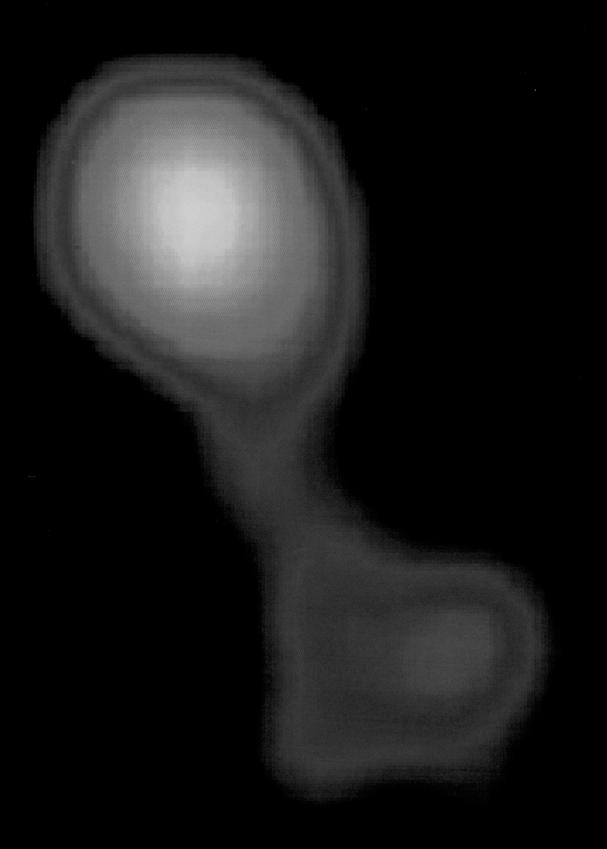

Mira

DEFINITION MIRA IS THE PROTOTYPE FOR A CLASS OF HIGHLY
EVOLVED STARS THAT SLOWLY PULSATE IN SIZE AND BRIGHTNESS.

DISCOVERY THIS STAR'S UNUSUAL BEHAVIOUR WAS FIRST NOTICED
BY DAVID FABRICIUS IN 1609.

KEY BREAKTHROUGH IN THE 20TH CENTURY, DEVELOPMENTS IN OUR
KNOWLEDGE OF STELLAR EVOLUTION SHOWED THAT MIRA-TYPE
STARS ARE RED GIANTS NEARING THE END OF THEIR LIVES.

IMPORTANCE MIRA REVEALS THE KIND OF PROCESSES THAT CAN
TRIGGER PULSATIONS IN A WIDE RANGE OF VARIABLE STARS.

Stars approaching the end of their lives often pass through an unstable phase during which their luminosity, size and surface temperatures grow and shrink in semi-regular ways. Among the most famous of these stars is Omicron Ceti, better known as Mira.

The first observer known to have recognized the unique nature of Omicron Ceti was German astronomer David Fabricius. In August 1596, he spotted a new red star in the constellation of Cetus, the Whale, which faded from view over the following months. At first the star appeared to be a short-lived nova (see page 315), but in 1609, Fabricius noticed that the star had returned.

In 1638, another German, the philosopher Johann Holwarda, determined that the star's brightness varied over a period of roughly 11 months. Polish astronomer Johannes Hevelius observed the star a year later, and brought it to widespread attention in a book of 1662, in which he named it Mira, from the Latin word meaning 'wonderful'. Subsequent observations determined that the star varies from a magnitude of around 3.5, easily seen with the naked eye, down to below magnitude 9 (visible only through a moderate telescope) with a period of 332 days. Neither maximum nor minimum is fixed, and Mira can get considerably brighter or fainter than these values, changing its brightness by a factor of well over a thousand.

Classifying variables

Over the next two centuries, astronomers discovered many more stars that changed their brightness. Some proved to be eclipsing binaries like Algol (see page 301), but the properties of the majority remained mysterious. These 'variable stars' seemed to fall into various categories, distinguished from

OPPOSITE An X-ray image from NASA's Chandra satellite captures Mira's interaction with its white dwarf companion star. The primary star (top) produced an outburst of X-rays during the observations, but fainter X-rays allow astronomers to trace hot gas being pulled towards the secondary star (bottom). The two stars are separated by roughly the diameter of Neptune's orbit around the Sun.

each other by the spectral properties of the stars, the period and intensity of their variations, and the shape of the 'light curves' produced when their changing brightness is plotted out on a graph. Mira's light curve, for instance, shows a rise in brightness over about 100 days, followed by a much slower decline.

Mira proved to be the prototype of a widespread variable category, and more than 250 Mira-type variables were known by the late 19th century (out of about 430 variable stars in total). From the 1890s, the rate of discovery accelerated, largely thanks to the work of Williamina Fleming at Harvard College Observatory. She discovered that Mira-type stars had distinctive spectral features, allowing them to be identified without years of observation. Twentieth-century advances led to the discovery of many more variables, frequently changing on much shorter timescales than Mira and its kin. Nevertheless, Mira-type stars, today known as Long-Period Variables (LPVs), remain an important group, and offer a key to understanding the kind of processes that trigger oscillations in many variable stars.

A pulsating red giant

It was only in the mid-20th century that astronomers properly established Mira's place in stellar evolution. It is a red giant – a star of similar mass to the Sun that is nearing the end of its life and has swollen to enormous size.

BELOW An ultraviolet image from NASA's Galaxy Evolution Explorer (GALEX) satellite shows hot gas trailing behind the star system on its journey through space.

As the supply of hydrogen fuel in a star's core becomes depleted at the end of its main-sequence lifetime (see page 83 and 266), the radiation pressure emanating from the centre of the star weakens. The outer layers fall inward, compressing and heating a shell around the core and allowing fusion to move out into this zone. In relatively low-mass stars like Mira, the ignition of 'shell burning' causes the star to brighten considerably – temperatures in the shell are even higher than they were in the core, and so fusion runs at a faster rate. The associated increase in radiation pressure now causes the star's outer layers to balloon outwards, so despite its hugely increased luminosity, the bloated star cools and reddens. Mira itself, for instance, shines with around 3,000–4,000 times the luminosity of the Sun, but because it has swollen to 300 times the Sun's diameter, its surface has cooled to 2,700°C (4,900°F).

Meanwhile, the star's inert core continues to contract, eventually reaching temperatures and pressures in which the helium products of hydrogen fusion can themselves begin to fuse, forming heavier elements such as oxygen, carbon and neon. The new energy from the core causes the hydrogen-burning shell to expand and cool, slowing its rate of fusion so that the star's overall luminosity falls. Stars in this phase move to the left on the Hertzsprung–Russell diagram (see page 266), along the 'horizontal branch'.

However the core's supply of helium is relatively small – when it too is exhausted, the core contracts again, the star's inner layers are compressed and heated, and a thin shell of helium fusion forms inside the hydrogen-burning shell. Stars in this phase move onto the asymptotic giant branch of the H–R diagram, and owing to the limited supply of helium in the shell, soon become unstable. Once the initial shell of helium is exhausted, compression intensifies the rate of hydrogen fusion in the outer shell. Waste helium generated by the hydrogen shell eventually allows helium fusion to resume, but this, in turn, suppresses the hydrogen burning until the helium is once again exhausted. In this way, the star begins a series of thermal pulses, each lasting from 10,000 to 100,000 years. The process also causes the relatively short-term instability witnessed in Mira and other LPVs.

A trail through space

Material dredged up from the interior during Mira's pulses enriches the star's outer layers with heavy elements, and strong stellar winds blow much of this material out into space, enriching the interstellar medium. Until recently, this process had only been inferred from spectroscopy, but in 2007 NASA's GALEX ultraviolet telescope produced the first direct image of a trail of hot gas, some 13 light years long, left behind on Mira's journey through space.

'In 2007, NASA's GALEX ultraviolet telescope produced the first direct image of a trail of hot gas, some 13 light years long, left behind on Mira's journey through space.'

Mira has long been known as a double star, but detailed images of the system were only obtained in 1997, using the Hubble Space Telescope. These revealed that Mira is distorted, with a trail of gas pulled out of its upper atmosphere extending towards a hot, dense companion. Mira B, as it is known, is almost certainly a white dwarf (see page 337) that has already passed through its red giant phase to the next and final step in its evolution.

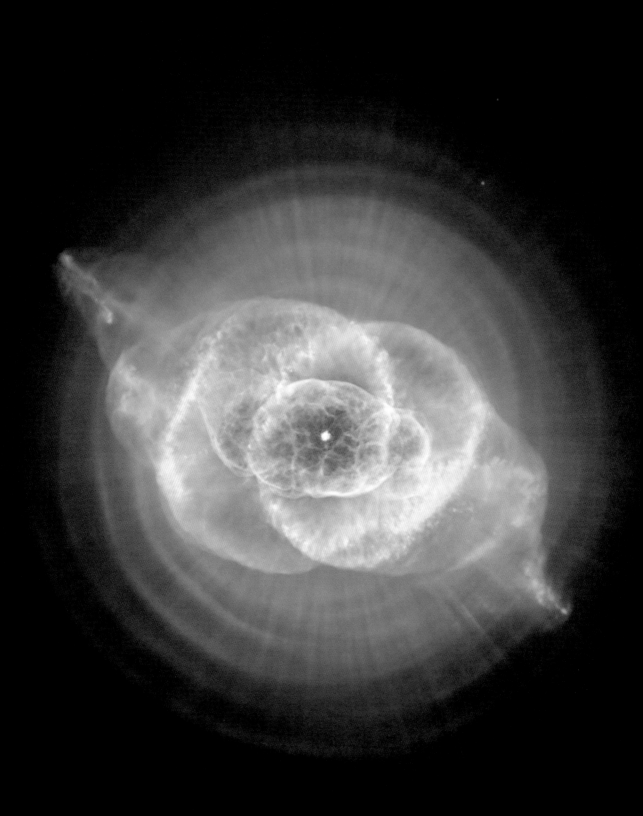

79 Complex planetary nebulae

DEFINITION BEAUTIFUL SHELLS OF GAS CAST OFF BY STARS LIKE THE SUN IN THE FINAL STAGES OF THEIR LIVES.

DISCOVERY WILLIAM HUGGINS IDENTIFIED THE GASEOUS NATURE OF PLANETARY NEBULAE USING SPECTROSCOPY IN 1864.

KEY BREAKTHROUGH IMAGES FROM SPACE-BASED TELESCOPES HAVE REVEALED UNEXPECTED COMPLEXITIES WITHIN THE NEBULAE.

IMPORTANCE PLANETARY NEBULAE OFFER US A GLIMPSE OF THE DEATH THROES OUR OWN SUN WILL EVENTUALLY EXPERIENCE.

Planetary nebulae are the elegant but short-lived final act of stars like the Sun. Once thought to be relatively simple interstellar smoke rings, recent discoveries have shown that they have far more complex structures that can tell us about the dying stars at their heart.

The term 'planetary nebula' was first coined by William Herschel, the discoverer of Uranus, in 1785, referring to a class of disc-shaped objects that resembled extremely faint versions of the gas giant planets. The first of these to be discovered, the Dumbbell Nebula in Vulpecula, was catalogued by the French comet hunter Charles Messier in 1764, and as Messier built up his catalogue of non-stellar objects, he added several more.

The true nature of planetary nebulae, however, was not established until 1864, when pioneering astrophotographer William Huggins (see page 26) obtained a spectrum of the Cat's Eye Nebula (NGC 6543), and found that it was characteristic of a glowing gas – largely dark, but with a few emission lines at specific wavelengths. The precise nature of these lines caused some confusion at first, since some could not be linked to the behaviour of known elements. At around the same time, helium had been newly discovered from studies of the Sun's spectrum, so astronomers naturally suspected the presence of another new element, which they named 'nebulium'.

However unlike helium, nebulium obstinately refused to be found on Earth, and in the 1920s, laboratory experiments revealed the truth: the puzzling lines are due to a range of energy transitions in common elements such as nitrogen and oxygen, which can only persist at very low-densities. Since they are impossible in normal conditions, they are known as forbidden lines.

OPPOSITE This Hubble Space Telescope image of the Cat's Eye Nebula shows a wide range of complex structures, from the orderly radiating pattern of its outer shells to the twisted bubbles of gas closer to the central star.

The presence of these lines confirms that planetary nebulae are extremely tenuous objects – their diffuse nature makes it very hard to measure their parallax, but based on the distance to a few nearby examples, they seem to be about a light year in diameter, and usually reveal an intensely hot star embedded at their centre. In 1922, Edwin Hubble showed that the apparent size of the nebula is related to the luminosity of the central star, and argued that the nebula's glow is produced as its gases absorb radiation from the central star and become energized at around 10,000°C (18,000°F).

Brief lives

Despite these breakthroughs, it was not until 1957 that Soviet astronomer Iosif Shklovsky deduced the role that planetary nebulae play in stellar evolution. By comparing their spectra with red giant and white dwarf stars, and measuring their rates of expansion and therefore their expected lifetimes, he concluded the nebulae mark an intermediate stage, in which an aging Sun-like star on the asymptotic giant branch (see page 319) becomes so unstable that it casts off its outer layers completely in a series of pulsations that reveal its hotter, inner layers. As the star's interior is exposed, the strength of its stellar winds increases and more and more material, including the shells in which the last of the star's fusion is taking place, is blown away into space until only the star's core remains as a hot, newly formed white dwarf.

BELOW This Hubble image peers into the heart of NGC 2818, a planetary nebula in the southern constellation of Pyxis. Colours in the image trace the presence of different elements – red indicates nitrogen, green represents hydrogen, and blue shows oxygen.

Because the appearance of a planetary nebula relies on a delicate balance between the density of material around the dying star and the intensity of radiation from the stellar core itself, nebulae are an extremely short-lived phase of stellar evolution, lasting perhaps just 10,000 years. This in turn explains why, despite being generated by common Sun-like stars, planetary nebulae are relatively rare – just 3,000 are known within the Milky Way.

Unexpected complexity

Since the 1990s, the study of planetary nebulae has been revolutionized by the observations of the Hubble Space Telescope. From its orbit high above the atmosphere, it has imaged dozens of nebulae, revealing hitherto unsuspected structures within and around them. Traditionally, planetary nebulae were viewed as roughly spherical smoke bubbles, appearing ring-like from Earth where we see through their thicker edges. Now, however, they have emerged as some of the most complex and beautiful structures in the galaxy. Many display bipolar outflow – 'butterfly wings' of gas emerging from the central star. In some cases, the effect can be startlingly geometric – the 'Red Rectangle' (HD 44179), for instance, displays two sets of nested triangles to either side of the central star, where we happen to see the conical outflows from side-on. In contrast, the Ring Nebula, once cited as the perfect example of a smoke bubble, is now thought to have a dense concentration of matter around its equator, and infrared images from the Spitzer Space Telescope have revealed complex outer clouds of expanding gas beyond the visible centre.

'Planetary nebulae mark an intermediate stage, in which an aging Sun-like star becomes so unstable that it casts off its outer layers completely in a series of pulsations that reveal its hotter, inner layers.'

Astronomers are still uncertain why the escaping material produces such complex patterns, and several different mechanisms are probably at work. In some cases, bipolar shapes may arise where escaping gas is constrained above the star's equator, either by a ring of denser, slower-moving material, or possibly by the presence of a close companion star in a binary system. Collisions between gas ejected at varying speeds and at different stages of the star's evolution can also help sculpt the nebula – for instance, observations made by the Chandra X-Ray Observatory in 2001 revealed an expanding bubble of hotter gas at the centre of the Cat's Eye Nebula, which creates the eye's central pupil as it collides with cooler and slower-moving material ejected in earlier phases. Infrared images obtained by the Spitzer Space Telescope in 2009, meanwhile, revealed the faint glow of shredded gas clouds far beyond the nebula's visible limits – the earliest material ejected from the star in its red giant phase. Finally, powerful magnetic fields may also play a role – in 2002 astronomers using the VLBA radio telescope array showed for the first time that highly evolved red giants have much more powerful magnetic fields than stars like the Sun, and in 2005, a team led by Stefan Jordan of the University of Heidelberg used the European Southern Observatory's Very Large Telescope to detect magnetism up to 1,000 times stronger than the Sun's in the central stars of complex planetary nebulae.

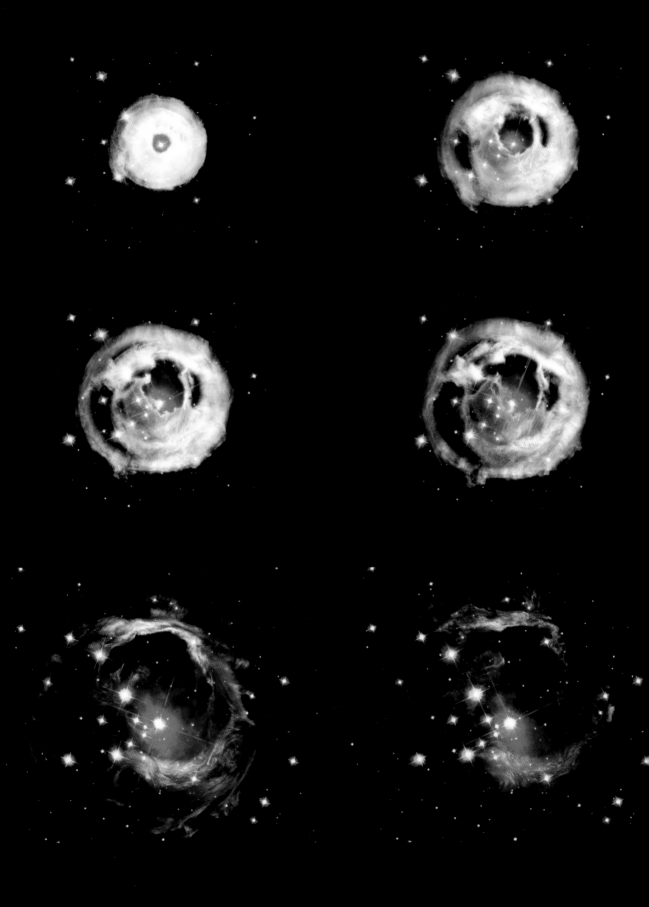

80 V838 Monocerotis

DEFINITION A STELLAR ERUPTION 20,000 LIGHT YEARS AWAY THAT
MAY HAVE BEEN TRIGGERED BY THE COLLISION OF TWO STARS.

DISCOVERY THE OUTBURST OF V838 MONOCEROTIS WAS SEEN
FROM EARTH IN 2002, AND ITS EXPANDING LIGHT ECHO HAS BEEN
TRACKED FOR MORE THAN A DECADE.

KEY BREAKTHROUGH IN 2005, ASTRONOMERS PRODUCED A DETAILED
ANALYSIS OF THE EXPLOSION'S PROGENITOR STAR.

IMPORTANCE V838 MONOCEROTIS REPRESENTS A NEW TYPE OF
MECHANISM TO CAUSE VIOLENT STELLAR EXPLOSIONS.

In 2002, astronomers identified what looked like a typical nova outburst in the constellation of the Unicorn. But as they have watched the explosion's beautiful aftermath develop over the past decade, they have also discovered that its cause could be something far rarer and more interesting.

The star now known as V838 Monocerotis was first observed on 6 January 2002, in a photograph taken by astronomer Nicholas Brown of Quinns Rocks, Western Australia. Identifying a faint new star shining where there had previously been none, Brown reported it as a likely nova – an explosion on the surface of a white dwarf star pulling material away from its companion in a binary system. The star grew brighter until early February and then began to fade away in visible light, but in March it began to brighten again in infrared wavelengths, remaining bright for a further two months before eventually subsiding back to its former obscurity. This unique behaviour marked V838 Mon out as something special, and astronomers scoured earlier images in search of information about the progenitor star.

Echoes of light

When the Hubble Space Telescope turned its gaze towards the star in May, however, it showed that the outburst was developing a remarkable afterlife. A bright cloudy halo now surrounded the central red star, which expanded rapidly into an increasingly complex series of more or less concentric rings over the following months. This strange phenomenon is known as a 'light echo' – while the rays of light that travelled directly from the original explosion towards Earth have long since faded away, the star happens to be surrounded by clouds of gas that reflect some of the explosion's light back towards Earth. The path taken by the reflected light is of course longer

OPPOSITE A sequence of Hubble Space Telescope images traces the evolving light echo from V838 Monocerotis between May 2002 and October 2004. V838 Mon itself is the red star at the centre of the eruption.

than that of light which came directly from the star, and so the further away from the star the reflecting material lies, the longer it takes to reach Earth. The result is rather like the lights of a train illuminating the sides of a dark tunnel, and creates an illusion of an object expanding faster than the speed of light. The light echo also offers a rare glimpse of normally invisible interstellar gas: astronomers are uncertain whether the gas creating the echoes is directly associated with the star itself – it could be material cast off in previous explosions, or it could be a remnant of the nebula from which V838 Mon was formed. Either possibility could have important implications for the nature of the eruption.

However, the light echoes are more than just a beautiful side effect of the explosion – they also offer astronomers an action replay of the brightening and fading involved in the explosion itself. For instance, the bluish outer edge of the echo seen in the first Hubble images reveals that the beginning of the explosion involved an intense outburst of short-wavelength light.

Redder than red

The progenitor of V838 Monocerotis was soon identified as an apparently unremarkable star around 20,000 light years from Earth, implying that, at its peak, the eruption shone with a million times the luminosity of the Sun. One of the strangest features of the outburst was that the star held itself together throughout. While most stellar explosions on this scale produce large shells of expanding debris, V838 Mon instead seems to have ballooned to enormous size, growing to roughly the diameter of Jupiter's orbit around the Sun. In a process similar to the growth of supergiant stars (though on a far shorter timescale), this led to an overall drop in the star's surface temperature, shifting its light towards a deep red L-type spectrum more commonly associated with feeble brown dwarf stars.

'A bright cloudy halo now surrounded the central red star, which expanded rapidly into an increasingly complex series of more or less concentric rings over the following months.'

In 2005, a team led by Romuald Tylenda of Poland's Nicolaus Copernicus Astronomical Centre published a detailed analysis of the progenitor star in which they concluded that it was an apparently normal B-type blue star with the mass of 5–10 Suns. Spectral analysis shows that it was just one element of a binary system, and that a near-twin blue star still orbits alongside the now-contracting progenitor.

Possible causes

So what could have caused this strange outburst? Various theories have been proposed, and some dismissed. For instance, it seems unlikely that the explosion really was some strange type of nova – the companion star of the V838 Mon system appears to be very young, and it's hard to see how a third star necessary for such an explosion could have evolved to become a white dwarf in the time available.

Another theory relies on disputed parallax measurements that put V838 Mon much further away (at roughly 36,000 light years) and therefore much brighter than is generally assumed. If this is indeed the case, then a team of astronomers led by Ulisse Munari of the Padua Observatory suggest that the explosion could have been a helium flash created as helium began to fuse into carbon in the core of a blue supergiant.

Perhaps the most intriguing suggestions, however, are those involving cosmic collisions. One idea, put forward by Tylenda and Noam Soker of the Israeli Institute of Technology, is that the explosion was a 'mergeburst', formed by the collision and merger of two stars. Computer simulations of such an event neatly describe various features including the multiple pulses in the original explosion, and the rapidly expanding envelope of the resulting merged star. A related idea, proposed by Alon Retter of Pennsylvania State University and others, is that the explosion was caused by nuclear fusion igniting in the outer layers of a star – an event triggered by the heating effect of a giant planet spiralling to its doom through the star's outer atmosphere.

ABOVE Hubble turned its gaze on V838 Monocerotis again in September 2006, uncovering yet more detail as the light echo illuminated new parts of the interstellar medium. The whorls and eddies clearly visible in this image are thought to be caused by magnetic fields flowing through space.

81 Eta Carinae

DEFINITION THIS GIANT STAR UNDERGOES PERIODIC OUTBURSTS AS IT EVOLVES TOWARDS A SUPERNOVA EXPLOSION.

DISCOVERY DURING AN OUTBURST IN 1843, ETA CARINAE ROSE TO BECOME THE SECOND BRIGHTEST STAR IN THE SKY.

KEY BREAKTHROUGH IN 2005, ASTRONOMERS CONFIRMED THAT ETA CARINAE IS ACTUALLY A BINARY SYSTEM.

IMPORTANCE ETA GIVES ASTRONOMERS A RARE CHANCE TO STUDY A STAR ON THE BRINK OF TURNING SUPERNOVA.

Embedded in the heart of the enormous Carina Nebula star-forming region lies the remarkable star Eta Carinae – a massive and unstable binary system that undergoes unpredictable outbursts as its stars hurtle towards their eventual destruction.

Although today it usually hovers around the limit of naked-eye visibility, Eta Carinae owes its fame to a brilliant eruption that saw it briefly become the second brightest star in the sky during 1843. With an estimated distance of 8,000 light years, the star's luminosity peaked at several million times that of the Sun, and ensured that the object has been closely studied ever since.

Early observations

Eta's variability was suspected from as early as 1677, when British astronomer Edmond Halley noted that the great Greek-Egyptian astronomer Ptolemy seemed to have 'missed' what Halley saw as a star of middling naked-eye brightness. Halley suspected this might be because the star had changed since Ptolemy's time. However, it was only in 1827 that English botanist and amateur astronomer W.J. Burchell concluded that the star was definitely changing its brightness. Then, during the 1820s and 1830s, John Herschel made frequent observations of the star's fluctuating brightness from the Cape of Good Hope in South Africa, until by 1843, the star reached its peak brightness. From then, Eta faded back to obscurity in the early 20th century, before increasing in brightness again around the turn of the millennium.

Eta lies in the midst of the Carina Nebula, NGC 3372 – a vast region of star-forming gas and dust around 400 light years across, and at the core of a

OPPOSITE This stunning view from the Curtis Schmidt Telescope at Chile's Cerro Tololo InterAmerican Observatory captures the full extent of the Carina Nebula. Eta Carinae is the bright star near the centre of the image, just to the right of the dark Keyhole Nebula.

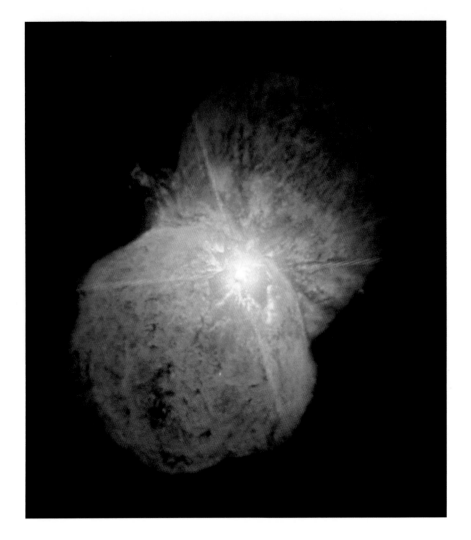

smaller, double-lobed cloud of material called the Homunculus Nebula. The
Homunculus has evolved rapidly since it was first observed in the mid-19th
century, and analysis of Doppler shifts in its spectrum has revealed that it
is expanding at a speed of roughly 2.4 million km/h (1.5 million miles per
hour). There seems little doubt that the double-lobed cloud was violently
ejected by Eta Carinae during its 1843 eruption.

Given its position near the centre of the Carina Nebula and its extreme
brilliance, astronomers generally concluded that Eta must be a young and
extremely massive star, of the type that age rapidly and die in supernova
explosions before they can move out of the nebulae that produced
them. Eta is evidently so massive that, even as it approaches the end of its
short life, its gravity has prevented it from swelling into a red supergiant
– instead its surface remains compact, and is heated by radiation escaping
the star to around 40,000°C (72,000°F). As a result of its instability, the star
is generally classed as a Luminous Blue Variable (LBV), and astronomers

suspected that it might be one of the most massive stars known, with a mass well in excess of 100 Suns. The explosion of 1843 was seen as a precursor to the star's eventual detonation in a spectacular supernova, and classed as a 'supernova impostor event'.

A complex system

However, recent developments have transformed our view of the Eta Carinae system. In 1996, astronomer Augusto Daminelli of the University of Sao Paolo, Brazil, reported his discovery of a 5.52-year cycle of changes in the spectrum of Eta and its surrounding nebulosity, which seems to be linked to the fluctuations in the star's overall brightness. This apparently reliable periodicity (albeit often complicated by larger-scale changes in the system's brightness), set a puzzle for astronomers. The spectral changes associated with them seemed like the result of a 'shell event', in which the star was casting off a huge spherical shell of material, but the precision of the cycle looked more like the work of two stars orbiting each other in an eclipsing binary system (see page 301). Perhaps the most telling clue was that, while Eta Carinae usually emits X-rays, they disappear for about three months of each cycle.

'Eta is evidently so massive that, even as it approaches the end of its short life, its gravity has prevented it from swelling into a red supergiant.'

In 2005, a team of astronomers using NASA's Far Ultraviolet Spectroscopic Explorer (FUSE) satellite confirmed the existence of a companion star around Eta for the first time. With a 5.5-year orbit, any companion star would orbit at roughly 10 astronomical units from the brighter component – making the system far too close to separate or resolve with current optical telescopes. But since the companion star was thought to be considerably hotter than Eta Carinae, the team led by Rosanna Iping of Washington's Catholic University of America reasoned that observations of the system at high-energy ultraviolet wavelengths would tend to dim the brightness of the more massive star, and amplify the brightness of the companion (which should pump out more ultraviolet radiation). They found that ultraviolet light associated with the companion star disappeared a couple of days before the onset of the 2003 'X-ray eclipse', confirming that it came from another object in the Eta Carinae system that is neither the main star, nor the X-ray source. This matched neatly with the proposed model of the system, in which the X-rays form at a 'hot spot' between the two stars, where their stellar winds collide and generate temperatures of millions of degrees.

Despite the fact that Eta turns out to be made of two stars rather than one, its bright primary is still thought to be a truly monstrous star, with the mass of more than 100 Suns alone. Its unstable outbursts cast off material that interacts with the complex stellar winds in ways that are still poorly understood, but astronomers remain certain that it is heading towards a spectacular death. Eta Carinae is still evolving towards a supernova explosion that will occur within the next million years, or possibly far sooner.

82

Supernovae

DEFINITION CATACLYSMIC EXPLOSIONS THAT MARK THE DEATH OF
STARS FAR MORE MASSIVE THAN THE SUN.

DISCOVERY RUDOLPH MINKOWSKI AND FRITZ ZWICKY IDENTIFIED
THE DIFFERENT TYPES OF SUPERNOVA EXPLOSION IN 1941.

KEY BREAKTHROUGH NEW COMPUTER SIMULATIONS HAVE REVEALED
PROBLEMS IN THE STANDARD MODEL OF TYPE II SUPERNOVAE.

IMPORTANCE SUPERNOVAE ARE SOME OF THE MOST VIOLENT EVENTS
IN THE UNIVERSE, PRODUCING AND DISTRIBUTING ALL OF THE
ELEMENTS HEAVIER THAN IRON.

Supernovae are the most spectacular of all cosmic events – enormous explosions that trigger huge amounts of nuclear fusion in a very short time. They mark the final end of the most massive stars, and can briefly outshine an entire galaxy as they seed the cosmos with heavy elements.

Astronomers classify supernovae in two main classes – Type I explosions (which involve the sudden collapse of a white dwarf into a neutron star – see page 315), and Type II supernovae, which involve the cataclysmic destruction of a supergiant star. The designations are purely coincidental and most supernovae are in fact of Type II form. Over the past few decades, these exploding stars have proved to be a remarkably fruitful target for astronomical research.

The supernova mechanism

As we've seen elsewhere (pages 82 and 318), stars with masses similar to the Sun pass through two phases of nuclear fusion, forcing hydrogen nuclei together to produce helium, and then fusing helium nuclei to create carbon, nitrogen and oxygen. Once the supplies of helium in their core are exhausted, they can never achieve the extreme conditions necessary to fuse the heavier elements, and so they are doomed to falter and die as planetary nebulae.

In contrast, a star with more than eight solar masses can carry things much further. As its helium-depleted core is compressed under the enormous weight of its outer layers, it becomes hot enough to begin fusion of the heavier elements to make still more complex ones such as neon, silicon and iron. As each new fusion process is exhausted, it moves out into its own shell around the core, until the star's central regions build up an onion-layer

OPPOSITE The Crab Nebula in Taurus is the expanding remnant of a supernova that was widely reported in AD 1055. Its shredded, asymmetric structure, revealed in this Hubble Space Telescope image, and the rapidly spinning pulsar lying at its heart both offer important clues to the nature of supernova explosions.

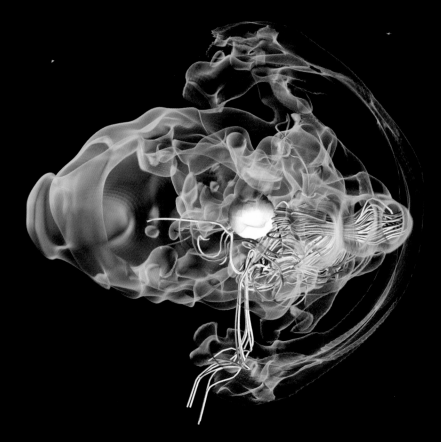

structure. However, this ability to keep shining for longer comes at a cost. Each new fusion reaction is less efficient than the previous one, and uses up its fuel more rapidly. The star becomes an unstable red supergiant as its interior becomes ever more complex and sensitive to minute changes in temperature and pressure.

Eventually, the star builds up a core of iron and, this time, there is nothing it can do to ward off the end. Fusion of iron to make heavier elements actually absorbs more energy than it creates, so when the star attempts this process, its power source – the only thing supporting the star's weight against gravity, abruptly cuts out. In a matter of seconds, the layers around the core collapse inwards at speeds that reach 70,000 km (44,000 miles) per second, compressing the core to a tiny size and raising its temperature enormously. During this process, electrons and protons within the core merge together in a process called electron capture, creating neutrons – subatomic particles that carry no electrical charge and are therefore no longer repelled from each other by the electromagnetic force. The core collapse is only brought to an end when the core reaches a diameter of around 30 km (19 miles) and a density roughly equivalent to an atomic nucleus, at which point the neutrons begin to repel each other thanks to the strong nuclear force (see page 35).

Core collapse problems

In the traditional model of the Type II supernova, the shock waves triggered by the sudden end of the core collapse were thought to tear apart the star's outer layers with tremendous force, raising their temperature to millions of degrees and providing enough energy to trigger a wave of nuclear fusion that consumed them. Because the vast majority of the star's outer envelope is still dominated by hydrogen and helium, the process is equivalent to burning off the energy of several Suns in a few days rather than billions of years. With so much energy around, the fusion process can also continue beyond the iron threshold, creating all the heavier elements familiar from our planet – everything from gold and platinum to radium and uranium.

But recent computer simulations such as those carried out at Oak Ridge National Laboratory in Tennessee, USA, suggest there is a problem with this model. While the external effects are clear and inarguable, the mechanism behind them seems to be far more complex. Using one of the world's most powerful supercomputers, the Oak Ridge scientists have shown that the energy of the expanding shock wave dissipates rapidly as it moves into the star's outer layers, and that most of it is lost in disintegrating heavy elements immediately around the core. As a result, a further huge injection of energy is required in order to produce the visible supernova explosion. Astronomers are turning to the strange properties of neutrinos, or possible heating effects associated with the collapse of the star's magnetic field (see pages 89 and 337) in an effort to solve the problem.

'The layers around the core collapse inwards at speeds that reach 70,000 km (44,000 miles) per second, compressing the core to a tiny size and raising its temperature enormously.'

Asymmetric explosions

Another problem with the standard model of supernovae lies in the pattern of debris they leave behind. The exploding star typically produces a rapidly expanding shell of shredded gas, enriched with heavy elements that are scattered across surrounding space. At the centre of this supernova remnant lie the remains of the star itself – the compressed stellar core or 'collapsar', transformed into a neutron star or black hole (see page 338). The problem is that the remnants are often asymmetrical in structure, and what is more, rather than remaining at the centre of the expanding remnant, the collapsar is often sent moving through space at high speed.

One possible explanation for this asymmetric behaviour is large-scale convection in the dying progenitor star. This might create variations in the local abundance of elements, resulting in uneven nuclear burning during the collapse, bounce and resulting explosion. Another possible explanation is that accretion of gas onto the forming neutron star creates a disc that drives highly directional jets, propelling matter at a high velocity out of the star, and helping to create the shock waves that disrupt its outer layers. This second theory is similar to that invoked to explain elusive bursts of gamma-rays linked to the most violent stellar explosions of all (see page 377).

83

Exotic stellar remnants

DEFINITION THE DENSE, COLLAPSED CORES OF BURNT-OUT STARS
THAT HAVE REACHED THE ENDS OF THEIR LIVES.

DISCOVERY THE STRANGE PROPERTIES OF WHITE DWARFS WERE
FIRST RECOGNIZED BY ASTRONOMERS AROUND 1910.

KEY BREAKTHROUGH IN 1967 ASTRONOMERS FOUND THE FIRST
NEUTRON STARS, AS BOTH PULSARS AND 'X-RAY BINARY' SYSTEMS.

IMPORTANCE NEUTRON STARS AND BLACK HOLES IN SYSTEMS
WITH OTHER STARS CAN CREATE SOME OF THE MOST VIOLENT
PHENOMENA IN THE UNIVERSE.

Throughout the 20th century, astronomers struggled to understand the strange objects that are left behind when stars die – white dwarfs, neutron stars and black holes. However, it now seems that there may be other types of extreme stellar remnants still awaiting discovery.

According to standard models of evolution, stars end their lives in three ways. Those with broadly Sun-like masses swell into red giants and shed their outer layers as planetary nebulae, leaving burnt-out, planet-sized remnants called white dwarfs. In contrast, a star with more than eight times the mass of the Sun detonates in a supernova explosion, leaving behind a city-sized neutron star or a black hole. However, new discoveries, coupled with improvements to our understanding of how particles interact at extreme densities, suggest that other types of 'exotic' stellar remnant may still await discovery.

The fate of Sun-like stars

The first white dwarf to be catalogued was 40 Eridani B, a dim member of a triple system discovered by William Herschel in 1783. Herschel had no way of knowing that this star was only 16.5 light years away, and it was only in 1910 that American astronomers Henry Norris Russell, Edward Charles Pickering and Williamina Fleming recognized its significance. According to accepted models of stellar evolution (see page 266), hot white stars should be very bright – in order to be faint yet white, a star must be very small indeed.

In 1915, American astronomer Walter Adams proved that Sirius B, the faint companion of the brightest star in the sky, was another white dwarf. From measurements of the pair's 50.1-year orbit, it was already clear that Sirius B had roughly the same mass as the Sun, so the star was clearly not only very

OPPOSITE In 2008, astronomers using the Very Large Telescope in Chile observed a series of flares from a young 'magnetar' – a recently formed neutron star with an intense magnetic field. These are the first visible-light flares seen from such an object, and may have been caused by a cloud of charged particles torn from the surface of the neutron star and sent spinning around in the magnetar's field.

small but also very dense. Further studies of white dwarf stars revealed that they typically contained roughly solar masses of material within volumes the size of Earth, and were rich in carbon, nitrogen and oxygen.

In 1926, English physicist R.H. Fowler used the newly discovered Pauli exclusion principle (see page 34), to show how tightly packed particles within the star create a 'degenerate electron pressure' that prevents it collapsing further under its own weight. This gives these remnants some strange properties – for instance, heavier white dwarfs are smaller and denser than those with less mass. It soon became clear that there must be an upper mass limit for a white dwarf, beyond which electron pressure could no longer support it against gravity. In 1931, Indian astrophysicist Subramanyan Chandrasekhar showed that this limit was roughly 1.4 solar masses.

Neutron stars and black holes

German and Swiss astronomers Walter Baade and Fritz Zwicky used the 1933 discovery of the neutron particle (see page 34) to describe the fate of stellar cores above the 'Chandrasekhar limit'. In such a situation, electrons and protons are forced together, combining to form a mass of neutrons that stabilizes, thanks to 'neutron degeneracy pressure', with a diameter of a few kilometres. Neutron stars are so small and faint that they can only be detected in special situations.

'Nothing can halt the collapse of the star's core, and it will dwindle to a singularity, a tiny point concentration of mass with enormously powerful gravity.'

In 1967, Cambridge radio astronomers Jocelyn Bell and Anthony Hewish discovered the first pulsar – a neutron star with a powerful magnetic field that channels its radiation into two rapidly spinning beams, which produce regular flashes if they happen to sweep across Earth. In the same year, Soviet astronomer Iosif Shklovsky suggested that the X-ray source Scorpius X-1 was produced by a neutron star drawing material from a binary companion to form an accretion disc in which matter is heated to millions of degrees. The vast majority of our knowledge of neutron stars comes from studying these pulsars and 'X-ray binaries', and it was not until the 1990s that a team led by Frederick M. Walter of the State University of New York used the ROSAT X-ray satellite and the Hubble Space Telescope to track down the first 'bare' neutron star. Astronomers are still uncertain of the exact conditions prevailing inside neutron stars but, as with white dwarfs, there appears to be an upper mass limit beyond which neutron degeneracy pressure can no longer support it. The exact value of this 'Tolman–Oppenheimer–Volkoff' (TOV) limit is not known, but is thought to be in the range of 1.5–3 solar masses.

What happens to a star whose mass is over the TOV limit? The most widely accepted view, put forward by American physicist J. Robert Oppenheimer in 1939, is that nothing else can halt the collapse of the star's core, and it will dwindle to a singularity, a tiny point concentration of mass with enormously powerful gravity. The singularity forms the core of a black hole, sealed off

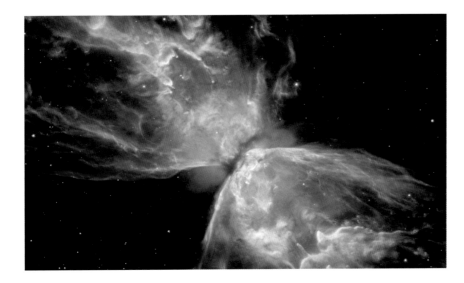

from the rest of the Universe by a boundary called the event horizon – the point at which the singularity's gravity becomes so strong that even light cannot escape. The possibility of black holes arises naturally from Einstein's theory of general relativity (see page 45), and was demonstrated by German physicist Karl Schwarzschild as early as 1916. However the name 'black hole' itself was only coined in the 1960s, and it was not until 1972 that a group led by American astronomer Charles Thomas Bolton identified the first possible candidate object within the X-ray binary system Cygnus X-1.

Strange intermediaries

Today, some astronomers and physicists believe there could be other stages between the TOV limit and singularity. Neutrons are known to be composed of quarks (see page 35), and so one possibility is that forces between the quarks create pressure that halts the collapse of a stellar core even after it has crossed the TOV threshold and its neutrons have disintegrated. Such theoretical bodies are known as quark stars or strange stars, and should be detectable as neutron stars that disobey the expected relationships between mass, diameter and temperature. A pulsar roughly 10,000 light years away in the constellation of Cassiopeia, named 3C 58, is one possible quark star, and some astronomers have argued that certain unusually brilliant supernova explosions in distant galaxies could be linked to their formation.

Stellar remnants even denser than quark stars become ever more hypothetical, since they rely on interactions and forms of matter that are themselves still only theoretical. 'Electroweak stars' may be apple-sized remnants that avoid collapse into a singularity by releasing radiation in a process called 'electroweak burning'. Preon stars, meanwhile, are made entirely from preons (hypothetical subunits of quarks and lepton particles). Whether such strange stellar corpses could ever be produced by the death of an actual star, however, is still open to question.

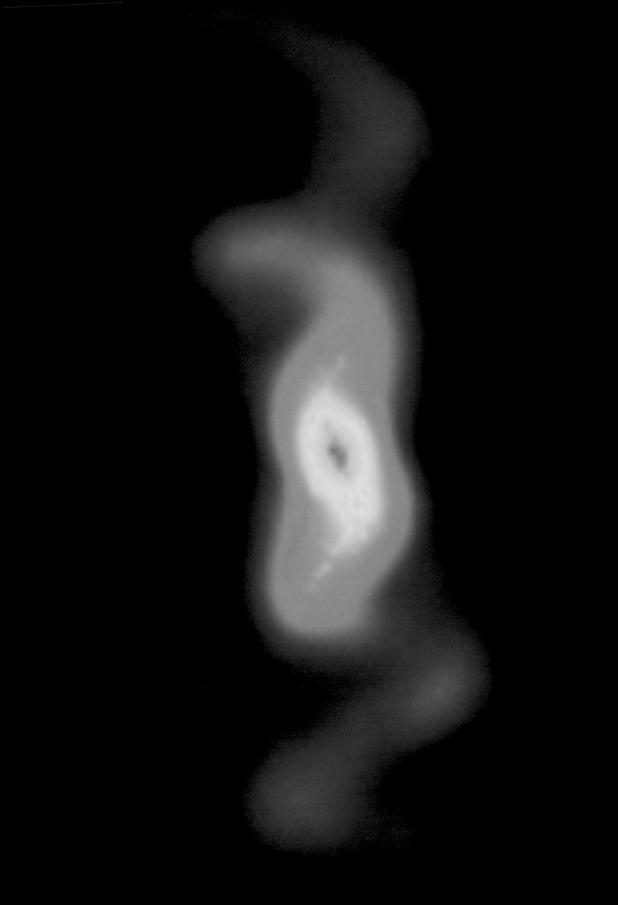

84

SS 433

DEFINITION A STRANGE STAR SYSTEM THAT APPEARS TO BE A MINIATURE VERSION OF A QUASAR.

DISCOVERY SS 433 WAS FIRST RECOGNIZED IN A STAR SURVEY OF 1977, AND INDEPENDENTLY DISCOVERED AS AN X-RAY AND RADIO OBJECT.

KEY BREAKTHROUGH IN 1979, TWO TEAMS OF ASTRONOMERS SHOWED HOW HIGH-SPEED JETS COULD EXPLAIN SS 433'S MOST PECULIAR FEATURES.

IMPORTANCE SS 433 GIVES ASTRONOMERS A RARE CHANCE TO STUDY A QUASAR-LIKE SYSTEM IN NEARBY SPACE.

The object known as SS 433 lies some 18,000 light years across the Milky Way and is one of the strangest star systems known. Its behaviour mimics those of far larger active galaxies and, for a while, astronomers were puzzled by its apparent ability to generate jets moving faster than the speed of light.

SS 433 takes its name from its entry in a 1977 catalogue of stars displaying strong emission lines in their spectra, drawn up by astronomers Nicholas Sanduleak and C. Bruce Stephenson of Case Western University. Sources of X-rays and radio waves had been identified from the same location in the sky in the previous two years, but it was not until 1978 that several groups of astronomers realized that the visible, X-ray and radio emissions were all coming from the same object. This intriguing discovery triggered a veritable avalanche of research into SS 433, with more than 200 separate scientific papers published in the five years after its discovery.

'Enigma of the century'

The features that had first attracted the attention of Sanduleak and Stephenson were strong, broad emission lines around specific wavelengths associated with hydrogen and helium, but there were also emissions that could not be linked to any known process or element. It eventually became clear that these mysterious emissions were in fact replicas of the hydrogen and helium lines in two sets – one showing a strong redshift (indicating rapid motion away from Earth), and another showing strong blue shift (swift movement towards Earth). The blue-shifted lines suggested the object was moving towards us at an appreciable fraction of the speed of light, while the redshift suggested it was moving away from us at roughly the same speed. What was more, the strength of the blue and redshifts varied in a

OPPOSITE This radio image of SS 433 as seen by the Very Large Array in New Mexico, clearly shows the corkscrew-paths followed by particles emerging from the central object.

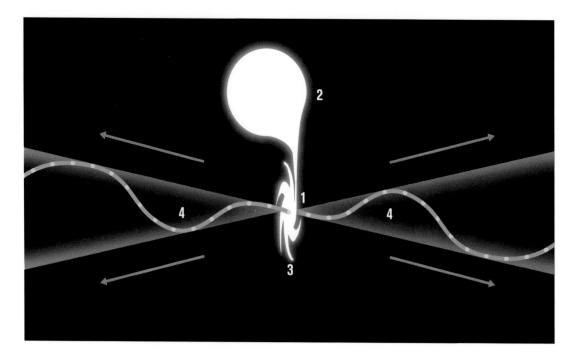

164-day cycle, while their average velocity remained a constant 12,000 km/s (7,500 miles per second) away from Earth. Measurement of the central set of relatively unshifted lines, meanwhile, showed that *their* source was moving at around 70 km/s (43 miles per second).

In 1979, British astronomers Andrew Fabian and Martin Rees, and Mordehai Milgrom of Israel, independently put forward models in which the shifted lines were the result of narrow jets emerging from the poles of an object tilted so that the jet axis rotated or 'precessed' slowly with respect to Earth. Americans George Abell and Bruce Margon developed this idea further, and were able to predict the shifts in the emission lines. According to their model, the jet's rotation inscribes the shape of a cone some 40 degrees wide, lying almost side-on to Earth with a central axis at an angle of 79 degrees. Material in the jets moves at 26 percent of the speed of light or 78,000 km/s (48,500 miles per second), and the change in its direction around the cone causes its speed to vary as seen from Earth. Perhaps the most remarkable aspect of the jet is that its relativistic motion creates a time-dilation effect (see page 43). Radiation from the jets is produced by vibrations in their atoms, so when time dilation cause them to vibrate more slowly, they produce longer wavelengths. It is this redshifting of light that was interpreted as the system's average motion of 12,000 km/s (7,500 miles per second) away from Earth.

Invisible evidence
Radio maps of SS 433 produced with the Very Large Array (VLA) at Socorro, New Mexico, confirmed the accuracy of this model by discovering the enormous corkscrew-like structure of radio-emission created as the

slowly spiralling jets sculpt a surrounding cloud of gas catalogued as radio source W50. However X-ray observations complicated matters still further. The object seemed to generate X-rays from two separate sources – a more or less constant source of soft (relatively low-energy) X-rays that wobbles or precesses with the radio jet, and another source of high-energy hard X-rays that disappear for roughly two days in every thirteen. Astronomers rapidly concluded that this central object was an X-ray binary – an extremely hot accretion disc surrounding a superdense object, which is regularly eclipsed by a nearby companion star. But what exactly is the object at the heart of SS 433? Astronomers believe that the answer lies with W50, the cloud of hot gas that surrounds the system: it appears to be an unusual supernova remnant, and has an estimated age of 10,000 years. This suggests that the object at the heart of the accretion disc is either a neutron star or a black hole.

'The blue-shifted lines suggested the object was moving towards us at an appreciable fraction of the speed of light, while the redshift suggested it was moving away from us at roughly the same speed.'

Putting it all together

According to the widely accepted 'standard model' of SS 433, the system started out as a tightly bound binary in which one star (the primary), was significantly heavier than the other. The more massive star destroyed itself in the supernova that created W50 while the companion or secondary star remains in relatively sedate middle age. Despite the havoc wreaked by the supernova explosion, the two stars remain in close orbit and exert a powerful influence on each other. Most importantly, the outer layers of the companion star fall within the supernova remnant's 'Roche lobe', a region where the remnant's gravity overcomes the companion's own, and material is siphoned out of the star's atmosphere. As this hot stolen gas spirals down towards the remnant, it forms a superhot accretion disc that generates powerful X-rays. Some of the material in the disc is accelerated to high speeds (perhaps by magnetic fields – see page 337), and escapes along the tightly aligned jets. Meanwhile, the companion star's own gravitational influence tugs on the disc and causes its periodic precession. Thanks to its similarity to the much larger and more powerful cores of active galaxies, SS 433 is often considered as the prototype for a class of objects called 'microquasars'.

Although this general model of SS 433 has stood the test of some two decades of research, there are still many unanswered questions about this intriguing object. In 2004, radio astronomers using the VLA discovered that the speed of the jets is not as constant as previously thought, but instead varies between 24 and 28 percent of the speed of light – and that these changes affect both jets at precisely the same time. What's more, attempts to weigh the system have produced widely different results, suggesting either a fairly average A-type companion star orbiting a neutron star primary, or an enormous white supergiant circling a truly massive black hole. The so-called 'enigma of the century' has not yet surrendered all of its secrets.

The shape of our galaxy

85

DEFINITION NEW COMPLEXITIES THAT HAVE RECENTLY BEEN FOUND WITHIN OUR GALAXY'S BASIC SPIRAL STRUCTURE.

DISCOVERY THE SPIRAL STRUCTURE OF THE MILKY WAY WAS CONFIRMED USING RADIO OBSERVATIONS IN THE 1950s.

KEY BREAKTHROUGH THE PRESENCE OF A LONG BAR OF STARS AT THE CENTRE OF OUR GALAXY WAS CONFIRMED IN 2005.

IMPORTANCE UNDERSTANDING THE STRUCTURE OF THE MILKY WAY HELPS US TO UNDERSTAND PROCESSES THAT AFFECT RATES OF STAR FORMATION.

Astronomers have attempted to measure the Milky Way since the 18th century. But, even today, our huge star system holds many surprises, and the galaxy we know today is very different from the one we imagined just a decade ago.

The first attempts to map the shape of our galaxy and identify the Sun's location within it were made by German-born British astronomers William and Caroline Herschel around 1785. Working on the assumption that all stars had roughly the same luminosity, they mapped the stellar populations of almost 700 areas of the sky, ending up with a chart of an amorphous blob, somewhat wider than it was deep, with the Sun somewhere near the centre.

Scaling the Milky Way

More than a century later in 1906, Dutch astronomer Jacobus Kapteyn tried again, co-ordinating an international project between 40 observatories that once again relied on the principle of 'star counts'. The end result was a similar, if somewhat flatter, galaxy, with a diameter of about 40,000 light years and again with the Sun at the centre.

It took the insight of American astronomer Harlow Shapley to put our place in the Milky Way into perspective. Studying the distribution of globular star clusters that orbit mostly above and below the plane of the Milky Way, he discovered around 1921 that they were concentrated around a distant region in the constellation Sagittarius, and realized that this was likely to be the true centre of the galaxy, with our own solar system on the outskirts. However, Shapley's estimates of the distance to globular clusters ultimately proved to

OPPOSITE Galaxy NGC 6744 in the southern constellation of Pavo is thought to be a near-twin of our own Milky Way galaxy, with two dominant spiral arms and a short bar extending from its nucleus. One major difference, however, is that the visible diameter of NGC 6744 is roughly twice that of the Milky Way.

be far too large – they led him to believe the galaxy's total diameter was some 300,000 light years, and ultimately put him on the wrong side of the 'Great Debate' about galaxies beyond the Milky Way.

In 1927, Dutch astronomer Jan Oort made another crucial discovery – different regions of the galaxy rotate at different speeds as they orbit the central hub (the Sun, for instance, orbits every 250 million years) This 'differential rotation', due to the Kepler's laws of motion (see page 14), allowed Oort to make greatly improved estimates of the scale of the Milky Way. His measurements put our galaxy's diameter at about 80,000 light years with the Sun roughly 19,000 light years from the centre (the widely accepted modern figures are 100,000 and 26,000 light years respectively).

Mapping the spiral arms

While the debate about the size of our galaxy continued, its structure remained unresolved. Evidence pointed to a disc-like distribution of stars, but suggestions that it might be a spiral relied mostly on comparison with other galaxies. A possible link with the newly discovered 'spiral nebulae' was proposed by American astronomer Stephen Alexander as early as 1852, but it was only in the 1920s, after Edwin Hubble proved these objects were distant star systems far beyond the Milky Way, that the idea gained momentum.

The first real signs of spiral structure were discovered in 1951 by William W. Morgan of Yerkes Observatory, Wisconsin. Morgan mapped the distribution of the bright open clusters that tend to define the spiral structure in other galaxies (see page 366), and identified three distinct chains that he interpreted as fragments of major arms. Later in the 1950s, Jan Oort and others used the new generation of giant radio telescopes to chart the locations of neutral hydrogen gas clouds. These could be detected even behind intervening clouds of stars and interstellar dust, across much greater distances than Morgan's bright cluster stars – they allowed Oort to confirm that the traces of structure in our own region of the galaxy in fact extended all the way across its disc.

Based on radio observations since the 1950s, along with studies of other galaxies, astronomers have generally assumed there are four major spiral arms – the Perseus Arm, Norma/Outer Arm, Scutum-Centaurus Arm and Carina-Sagittarius Arm – and several smaller structures or spurs between them, one of which, the Orion-Cygnus arm, lies close to our own solar system. However new infrared mapping by the Spitzer Space Telescope suggests that our galaxy has just two major arms, with the other two relegated to the status of minor spurs.

New discoveries

The presence of two major arms makes sense in the context of another recent discovery: it has become clear that our galaxy is in fact a barred spiral, and galaxies with elongated bars emerging from their cores often show just two major arms. The first evidence for a central bar of stars came from radio observations in the 1980s, and was bolstered by maps of star formation made using the Compton Gamma-Ray Observatory in the 1990s. But it was only in 2005 that Spitzer observations allowed a team led by Ed Churchwell and Robert Benjamin of the University of Wisconsin to confirm the bar's presence by mapping the distribution of cool red giant stars within it. These new studies also revealed the bar's surprising scale – with a length of 28,000 light years it is fully one quarter of our galaxy's entire diameter.

'The outer region of the galactic disc appears to be buckled or warped, with its outer edge lying up to 7,500 light years out of the main plane of the galaxy.'

Meanwhile, other new discoveries are changing how we measure the size of the Milky Way once again. The orbital speeds of the outermost stars betray the presence of large amounts of 'dark matter' in and around our galaxy (see page 397), but for several decades astronomers have also been aware of atomic hydrogen clouds extending to around 75,000 light years from the galactic centre. What is more, this outer region of the galactic disc appears to be distinctly warped, with its outer edge some 7,500 light years out of the main plane of the galaxy. Seen edge-on, our galaxy may appear somewhat similar to ESO 510-G13, a spiral galaxy in the constellation of Hydra. The origins of the Milky Way's warp have long puzzled astronomers, but in 2006 a team led by Leo Blitz of the University of California at Berkeley showed that it could be caused by the gravity from a dark-matter 'wake' pulled behind our galaxy's largest satellites, the Magellanic Clouds. According to this model, the warp is a dynamic, rotating structure that ripples around the Milky Way – amazingly, it seems that our galaxy is vibrating like an enormous gong.

86 The Milky Way's central black hole

DEFINITION THE SUPERMASSIVE BLACK HOLE THAT LIES AT THE CENTRE OF OUR GALAXY.

DISCOVERY THE CORE OF THE MILKY WAY WAS FIRST MAPPED WITH RADIO WAVES IN THE 1970s.

KEY BREAKTHROUGH IN 2002, ASTRONOMERS CONFIRMED THE BLACK HOLE'S PRESENCE FROM THE ORBITS OF NEARBY STARS.

IMPORTANCE THE EXISTENCE OF SUPERMASSIVE BLACK HOLES AT THE HEART OF MANY GALAXIES ANSWERS MANY QUESTIONS ABOUT THEIR ORIGINS, BUT RAISES OTHERS.

A slumbering giant lies at the heart of our galaxy, in the form of a supermassive black hole with the mass of several million Suns, embedded in a violent region of huge gas clouds, supermassive stars, and antimatter outbursts.

The nature of the centre of our galaxy has been a long-standing puzzle for astronomers. Lying some 26,000 light years away in the direction of the constellation Sagittarius, it is hidden from our direct view in either visible or infrared light by dense star clouds and interstellar dust in the intervening spiral arms, and billions of old red and yellow stars in the region of the galactic hub. Ultimately it is the gravity of all these stars that holds our galaxy together, but what keeps the hub itself intact? It is only since the 1990s that astronomers have begun to understand the strange objects and violent processes at work around the galactic centre.

Astronomers have suspected for some time that our galaxy and others are anchored at their centres by enormous concentrations of matter. Stars in the hub follow far less orderly orbits than those of the galactic disc, on elliptical paths that are tilted at extreme angles to the plane of the galaxy. The cumulative effect of the overlapping orbits makes the hub resemble a flattened ball, but amid this apparent chaos, the orbits all seem to focus around a relatively small region at the centre of the hub.

Mapping the core
The first attempts to probe this region with radio waves during 1974 resulted in the discovery of a group of radio sources collectively known as Sagittarius A. Sagittarius A East is a bubble of hot gas that is probably an expanding

OPPOSITE This Chandra X-ray Observatory image shows the turbulent region surrounding the central black hole at the heart of our galaxy. X-rays are colour-coded according to their energy, with red the weakest and blue the most powerful. The black hole itself lies near the top of the bright central region, surrounded by a cloud of hot gas emitted by nearby monster stars.

supernova remnant, while Sagittarius A West is a remarkable three-armed spiral of gas falling towards the galactic centre, sculpted by radiation from two dense clusters of giant stars. These clusters, known as the Arches and the Quintuplet contain some of the most massive stars known: they are thought to have formed in relatively brief 'starbursts' triggered by the large-scale compression of gas in the unique conditions just 100 light years from the galactic centre.

Embedded in the midst of Sagittarius A East, meanwhile, lies a third, compact radio source, called Sagittarius A*. Lying within another massive star cluster, it seems to mark the precise location of the galaxy's heart – and the supermassive black hole that lies at the very centre of the Milky Way.

Invisible heart

The presence of superdense massive objects at the core of so-called active galaxies was suspected as early as the 1950s (see page 369), but astronomers only linked them to black holes in the 1970s. Even then, many expressed doubts about the mechanism by which a black hole could grow to such enormous size. It was only in the 1980s, when detailed measurements of stellar orbits close to the centre of our galaxy confirmed the compact nature

RIGHT This map of the central Milky Way plots the motion of several bright stars over the period 1995–2008. Trails indicate the paths of stars orbiting an invisible but extremely massive object, while the background image shows the positions of the stars as seen in a single observation.

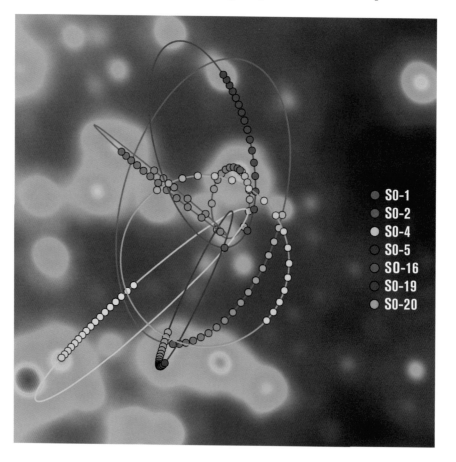

- S0-1
- S0-2
- S0-4
- S0-5
- S0-16
- S0-19
- S0-20

of its core, that astronomers began to speculate about the existence of a similar monster in the centre of the Milky Way.

Strong evidence that Sagittarius A* was in fact an enormous black hole came in 1998, when Andrea Ghez of the University of California at Los Angeles used the giant Keck Telescopes on Mauna Kea in Hawaii to observe fast-moving stars very close to the galactic centre. Using new techniques to resolve the closely packed stars and measure their movements, she identified individual objects moving at up to 12,000 km/s (7,500 miles per second) in orbit around an unseen central object. Calculations revealed that the object had a mass of at least 3.7 million Suns, concentrated into a region just a few light days across.

In 2002, the case for a black hole was clinched by similar measurements carried out using the Very Large Telescope in Chile. An international team led by Rainer Schödel of Germany's Max Planck Institute for Extraterrestrial Physics identified a star called S2 following a 15-year orbit that brings it within 17 light hours or 120 astronomical units of the central object itself. Further observations of stellar motions in the decade since have helped constrain the black hole's mass to 4.31 ± 0.38 million solar masses.

'The monster that once fed voraciously on stars and gas that came within its grasp has cleared out the region of space directly around it, and now feeds only on the slower-moving particles from the stellar winds of nearby stars.'

Sleeping giant

The presence of a supermassive black hole at the heart of the Milky Way raises an obvious question – why isn't the centre of our galaxy ablaze with radiation like the cores of active galaxies? The most likely explanation is that activity is simply a phase all galaxies go through early in their lives – and one which our galaxy has outgrown. The monster that once fed voraciously on stars and gas that came within its grasp has cleared out the region of space directly around it, and now feeds only on the slower-moving particles from the stellar winds of nearby stars. A 2009 study by scientists from Harvard and the Massachusetts Institute of Technology showed that the black hole consumes even less than previously thought, suggesting that it is shielded by a barrier of hot, fast-moving particles that keep most of the stellar wind out.

But there is evidence that the black hole is still subject to occasional outbursts. An antimatter 'fountain' above the galactic centre, discovered by the Compton Gamma-Ray Observatory in 1997 (see page 67) was initially attributed to past activity by the black hole, but is now thought to be created by violent stellar remnants in the neighbourhood. However in 2007 scientists using NASA's Chandra X-ray Observatory detected a rapidly evolving X-ray source close to Sgr A*. This source is believed to be the reflection or light echo (see page 325) from a brief flare of X-rays released 50 years earlier, when the black hole swallowed up a cloud of gas with roughly the mass of the planet Mercury. It's impossible to predict when this sleeping giant may next stir in its slumber.

Our nearest galactic neighbours

DEFINITION NEARBY SMALL GALAXIES THAT ARE CURRENTLY BEING ABSORBED INTO THE MILKY WAY.

DISCOVERY THE SAGITTARIUS DWARF ELLIPTICAL GALAXY WAS IDENTIFIED FROM ANOMALOUS DISTRIBUTION OF STARS IN 1994.

KEY BREAKTHROUGH IN 2003, SCIENTISTS USED INFRARED SURVEY DATA TO TRACK STARS BEING TORN AWAY FROM THE GALAXY.

IMPORTANCE SMALL GALAXIES LIKE SAGDEG AND THE CANIS MAJOR DWARF PLAY A SIGNIFICANT ROLE IN THE DEVELOPMENT OF LARGER GALAXIES SUCH AS OUR OWN.

Since the 1990s, astronomers have discovered two new dwarf galaxies orbiting the Milky Way, along with plentiful evidence that our galaxy has cannibalized its smaller neighbours in the past, and will do so again in the future.

In 1994, while carrying out a survey of stars on the far side of our galaxy's central hub in the direction of Sagittarius, astronomers Rodrigo Ibata, Gerard Gilmore and Michael Irwin from Cambridge's Institute of Astronomy and Royal Greenwich Observatory discovered an unusual concentration of stars, all of which were moving in a direction quite different from that which was expected. The only explanation for this startling discovery was that the stars belonged to another independent galaxy, lying just above the plane of the Milky Way on the far side of the galactic hub, about 80,000 light years from Earth. What's more, this galaxy, named the Sagittarius Dwarf Elliptical Galaxy or SagDEG, is in the process of colliding with our own.

A galaxy on our doorstep

At the time of its discovery, SagDEG was by far the closest satellite galaxy to the Milky Way. As its name suggests, it was classified as an elliptical (or spheroidal) galaxy on account of its apparently ancient stars and lack of star-forming gas and dust (see page 367), but its shape has been stretched beyond recognition by the Milky Way's powerful gravity. Further studies identified four globular star clusters associated with the galaxy's loose star clouds, the brightest of which, Messier 54 (known to astronomers since 1778), is now thought to mark the surviving core of the galaxy, and more recent work suggests that another globular, Palomar 12, started out as a component of SagDEG before being captured into orbit around the Milky Way.

OPPOSITE A computer model produced by astronomers at the University of California Irvine shows the interaction between the Milky Way and the SagDEG galaxy. According to this simulation, SagDEG's influence over the past 2 billion years may have given rise to our own galaxy's spiral arms.

At first, astronomers assumed that such a small and apparently empty galaxy could not survive for long in orbit around the Milky Way without being destroyed completely, and that SagDEG must therefore be a relatively new arrival in our galactic neighbourhood. But a 2001 study of ancient carbon-rich stars in our galaxy's halo suggested they had originated in SagDEG but had been commandeered by the Milky Way billions of years ago. It seems that the two galaxies have been associated with each other for much of their history, and that SagDEG may have completed at least ten billion-year orbits of the Milky Way. So how has this small galaxy managed to stay together for so long? The general assumption is that it must be much heavier than the sum of its visible stars – in other words, it is very rich in undetectable dark matter (see page 397). This may also explain why the seemingly feeble SagDEG is apparently affecting the shape of our own, far more massive galaxy (see page 345).

'The stars belonged to another independent galaxy, lying about 80,000 light years from Earth. What's more, this galaxy is in the process of colliding with our own.'

In 2003, a team led by Steve Majewski of the University of Virginia used data from the infrared 2-Micron All-Sky Survey (2MASS) to chart the stream of cannibalized stars torn away from SagDEG by the Milky Way, but still following it around its orbit. They discovered that the stream passes through the near side of our galaxy very close to our own current location, and that SagDEG itself has therefore passed close to the Sun in the last half-billion years or so. An interesting side-effect of the work carried out by Majewski's group was to demonstrate that our own galaxy's dark matter is distributed in a spherical halo – other distributions would have caused far greater disruption to the stream of stars from SagDEG.

One other intriguing feature of SagDEG is worth mentioning – in 2001 Patrick Cseresnjes of New York's Columbia University found a remarkable similarity between the galaxy's stars and those of the more distant Large Magellanic Cloud. It seems the two galaxies may share an origin as fragments of a larger original, although the dynamics involved in tearing such a system apart and producing the current configuration of galaxies are still uncertain.

The Canis Major Dwarf

In 2003, an even closer satellite galaxy came to light in the constellation of Canis Major. This time, an international team of astronomers from France, Italy, the UK and Australia were investigating an unusual feature in the galactic halo known as the Monoceros Ring. This stream of stars, with the mass of 100 million Suns and a total length of roughly 200,000 light years, loops its way around our galaxy three times, passing through a closely spaced group of globular clusters just to the south of Canis Major itself. While studying 2MASS data for this area of the sky, the team found a surprising excess of 'M-class' red giants, roughly 42,000 light years from the galactic centre and only 25,000 light years from our own solar system. The new system was named the Canis Major Dwarf Galaxy, and it appears to

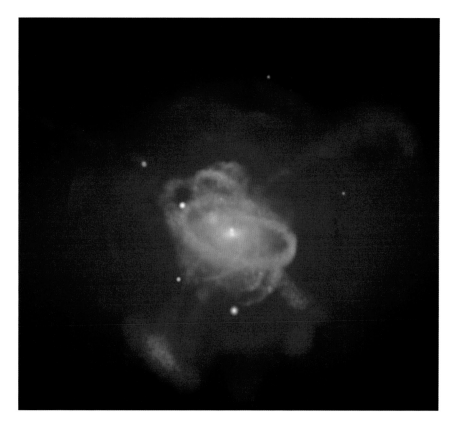

be a dwarf elliptical with about the same number of stars as SagDEG. The original team also identified streams of stars linked to the central galaxy, showing that it, too, is being torn apart by the Milky Way's tidal forces.

So far, the Canis Major Dwarf has not been studied as closely as SagDEG, but some differences have already become clear. For one thing, the closer galaxy is far more degraded than its companion, and has clearly been fragmented and all-but-absorbed by the Milky Way over the course of several recent orbits. For another, the new discovery seems to contain at least some star-forming material, since several small open clusters of relatively young stars can be linked to it. Such new star formation ties neatly to the 'starbursts' we see in the wider Universe when gas-rich galaxies interact (see page 382).

However, some astronomers have cast doubt on the new galaxy's very existence. A 2006 study led by astronomers at the University of Padua looked again at the 2MASS data for the Monoceros Ring and the unusual concentration of stars in Canis Major, and suggested that they are in fact results of our galaxy's warped disc rather than any external cause (ironically linking their origin back to SagDEG). In response, a 2007 survey with the Anglo-Australian Telescope's wide-field camera identified new structures in the Ring that cannot be explained by the 'warped disc' model, throwing the spotlight back onto an extragalactic origin.

88 Supernova 1987A

DEFINITION THE MOST RECENT SUPERNOVA EXPLOSION IN OUR COSMIC NEIGHBOURHOOD, IN THE LARGE MAGELLANIC CLOUD.

DISCOVERY THE SUPERNOVA WAS SPOTTED IN FEBRUARY 1987 AND TOOK THREE MONTHS TO REACH ITS PEAK BRIGHTNESS.

KEY BREAKTHROUGH IN 2010, EUROPEAN SOUTHERN OBSERVATORY ASTRONOMERS MAPPED THE EXPANDING SUPERNOVA REMNANT IN THREE DIMENSIONS FOR THE FIRST TIME.

IMPORTANCE THE STRANGE BEHAVIOUR OF SUPERNOVA 1987A HAS FORCED ASTRONOMERS TO RETHINK MANY LONG-HELD THEORIES.

The closest supernova explosion to Earth for more than three centuries was seen in the Large Magellanic Cloud during 1987. In the decades since, astronomers have continued to study this cosmic eruption, and it has changed their understanding of supernovae forever.

One abiding frustration for astronomers is that some of the most interesting events in the Universe, such as the spectacular explosions of supernovae, are so rare. Although according to estimates supernovae should occur in the Milky Way at a rate of roughly one per century, none has been seen in our galaxy since the invention of the telescope, more than four centuries ago (and the only one that we know to have occurred in this period was blocked from view by clouds of obscuring dust). However in February 1987, astronomers got the next best thing – a supernova on our galactic doorstep, roughly 168,000 light years away in the Large Magellanic Cloud.

Supernova 1987A, as it became known, marked the sudden death of a massive star (see page 333), and was so bright that it became obvious to observers just hours after the events that triggered it. This gave scientists a unique opportunity to study it from its earliest stages.

Tracking the outburst

The explosion was first noticed by two astronomers working at Las Campanas Observatory in the Chilean Andes. University of Toronto researcher Ian Shelton spotted the bright new star while developing a photographic plate from a long-exposure image of the LMC taken on the evening of 23 February, while telescope operator Oscar Duhalde identified the supernova visually at around the same time. On the same evening

OPPOSITE This 1999 Hubble Space Telescope view covers an area of the Large Magellanic Cloud roughly 130 light years across. The expanding double-lobed remnant of SN1987A can be clearly seen, embedded in the outskirts of the Tarantula Nebula.

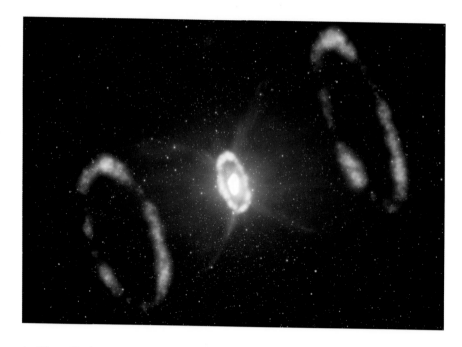

in New Zealand, amateur astronomer Albert Jones spotted the supernova and kept it under observation for several hours. By the following day, observatories around the world had been alerted, and both professional scientists and amateur stargazers subjected the exploding star to unprecedented scrutiny.

One important question was exactly when the explosion had begun. About 15 hours before its light was first observed, neutrino detectors in Japan, Russia and Italy (see page 90) detected bursts of these elusive particles, released in the instant that the star's core collapsed, from the direction of the LMC. When they sifted through other observations, astronomers found that the supernova began to brighten two hours after the neutrino burst. Once the supernova's progenitor star (known only by the clumsy catalogue name of Sanduleak −69° 202) was identified, it became clear that the star increased its light output by a factor of 600 in its first 13 hours.

But from the outset, SN1987A proved to be an awkward fit for astronomers' models of how supernovae should behave. The most obvious anomaly was that, while typical 'Type II' supernovae (see page 333) brighten rapidly to a maximum before slowly declining, SN1987A's energy output dipped in late February, before climbing again to a maximum of magnitude 2.9 (about 4,500 times brighter than the progenitor star) in late May, and then slowly fading over the next 18 months. Astronomers monitoring the supernova's rise and decline concluded that, while the energy released in the original collapse had begun to fade by late March, it was supplemented by a secondary power source – the decay of radioactive cobalt that had itself been generated in the firestorm of nuclear fission associated with the initial outburst.

Puzzling origins

But in that case, why did SN1987A produce more cobalt than a normal supernova? One clue to this lay in the nature of Sanduleak –69° 202. When astronomers searched their records to identify the progenitor star, they were surprised to find a blue supergiant occupying the spot – theory said that all Type II supernovae were caused by the deaths of much larger and more luminous red supergiants. But although it caused problems for theoretical models, the progenitor's unusual nature explained a few things – with its smaller size and mass of roughly 18 Suns, it would be much denser than a red supergiant, and would release far less energy during its collapse. This explained why SN1987A was roughly ten times fainter at its peak than a typical Type II supernova, and also offers a possible reason for the strange behaviour of its 'light curve' – the cobalt-related energy 'spike' is probably present in other supernovae, but is normally 'swamped' by their much greater overall brightness.

Nevertheless, the precise process that drove a blue supergiant to turn supernova without first swelling into a red supergiant remains unresolved. In a 1989 review, W. David Arnett of the University of Arizona and others proposed that it could be related to the progenitor's unusually low complement of heavy elements, while in 1992, Philipp Podsiadlowski of Oxford University pointed to evidence that Sanduleak –69° 202 could have collided with, and absorbed, another, smaller star prior to the explosion, perhaps creating a fatal instability (see also page 327). A third possibility (not necessarily excluding the other two) is that such blue supergiant explosions are more common than previously believed, but tend to be overlooked in distant galaxies because of their relative faintness.

> 'Expanding rings of incandescent material are caused by the supernova shock wave colliding with and heating the stellar wind previously ejected by the dying star.'

The developing remnant

In the years since the explosion faded from view, astronomers have continued to study its location, watching as matter blasted off the exploding star has begun to form an expanding supernova remnant. Here again, SN1987A has presented many puzzles. Expanding rings of incandescent material were unexpected, but have now been explained as an effect of the supernova shock wave colliding with and heating the stellar wind previously ejected by the dying star. More problematically, there seems to be no sign of the expected neutron star at the heart of the remnant. This superdense object should have formed from the collapse of the star's core, and should be obvious from its heating effect on debris around it, but it is nowhere to be seen. Possible explanations include the idea that the neutron star is surrounded by a dense dust cloud, or that (despite other indications), the progenitor star was in fact large enough to form a back hole. In 2009, a group led by T.C. Chan of the University of Hong Kong suggested a third alternative – a hypothetical compact object called a quark star that is even denser than a neutron star, but not quite massive enough to form a black hole.

89

Monster stars of the Tarantula Nebula

DEFINITION THE LARGEST KNOWN STARS LIE AT THE HEART OF A GIANT STAR-FORMING NEBULA IN THE LARGE MAGELLANIC CLOUD.

DISCOVERY SPECTRAL ANALYSIS OF THE STAR R136A IN THE 1980s SUGGESTED THAT IT COULD BE A HYPERGIANT STAR.

KEY BREAKTHROUGH IN 2010, ASTRONOMERS IDENTIFIED A SINGLE MEMBER OF R136A WITH THE MASS OF 265 SUNS.

IMPORTANCE THESE MASSIVE STARS PUSH CURRENT THEORIES OF STELLAR EVOLUTION TO THEIR LIMIT.

The Tarantula Nebula in the Large Magellanic Cloud is the largest star-forming zone in our region of the Universe, and plays host to clusters of brilliant young heavyweight stars, including the most massive stars yet discovered.

Also known as 30 Doradus or NGC 2070, the Tarantula Nebula is a large knot of gas within the Large Magellanic Cloud (LMC). Although its enormous distance of around 165,000 light years renders it visible only through binoculars (and once saw it classified as a faint star), it is in fact the biggest and brightest nebula in our Local Group of galaxies. If the Tarantula Nebula lay at the same distance as the Great Orion Nebula M42 (some 1,350 light years from Earth), it would be bright enough to cast shadows.

This enormous cloud of gas and dust has an overall diameter of around 650 light years, and contains about a million solar masses of material, with bright tendrils spread out like the legs of an enormous spider. At its heart lie two enormous star clusters known as Hodge 301 and R136.

Heart of the matter

R136 lies closest to the centre of the nebula, and is thought to be just 1 or 2 million years old. Strong stellar winds from the cluster's young stars are driving back or eroding the nebula from the inside, creating a cavern-like hollow, while fierce ultraviolet radiation excites gas molecules within the nebula and causes them to glow intensely. Several of the cluster's member are Wolf–Rayet stars, radiating so ferociously that their outer layers are being stripped away to expose hotter material from their interior.

OPPOSITE This wide-field image of the Tarantula Nebula was captured by the European Southern Observatory's 2.2-metre (88-inch) telescope at La Silla, Chile. R136 and Hodge 301 are embedded in the bright yellow-white region near the top of the picture.

In contrast, Hodge 301 is about 150 light years from the nebula's present centre, and considerably older than R136, with an age of 20–25 million years. The cluster probably formed in the same region as R136, but has drifted away throughout its life, with its stars gradually spreading out and its structure becoming looser.

The stars of Hodge 301 and R136 showcase the way in which clusters change their character throughout their lives – while R136 is so young that even its most massive and short-lived stars are still shining, Hodge 301 is peppered with at least 40 supernova remnants, the shredded remnants of heavyweight stars that have exhausted their nuclear fuel and exploded. As the expanding supernova remnants slam into the surrounding nebulosity of the Tarantula, they heat it to tremendous temperatures, generating X-ray emission.

R136's young age, and the enormous amounts of material it contains (estimated at some 450,000 solar masses) make it an ideal place to look for the most massive stars of all – the very stars that have already disappeared from older clusters like Hodge 301. While many of R136's individual stars can be imaged separately, and then studied through their separate motions in relation to the rest of the cluster, the brilliant central object, known as R136a, defied explanation until recently.

In the early 1980s, spectroscopic analysis of light from R136a, along with other evidence, led astronomers to suspect that it might be a hypergiant – a star shining with the brightness of some 30 million Suns. An enormous mass would be needed simply to hold such a star together against the tremendous

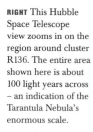

RIGHT This Hubble Space Telescope view zooms in on the region around cluster R136. The entire area shown here is about 100 light years across – an indication of the Tarantula Nebula's enormous scale.

pressure of radiation tearing it apart from inside, and some estimates put the mass of R136a at as much as 3,000 solar masses. At the time, though, theoretical models suggested that stars could never grow to such a huge mass – the pressures and temperatures created during the collapse of a protostellar nebula big enough to form such a star would blow it apart before it could even begin to shine through nuclear reactions. Despite the theory, however, the weight of evidence for a stellar mass limit much lower than this comes from observations – in 2005, astronomers Sally Oey of the University of Michigan and C.J. Clarke of the University of Cambridge Institute of Astronomy used statistical methods based on a study of clusters in the Milky Way and the Magellanic Clouds to show that stars of more than around 120–200 solar masses simply shouldn't occur. In the same year, a similar study of the Arches Cluster, one of the most massive clusters in the Milky Way, narrowed the mass limit to 150 solar masses.

Tracking down a monster

So what of R136a? The only alternative to a single bright hypergiant star is a tightly bound cluster of more modest, though still enormous, blue-white giants. By the late 1990s, technological advances finally allowed the mystery of the cluster's heart to be resolved, and this proved to be the case.

However, the stars of R136a are still forcing astronomers to rewrite their theories of stellar evolution. In 2010, an international team led by Paul Crowther of the University of Sheffield completed a detailed spectral analysis based on observations from the Hubble Space Telescope and the European Southern Observatory's Very Large Telescope. They concluded that several of the cluster's stars weigh considerably more than the widely accepted 150-Sun limit, and the brightest, catalogued as R136a1, contains a staggering 265 solar masses of material. The star's radiation is so fierce that it has probably lost around 20 percent of its mass in the million years since its birth, suggesting that it initially weighed as much as 320 Suns.

'Several of the cluster's stars weigh considerably more than the widely accepted 150-Sun limit, and the brightest, catalogued as R136a1, contains a staggering 265 solar masses of material.'

So it seems that the heart of R136 contains dozens of extremely massive stars in an extremely compact area of space, exerting tremendous gravitational forces on each other. These circumstances are ideal for producing runaway stars, catapulted out of the cluster by close encounters with their more massive neighbours (see page 310). And in 2010, astronomers identified just such a stellar refugee on the outskirts of the Tarantula Nebula. Using the Hubble Space Telescope's newly installed Cosmic Origins Spectrograph, a team led by Ian Howarth of University College London were able to study the torrent of ultraviolet radiation emanating from the star and estimate its mass at roughly 90 times that of the Sun. They also showed that it is moving at an impressive 400,000 km/h (250,000 mph) on a path that has carried it some 375 light years from its origins in R136 over a million years or so.

90

Galaxy classification

DEFINITION WAYS OF GROUPING GALAXIES BY THEIR APPEARANCE
AND COMPOSITION, AND UNDERSTANDING THEIR STRUCTURE.

DISCOVERY THE FIRST SYSTEM OF GALAXY CLASSIFICATION WAS
DEVELOPED BY EDWIN HUBBLE IN THE 1920s AND 1930s.

KEY BREAKTHROUGH IN 1966, LIN AND SHU PRODUCED A 'DENSITY
WAVE THEORY' TO EXPLAIN THE ORIGIN OF SPIRAL ARMS.

IMPORTANCE UNDERSTANDING THE COMPOSITION AND VARIETY
OF GALAXIES IS A KEY FIRST STEP TOWARDS MODELLING
THEIR EVOLUTION.

Following Edwin Hubble's confirmation of the distance to spiral nebulae in the 1920s, astronomers soon realized that there were many other types of galaxy, displaying a variety of structures. However, the processes that create the various galaxy types took longer to explain.

The first attempt to classify galaxies beyond the Milky Way was made by Hubble in 1936. He identified four major groups: spirals (type S), barred spirals (SB), ellipticals (E) and irregulars (Irr). Within each category there were subgroups – spirals and barred spirals were categorized by the tightness of the spiral arms, ranging from Sa and SBa (the most compact) to Sc and SBc (the loosest). Ball-shaped ellipticals were defined by their eccentricity, from spherical E0 to elongated E7. Finally, irregulars were subdivided into Irr-I (showing some traces of structure), and truly amorphous Irr-II galaxies.

Hubble represented the major groups of galaxies on a diagram in the shape of a tuning fork, with ellipticals running from E0 to E7 along the 'handle', and the two groups of spirals forming the 'prongs'. At the junction lies a group known as the lenticular galaxies, which have a spiral-like central bulge surrounded by a disc of gas and stars, but no actual spiral structure. The tuning-fork diagram is suggestive of an evolutionary sequence, and although Hubble himself never intended this, it has often been read as indicating a progression from ellipticals, through lenticulars to spirals.

Today, Hubble's scheme is seen as overly simplistic, and astronomers tend to use an improved scheme introduced by French astronomer Gérard de Vaucouleurs in 1959. This takes into account more recent discoveries, about both galaxy morphology and other properties such as stellar populations.

OPPOSITE Galaxy M74, some 32 million light years away in the constellation of Pisces, is displayed in stunning detail in this Hubble Space Telescope view. Pinkish star-forming regions and bright blue-white open star clusters are clearly visible along the galaxy's spiral arms, but the fainter disc star lying between the arms are also obvious.

Spiral galaxies

The first 'spiral nebulae' were identified by Irish astronomer William Parsons in the 1840s using his huge 'Leviathan' telescope, and it was Cepheid variables within spirals that helped Hubble to prove the distance of other galaxies (see page 31). In the early 1940s, German astronomer Walter Baade, working at California's Mount Wilson Observatory, identified differences in the distribution of stars within the Andromeda Galaxy, our closest neighbouring spiral, establishing a pattern that is found in nearly all spirals. The central hub is composed of old red and yellow 'Population II' stars, similar to those found near the centre of our own Milky Way and in globular clusters that orbit in the galactic halo (see page 314). These stars contain few heavy elements ('metals'), and there is little interstellar gas or ongoing star formation. In contrast, the outer disc contains plentiful gas and dust, and is dominated by 'Population I' stars with higher metal content. Relatively faint, Sun-like stars are scattered around the disc, but the brightest stars, embedded in recently formed open star clusters, are concentrated close to the major star-forming regions, within spiral arms that cross the disc.

'Hubble represented the major groups of galaxies on a diagram in the shape of a tuning fork, with ellipticals running along the "handle", and the two groups of spirals forming the "prongs". '

The origin of the spiral arms themselves is a subject of debate even today. In 1925, Swedish astronomer Bertil Lindblad predicted that the galaxies would experience differential rotation, so that inner regions of the disc would orbit the hub more rapidly than the outer parts (a phenomenon confirmed in our own galaxy by Jan Oort in 1927 – see page 346). Lindblad showed that if the spiral arms were fixed physical structures, differential rotation would cause them to rapidly 'wind up' around the hub and disappear. Because they are such common structures, they must persist for long periods of time, and therefore must be continuously regenerated – Lindblad argued that the spirals mark slowly rotating regions of higher density, which trigger compression and star formation in material passing through them.

A possible origin for this spiral wave was proposed by C.C. Lin and Frank Shu of the Massachusetts Institute of Technology in 1964. They suggested that if stars and other disc material follow slightly elliptical orbits, then the gravitational pull of the hub can cause them to form a neat pattern in which stars and gas are at their slowest-moving and most densely packed along spiral curves. This 'density wave theory' is now widely accepted, and a related effect is thought to produce the bars found in a majority of spirals. But astronomers still struggle to understand the precise factors that create the full range of spiral patterns, and which apparently fail completely in lenticulars. Tides raised during gravitational interactions with other nearby galaxies are thought to play a crucial role. Furthermore, spiral galaxies have a fairly limited range of sizes, suggesting that the spiral pattern only emerges in larger star systems (and offering a neat explanation for the two types of irregular galaxies).

LEFT Galaxy cluster
Abell S0740, some
450 million light
years away in the
constellation of
Centaurus, contains
a diverse range of
galaxies including
various spiral types
and a dominant
giant elliptical galaxy
at its centre.

Understanding ellipticals

In comparison to the complexities of spirals, elliptical galaxies have
comparatively simple structures – they are simply huge clouds of stars
following elliptical orbits, which overlap to produce a more or less elongated
ball structure. Like the hubs of spirals, they are dominated by old Population
II stars, and contain few signs of ongoing star formation. In any galaxy,
collisions and close encounters between stars will be very rare, so it is
thought that collisions between interstellar gas clouds play a crucial role in
'flattening' the structure of spirals – the lack of such clouds in ellipticals allows
them to retain their ball-like shape. Ellipticals also vary hugely in size, from
giants far larger than the Milky Way (such as M87, discovered by French
astronomer Charles Messier in 1781), down to small 'dwarf ellipticals' (such
as the brightest satellites of the Andromeda Spiral). The largest ellipticals are
generally found near the centres of large galaxy clusters, and this has proved
to be an important clue to the true pattern of galactic evolution.

91 Active galaxies

DEFINITION GALAXIES THAT DISPLAY ACTIVE CORES GENERATING LARGE AMOUNTS OF RADIATION AND PARTICLE JETS.

DISCOVERY SEYFERT GALAXIES WERE IDENTIFIED IN 1943, RADIO GALAXIES IN THE 1950S, AND THE FIRST QUASAR IN 1960.

KEY BREAKTHROUGH IMPROVED OBSERVATIONS ALLOWED ASTRONOMERS TO DEVELOP A UNIFIED MODEL OF ACTIVE GALACTIC NUCLEI IN THE 1980S.

IMPORTANCE ACTIVE GALAXIES CAN BE SEEN OVER ENORMOUS DISTANCES, PROVIDING ASTRONOMERS WITH A PROBE INTO THE DEPTHS OF THE UNIVERSE.

A wide range of galaxies have unusually bright nuclei or other kinds of strange activity associated with them. Together, the various types of 'active galaxy' can reveal a great deal not just about the structure of galaxies themselves, but about the long-term evolution of the Universe as a whole.

The first active galaxies were identified by American astronomer Carl Seyfert in a paper of 1943. He noted that certain spiral galaxies showed unusual spectral features – emission lines that were spread across a range of wavelengths by the Doppler effect, indicating that they were produced by gas moving at a range of speeds. The spectral features seemed to be generated around a bright, starlike nucleus embedded within the galaxy's hub.

Radio discoveries

The construction of the first large dish radio antennae in the 1950s was largely driven by the onset of the Space Race and the need to track satellites. However the first such dish to be completed, at Jodrell Bank near Manchester, England, was championed by British radio astronomer Bernard Lovell. The long wavelengths of radio waves make their origins difficult to pin down, and dish antennae allowed the radio sky to be mapped in greater detail than ever before, producing the first images of individual radio sources. Many showed a distinctive structure, with a pair of radio 'lobes' to either side of an apparently innocuous central galaxy.

Other radio sources, however, refused to conform to this pattern, lacking the double-lobed appearance or the central galaxy. In 1960, astronomers led by Allan Sandage at California's Mount Wilson and Palomar Observatories photographed the sky around some of these radio sources. The only objects

OPPOSITE An image from the National Radio Astronomy Observatory's Very Large Array shows huge radio-emitting clouds billowing out to either side of a lenticular galaxy called NGC 1316, some 70 million light years from Earth. This radio source, known as Fornax A, is one of the most powerful in the sky.

RIGHT The Circinus Galaxy is one of the closest active galaxies to Earth, but was only discovered in the 1970s because it happens to lie behind a dense region of the Milky Way. It is a Seyfert galaxy, in which gas is being ejected from the region around the Active Galactic Nucleus at high speeds.

that coincided with their location appeared to be stars, and this new class of objects was named quasi-stellar radio sources or 'quasars'.

Aside from their radio emissions, quasars showed other strange features. When the spectrum of a bright quasar called 3C 48 was analysed, it showed emission lines that did not match any known element. It was only in 1963 that Sandage's colleague, Dutch astronomer Maarten Schmidt, recognized that lines in the spectrum of another bright quasar called 3C 273 were in fact the familiar ones produced by hydrogen, only Doppler shifted towards the red end of the spectrum to an unprecedented degree. In fact, 3C 273 turned out to be moving away from Earth at about one sixth the speed of light. Some astronomers argued that 3C 273 was an extreme runaway star (see page 309), but more quasars with extreme redshifts soon came to light, and British scientists Dennis Sciama and Martin Rees pointed out that, if they really were local runaways, there should also be quasars with extreme blue shifts approaching us. The lack of such objects, they argued, showed that quasar redshifts were a result of cosmic expansion (see page 49), and that 3C 273 was an astonishing 2 billion light years away.

The tremendous distance of 3C 273 was soon confirmed in other cases, and eventually the tenuous traces of faint 'host galaxies' were found around some bright quasars, confirming that they lie at the heart of distant galaxies and are effectively much brighter versions of the nearby Seyfert galaxies. However, these breakthroughs simply presented astronomers with another puzzle: in order to be visible over such huge distances, quasars must be the most luminous objects in the Universe, shining with the light of trillions of Suns. Furthermore, the actual energy-producing regions must be tiny in astronomical terms: short-term and unpredictable variations in brightness showed they could only be a few light days across at most.

Solving the mystery

As ground- and space-based telescope technology improved through the 1960s and 1970s, a series of discoveries began to show connections between the various types of 'active galaxy'. Quasars turned out to emit radiation at a wide range of wavelengths including X-rays, and often produced the same double-lobed radio emission as the nearby 'radio galaxies'. From 1965, Sandage began to discover 'radio-quiet' quasars that were effectively superluminous versions of the Seyfert galaxies. Conversely, some Seyferts revealed weak radio activity, while high-speed gas jets were identified in galaxies that showed no obvious bright nucleus. In the late 1970s, another group of active galaxies was discovered, the first of which was the mysterious BL Lacertae, initially classified as a variable star. These 'BL Lac objects' or 'blazars' change their brightness rapidly and show a complete absence of spectral lines. They proved to be the final piece of the puzzle.

'In order to be visible over such huge distances, quasars must be the most luminous objects in the Universe, shining with the light of trillions of Suns.'

Throughout the 1980s, astronomers developed a unified model, in which a single type of object – an 'Active Galactic Nucleus' (AGN) gives rise to different phenomena when seen from different angles. The AGN is thought to be created by an accretion disc around a supermassive black hole, surrounded by a doughnut-shaped torus of gas and dust. Material spiralling into the disc is heated to millions of degrees generating intense but variable radiation, while particle jets escaping along the disc's central axis collide with the surrounding intergalactic medium to generate clouds of radio emission. So quasars and Seyfert galaxies arise when we see an AGN at a range of angles, while a radio galaxy is produced when the galaxy lies 'edge-on' and the accretion disc is hidden by the outer torus. Finally, blazars occur when we look straight down one of the jets emerging from the nucleus, and radiation from these high-speed particles obscures the spectral features of the AGN itself.

Although the 'unified model' of AGNs has withstood two decades of scrutiny and new discoveries, the precise mechanisms that generate some types of activity are still poorly understood, and certain questions, such as the difference between 'radio-quiet' and 'radio-loud' galaxies, still defy a neat explanation. Active galaxies have proved to be surprisingly common, with a new type, in which the AGN is completely hidden by a surrounding cloud of gas and dust, discovered by NASA's Swift X-ray Telescope as recently as 2007. Furthermore, confirmation of supermassive black holes in galaxies like our own (see page 349) raises the prospect that many galaxies go through an active phase, offering clues to the way that galaxies evolve.

92

Cosmic rays

DEFINITION FAST-MOVING PARTICLES FROM SPACE, WITH A VARIETY
OF ORIGINS, THAT BOMBARD EARTH'S ATMOSPHERE.

DISCOVERY THE INCREASE IN RADIATION AT HIGHER ALTITUDES WAS
DISCOVERED BY WULF AND HESS AROUND 1910.

KEY BREAKTHROUGH IN THE 1930s, BRUNO ROSSI AND PIERRE AUGER
IDENTIFIED GROUND-LEVEL PARTICLE SHOWERS TRIGGERED BY
INCOMING COSMIC RAYS.

IMPORTANCE COSMIC RAYS HAVE IMPORTANT EFFECTS ON EARTH'S
ENVIRONMENT AND PROVIDE A POWERFUL TOOL FOR STUDYING
OBJECTS IN DISTANT SPACE.

Despite their name, cosmic rays are actually high-energy particles that disintegrate in Earth's upper atmosphere. Produced by a variety of processes in the depths of space, even detecting them on Earth presents unique challenges for astronomers.

The existence of cosmic rays was unsuspected until the early 1900s, when physicists were eager to investigate every aspect of the newly discovered 'ionizing radiations' associated with certain radioactive substances. In 1909, German physicist Theodor Wulf detected higher levels of ionization (fragmentation of air molecules into electrically charged ions) at the top of the Eiffel Tower in Paris than at the bottom, and from 1911, the Austrian Victor Hess began a series of balloon ascents, during which he discovered that radiation increased fourfold at altitudes of around 5 kilometres (3 miles). By repeating his observations at night and during a solar eclipse, Hess proved that the Sun was not the cause of the ionization.

However, the term 'cosmic rays' was not coined until 1925, when American physicist Robert Millikan showed that they were coming from space rather than the upper atmosphere. In the 1930s, Italian scientist Bruno Rossi and French physicist Pierre Auger independently made an important breakthrough with the discovery that cosmic rays produce showers of particles at ground level. The initial evidence came from the simultaneous triggering of widely separated Geiger counters during an experiment carried out by Rossi, but it was Auger who concluded that the 'air showers' were generated by interactions between incoming cosmic rays and air particles high in the atmosphere. These events triggered a series of secondary collisions that generated more particles, which eventually reached the ground.

OPPOSITE An image from the Japanese Super-Kamiokande experiment (see page 89) traces the path of a muon neutrino through the main detector tank. Generated by a cosmic ray entering the atmosphere on the far side of Earth, the neutrino entered the detector through its base, and left through one of the side walls, generating a cone of light during its passage.

Cosmic particles

Despite these discoveries, the nature of the cosmic rays themselves remained elusive until 1948, when American physicists Melvin Gottlieb and James Van Allen detected their traces on special photographic plates carried on high-altitude balloons. Distinctive tracks left as the rays crossed the plates left no doubt – they were the signs of protons, helium nuclei and (rarely) heavier atoms travelling at high speeds. Cosmic rays were not rays after all, but particles.

In the 1950s, astronomers found ways to extract more information about cosmic rays from the air showers that they create. The first detector 'array', consisting of a large ring of particle detectors, was built by Rossi and others at Harvard College Observatory in 1954. By measuring the minute differences in time and energy when air shower particles triggered different detectors, Rossi's group could begin to measure the speed of cosmic rays and even the direction from which they came (since detectors closer to the source would be triggered fractionally before those further away). In the mid-1960s, Rossi's student Kenneth Greisen pioneered another detection technique, using telescopes with sensitive electronic detectors to look for fluorescence – flashes of light released by particle interactions during air showers.

Studies through the 1970s began to suggest that cosmic rays came from a variety of sources. There are two distinct populations: 'primary' rays consisting of the lighter, fastest-moving particles; and 'secondary' rays, heavier nuclei that are thought to be created when primary rays interact with the interstellar medium. The primary rays display a wide range of energy and speed. Low-energy rays appear to originate in the atmospheres of the Sun and other stars, and are boosted to unusually high speeds (though still slow by cosmic ray standards) by stellar flares. The production of certain radioactive isotopes in Earth's atmosphere is thought to be linked to these plentiful low-energy rays, and according to some models they may even affect Earth's climate (see page 95). In addition, they present a significant problem for astronauts and electronic circuits operating beyond Earth's atmosphere.

'Astronomers were astonished to discover a cosmic ray with unprecedented energy – a subatomic particle with the kinetic energy of a baseball moving at 100 km/h (60 mph).'

Intermediate-energy 'galactic cosmic rays', meanwhile, seem to be trapped by the Milky Way's magnetic field, rebounding back and forth across our galaxy. In 2004, European astronomers using the High-Energy Stereoscopic System (HESS) telescope in Namibia detected a stream of gamma rays from a thousand-year-old supernova remnant called RX J1713.7–3946 – the first evidence confirming a long-held theory that the galactic cosmic rays are accelerated to high speeds by the extreme magnetic fields around stellar remnants (see page 337).

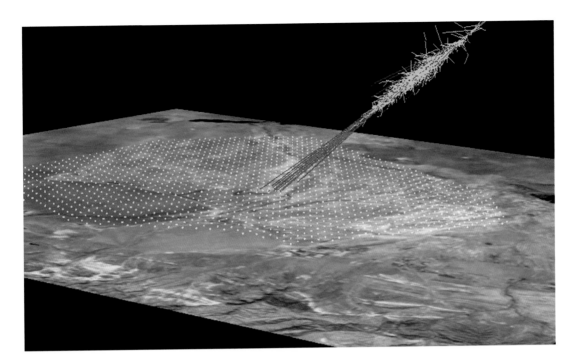

Extreme rays

In 1991, astronomers using the 'Fly's Eye' fluorescence detector at Utah's Dugway Proving Ground were astonished by the discovery of a cosmic ray with unprecedented energy – a subatomic particle with the kinetic energy of a baseball moving at 100 km/h (60 mph). Assuming that it was a proton, this particle must have been moving at just a fraction below the speed of light, giving it more than 10 billion times the energy of the fastest galactic cosmic rays. This was the first confirmation of the existence of 'ultra-high-energy cosmic rays', and they have become the subject for intense study ever since.

The most ambitious project to study these extreme cosmic rays is the Pierre Auger Observatory, a huge array of air shower detectors spread across the Argentinian pampas, with an overall area of some 3,000 square kilometres (1,160 square miles). Each of the 1,600 detector units is a large water tank – the experiment looks for the telltale flashes of Cerenkov radiation (see page 42) triggered when the high-energy air shower particles produced by an incoming ray pass through the tank, moving faster than the speed of light in water. The enormous detection area is required to increase the chance of capturing these rare events, and the accuracy with which the speed and direction of the incoming rays can be measured.

In 2007, the observatory produced its first results, confirming a link between 27 high-energy events and nearby active galactic nuclei (see page 371). This appears to confirm the theory that ultra-high-energy cosmic rays are produced by similar processes to those responsible for the galactic rays, but in the far more extreme environments around supermassive black holes.

ABOVE This schematic shows how the shower of particles, generated by a single cosmic ray entering the atmosphere, reaches the ground in a distinctive pattern that can be measured by the Pierre Auger Observatory's huge array of detectors.

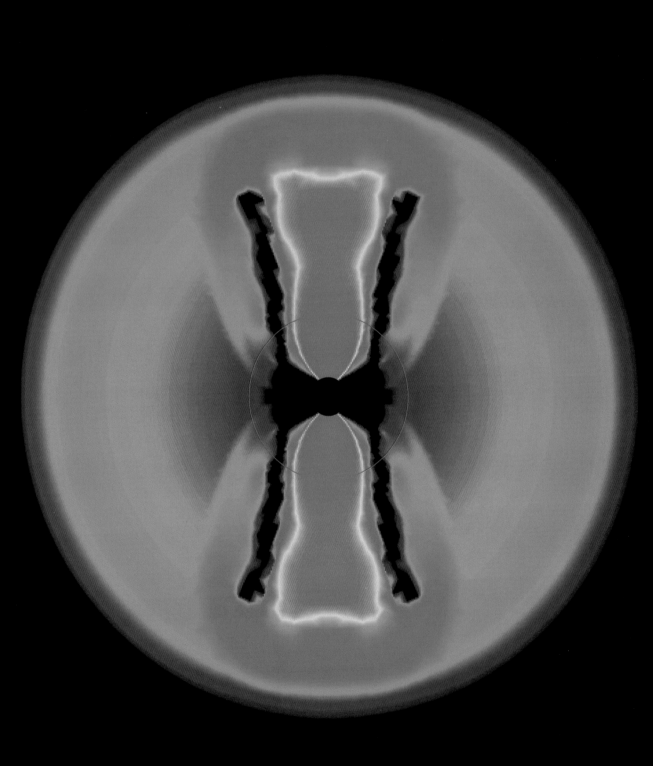

93

Gamma-ray bursts

DEFINITION SHORT-LIVED BLASTS OF HIGH-ENERGY RADIATION FROM
THE DEPTHS OF THE UNIVERSE.

DISCOVERY THE FIRST GAMMA-RAY BURST (GRB) WAS DETECTED BY A
US MILITARY SATELLITE IN 1967.

KEY BREAKTHROUGH IN 1997, X-RAY SPECTROSCOPY OF A FADING
GRB CONFIRMED THAT THESE OBJECTS ARE USUALLY BILLIONS OF
LIGHT YEARS FROM EARTH.

IMPORTANCE NOT ONLY FASCINATING ASTROPHYSICAL OBJECTS, A
FUTURE NEARBY GRB COULD ALSO PRESENT A DIRECT THREAT TO
LIFE ON EARTH.

Gamma-ray bursts are the most violent events in the Universe and, despite decades of research, still one of the least understood. Astronomers suspect that many of these explosions are caused by the formation of black holes that consume dying stars from the inside.

The first sign that natural objects in the Universe could release sudden and violent bursts of high-energy gamma rays came in 1967 when Vela 4a, a US military satellite designed to detect the gamma-ray emissions from nuclear tests, detected an unexpected signal. This powerful burst of gamma rays rose to a peak in a matter of seconds, then took several days to fade completely. Its behaviour was completely unlike that of a nuclear warhead, and the limitations of technology prevented the satellite from identifying the direction of the gamma-ray source, so for the moment it was classed as a mystery gamma-ray burst (GRB), and treated as classified information.

Vela 4a's successors detected a further 15 GRBs over the following six years, and all remained classified until after NASA scientists, analysing data from the Orbiting Solar Observatory and Imp 6 satellites, announced their own discovery of something unusual in 1973. The following year, the Soviet Union announced that its own satellites had detected similar signals.

Identifying the sources

Despite numerous gamma-ray experiments piggybacked onto solar observation satellites in the next decade and a half, the source of GRBs remained a mystery – though most scientists assumed, based on GRBs' power, that they lay somewhere inside our galaxy. It was only

OPPOSITE A computer simulation by Andrew McFadyen of New York University shows the development of two powerful jets channelling radiation from a 'collapsar' – the likely cause of many gamma-ray bursts.

in 1991, with the launch of the Compton Gamma-Ray Observatory (CGRO), that astronomers were able to measure the direction of GRBs for the first time.

Gamma rays are the hardest of all radiations to pin down because their high energies allow them to pass through any device that might be used to focus them. While visible light and nearby wavelengths can be imaged with normal telescopes, and radio waves mostly present a problem of scale, high-energy X-rays and gamma rays pass straight through reflective mirrors or metal sheets. X-rays can be focused using 'grazing incidence' mirrors which rely on the ricochet effect when rays strike at shallow angles, but even this does not work for gamma rays. Instead, CGRO carried a battery of eight detectors (one at each corner): minute delays in the detection of rays on different parts of the spacecraft allowed the direction of their origin to be estimated. Through nine years of operation, CGRO detected 2704 GRB events, coming from all over the sky and showing no discernible bias to the plane of the Milky Way. It seemed GRBs were extragalactic after all.

Further breakthroughs came with the 1997 launch of BeppoSAX, an Italian–Dutch X-ray observatory that was able to detect the lower-energy 'afterglow' of GRBs, allowing their spectra to be analysed. This revealed strong redshifts in their spectral lines, indicating distances of hundreds of millions to billions of light years. It soon became clear that GRBs produce radiation across a range of wavelengths, and measurements of the radio waves from a 1997 GRB allowed Dale Frail of the US National Radio Astronomy Observatory

BELOW This supercomputer simulation shows a merger between two neutron stars. Colours map the intensity of magnetic fields associated with the stellar remnants – short-duration gamma-ray bursts may be produced by an enormous release of magnetic field energy as the stars finally coalesce.

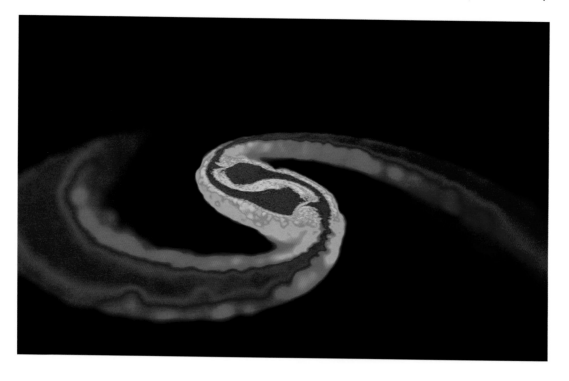

to show that the GRB involved an explosion at relativistic speeds (close to the speed of light). In 1999, the Hubble Space Telescope tracked down one of the first GRBs to be studied in visible light, revealing an object that produced the energy of 100 million billion Suns.

To aid the rapid tracking down of GRBs, international collaborations led by NASA launched the High-Energy Transient Explorer (HETE) in 2000 and the Swift Gamma-Ray Burst Mission in 2004. Observations triggered by these satellites have begun to at last shed light on the origins of GRBs, and there seem to be two distinct mechanisms at work.

GRB types and mechanisms

Astronomers divide GRBs into two major groups: short-duration bursts last from a few milliseconds to two seconds, and long-duration bursts last from a few seconds to a few hundred. The long-duration bursts seem to be linked to hypernovae – stellar explosions whose brilliance dwarfs normal supernovae. A hypernova is thought to be created by the violent death of an extremely massive star and the formation of an object known as a collapsar.

'In 1999, the Hubble Space Telescope tracked down one of the first GRBs to be studied in visible light, revealing an object that produced the energy of 100 million billion Suns.'

The heaviest stars have cores so massive that, when their nuclear fusion processes finally come to an end, they collapse to create a black hole. This superdense object begins to swallow the star from the inside, drawing material into a rapidly developing 'accretion disc', but at the same time a powerful shock wave rips through the star's outer layers, generating a huge wave of nuclear fusion, with accompanying radiation including intense gamma rays. Escaping matter and energy are channelled along narrow jets aligned to the black hole's axis of rotation, intensifying the effects of an already brilliant explosion.

Although GRBs are so distant that it's impossible to observe their progenitor stars directly, spectral studies suggest that they may be linked to 'Wolf–Rayet' stars – stellar heavyweights that generate such fierce stellar winds that they shed most of their outer hydrogen envelope during their brief lifetimes, creating an unusually dense dying star. Tracking the origin of bursts is particularly important because a nearby GRB directed towards Earth could have devastating consequences for the environment and life.

The origins of short-duration GRBs are less well-established, but in 2005 astronomers tracked the afterglow of two such bursts for the first time. They proved to lie in elliptical galaxies dominated by aged, low-mass stars – not the most promising environment for the creation of a hypernova. Instead, it seems likely that short GRBs are triggered by the collisions and mergers of old stellar remnants – either the collision of two neutron stars to create a black hole, or the absorption of a neutron star by a pre-existing black hole. Whatever the precise mechanism, the results are undeniably spectacular.

Interacting galaxies

94

DEFINITION COLLISIONS AND CLOSE ENCOUNTERS BETWEEN GALAXIES BOTH LARGE AND SMALL.

DISCOVERY IN 1967, HALTON ARP PUBLISHED HIS CATALOGUE OF PECULIAR GALAXIES, CONTAINING MANY OBJECTS THAT DID NOT FIT THE ESTABLISHED CLASSIFICATION SCHEMES.

KEY BREAKTHROUGH IN 1972, THE TOOMRE BROTHERS PUBLISHED THE FIRST MODERN COMPUTER MODELS OF THE PROCESSES AT WORK DURING GALAXY COLLISIONS.

IMPORTANCE INTERACTION BETWEEN GALAXIES PLAYS A MAJOR ROLE IN PRODUCING NEW GENERATIONS OF STARS.

On a cosmic scale, galaxies are relatively closely packed together, and the largest ones exert enormous gravitational pull on their neighbours. As a result, collisions and close encounters are quite common, and astronomers now believe they play an important role in the evolution of galaxies.

Groups of 'nebulae' had been observed since the 18th century, although their true significance was only appreciated from the 1920s, after Edwin Hubble proved that they were independent galaxies millions of light years away. Astronomers accepted that these clusters were bound together by the gravity of their individual members, but still generally denied the possibility that collisions were common or widespread. Nevertheless, a few compact galaxy groups, most notably the quintet of galaxies in Pegasus discovered by French astronomer Édouard Stephan in 1877, seemed to cluster so closely together that some kind of interaction must be unavoidable.

Early simulations

During the 1940s, Swedish astronomer Erik Holmberg set out to investigate what might happen if galaxies did collide, constructing a remarkable analogue computer to aid his studies. He concluded that collisions would generate huge tidal forces, distorting the galaxies, robbing them of momentum through space and ultimately causing them to slow down and coalesce together. Holmberg's simple models turned out to be remarkably accurate. During the 1950s, Swiss astronomer Fritz Zwicky photographed a number of galaxies that he suspected were interacting with their neighbours, identifying starry 'tails' trailing away from their central regions. However, Zwicky's theories were largely ignored, and most astronomers persisted in their belief that galaxy interactions, if they occurred, were rare events.

OPPOSITE A composite image shows the central region of the colliding Antennae galaxies NGC 4038 and 4039. X-ray data from the Chandra satellite is shown in blue, visible light from the Hubble Space Telescope in brown and yellow, and infrared radiation recorded by the Spitzer Space Telescope in red.

Attitudes only began to change in the late 1960s, when Halton Arp of the Palomar Observatory in California published the first catalogue of 'peculiar' galaxies that stubbornly refused to fit into Hubble's neat classification. Arp listed some 338 objects, many of which were little more than misshapen blurs through even the largest telescopes of the time. However, he argued persuasively that these systems were the result of close encounters and collisions between galaxies, and began to interest others.

> 'Stars within a galaxy are so widely scattered that close encounters are rare. Clouds of gas and dust are diffuse but much more widely spread, and galactic encounters drive huge shock waves through them.'

In 1972, Estonian-born US astronomers Alar and Jüri Toomre published the first detailed simulations of galaxy collisions made using modern, digital computers. Their models showed how the tidal forces would cause the arms of spiral galaxies to 'unwind', forming tails of stars such as those photographed by Zwicky. The Toomre brothers were even able to model specific galaxy collisions, creating results that produced good matches with well-known peculiar galaxies such as the Mice (NGC 4576A and B) and the Antennae (NGC 4038/9). In 1977, Alar Toomre suggested that elliptical galaxies are the ultimate product of mergers between spirals – a controversial theory that ultimately had far-reaching consequences for models of galactic evolution (see page 389).

Active nuclei and starbursts

Since the 1970s, astronomers have discovered, through both computer simulations and direct observations, that galaxy collisions and interactions are even more common than Arp and the Toomres suspected, and that they can have a variety of effects.

Arp's catalogue included a wide range of galaxies with unusual brightness. Some have bright cores that can now be attributed to active galactic nuclei (see page 369). One well known example is NGC 5128, an elliptical galaxy around 15 million light years from Earth, with a dark dust lane running across its centre. NGC 5128 is associated with a strong radio source called Centaurus A – a pair of radio-emitting lobes created where powerful jets of particles from the core billow out into intergalactic space. In the past decade, infrared images of the galaxy's core have confirmed that the galaxy's dust lane is the surviving 'ghost' of a spiral galaxy that has otherwise been completely absorbed – it seems that this collision has also supplied large amounts of fresh material to the supermassive black hole at the centre of the galaxy, sparking its current activity.

Other Arp galaxies are amorphous, and unusually bright across large areas. In these cases, the brightness is due to stars that are forming inside them at a tremendous rate – a so-called 'starburst'. The best known starburst galaxy is the Cigar Galaxy M82, which lies close to the bright spiral M81 and about

12 million light years from Earth. The pair were discovered by German astronomer Johann Elert Bode in 1774, and early observers believed M82 was actually in the process of exploding. It's only since the 1980s that images of the galaxy from space-based observatories have revealed the truth – strong stellar winds and supernova shock waves in the heart of the galaxy are blasting huge amounts of interstellar material out into the surrounding interstellar space. In 2005, new infrared observations showed that M82 is not as shapeless as it appears, revealing two faint spiral arms that extend from its central disc and are aligned edge-on to Earth. M82's close encounter with its neighbour began around 100 million years ago, and the enormous tides raised by the larger galaxy's gravity have compressed star-forming material together in its core, driving a wave of starbirth.

Both of these examples show that the behaviour of interstellar gas, rather than stars, is the main trigger for activity in interacting galaxies. Stars within a galaxy are so widely scattered that, even when two galaxies collide head on, close stellar encounters are rare. Clouds of gas and dust, in contrast, are diffuse but much more widely spread, and galactic encounters drive huge shock waves through them.

In the short term, this triggers enormous waves of star formation such as those seen in starburst galaxies. Since the late 1990s, based on images of concentrated starbirth regions obtained by the Hubble Space Telescope, astronomers have concluded that starbursts often trigger the formation of 'super star clusters' containing millions of stars. As the heavier stars within such giant clusters age and die, they leave behind the more sedate, lower-mass stars to persist as globular clusters. However, in the long term, the same shock waves heat the star-forming gas and drive it out of its host galaxies – a process that plays a key role in galactic evolution.

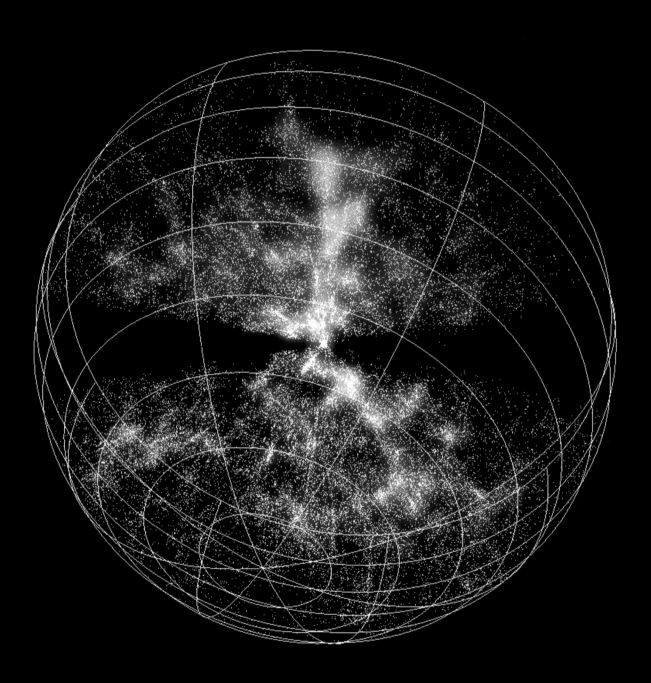

95 Mapping the Universe

DEFINITION EFFORTS TO CHART THE DISTRIBUTION OF LARGE
NUMBERS OF GALAXIES BY MEASURING THEIR REDSHIFTS.

DISCOVERY THE FIRST REDSHIFT SURVEY WAS BEGUN AT THE
HARVARD–SMITHSONIAN CENTRE FOR ASTROPHYSICS IN 1977.

KEY BREAKTHROUGH THE 1986 PUBLICATION OF THE FIRST CFA
MAPS REVEALED THAT GALAXIES CONCENTRATE IN CHAIN-LIKE
FILAMENTS AROUND HUGE, APPARENTLY EMPTY VOIDS.

IMPORTANCE THE FILAMENTS AND VOIDS REVEALED BY REDSHIFT
MAPS ARE THE LARGEST KNOWN STRUCTURES IN THE UNIVERSE,
AND PLACE IMPORTANT CONSTRAINTS ON THE BIG BANG THEORY.

Charting the distribution of galaxies on the largest scale reveals intriguing patterns and large-scale structure in the Universe. The origins of such structure can be traced back to the earliest times, and the aftermath of the Big Bang itself.

By combining the positions of galaxies in the sky with accurate measurements of their spectroscopic redshifts, astronomers can build up a three-dimensional view of the Universe around us. Such surveys rely on the cosmic expansion discovered by Edwin Hubble (see page 49), assuming that a galaxy's redshift (caused by its motion away from Earth) increases with distance. They ignore small local variations in the motion of galaxies caused by their mutual gravitational attraction in favour of building up a grand map of the Universe as a whole – or at least our region of it.

The first of these surveys, began in 1977 by Marc Davis, John Huchra, Dave Latham and John Tonry of the Harvard Smithsonian Centre for Astrophysics (CfA), was completed in 1982. It measured the redshifts of almost 13,000 galaxies in the northern sky, down to a magnitude of 14.5 – roughly 2,500 times fainter than the limit of naked-eye visibility. Between 1985 and 1995, a team led by John Huchra and Margaret Geller expanded the survey to some 18,000 galaxies.

When plotted using the galactic coordinate system (based on the orientation of the Milky Way) the resulting map formed a broad cone (since galaxies are only visible at high 'galactic latitudes' away from the obscuring stars and dust of the Milky Way's central plane). At first, the distribution of galaxies appeared somewhat random, but in 1986, Huchra, Geller and Valérie de

OPPOSITE A computer-generated map plots the positions of more than 100,000 galaxies visible from Earth's southern skies in three dimensions. Large-scale cosmic structure takes the form of filaments and sheets of matter around apparently empty voids.

Lapparent produced a 'slice' of the sky, revealing remarkable patterns. Galaxies, it appeared, were concentrated in long chains around large and apparently empty regions of space.

Large-scale structure

The existence of concentrations of distinct galaxy clusters and looser groups had been understood for a long time – concentrations of 'nebulae' in and around the constellations of Virgo and Coma were obvious as early as the 18th century, and numerous fainter concentrations came to light in the 19th century. As soon as the true nature of galaxies was recognized, it became clear that these regions were hosts to huge galaxy clusters, pulled together by their mutual gravitational attraction. In the 1950s, American astronomer George Abell compiled the first catalogue of these clusters.

However, the idea that clusters were themselves gregarious, gathering together in some regions of the Universe and apparently shunning others, was largely ignored – a general principle of cosmology is that the Universe should be essentially uniform, and so at the time astronomers assumed that clusters would be distributed randomly through space. French astronomer Gérard de Vaucouleurs suggested in the 1950s that the Virgo Cluster might form the core of a larger 'supercluster', but the reality of such large structures remained uncertain for the next two decades.

'Between 1997 and 2002, the 2dF Galaxy Redshift Survey measured more than 230,000 galaxies visible from Australian skies, using a camera that allowed it to record the spectra of 400 objects simultaneously.'

Then in 1977, astronomers Mihkel Jõeveer and Jean Einasto, working at the Estonian Astrophysical Observatory, suggested the presence of a 'cellular' structure in the Universe based on their discovery of a supercluster centred on the well-known Perseus galaxy cluster. Galaxies within the supercluster formed a huge curving wall around one side of an almost galaxy-free void covering much of the constellation Taurus. A year later, Stephen Gregory and Laird Thomson of the Kitt Peak National Observatory published their evidence for a similar supercluster in the constellation of Coma.

The slice of sky covered by the CfA map confirmed these theories in dramatic fashion. It happened to include the core of the Coma Supercluster, roughly 300 million light years from Earth forming a shape that instantly became known as the 'Stick Man'. This in turn formed part of an even larger structure named the 'Great Wall', some 600 million light years long.

Confirmation of large-scale structures in the Universe (today known as filaments and voids) raised major issues for cosmologists, who had spent the previous few decades developing a Big Bang theory that would produce a smooth distribution of matter in the early Universe (see pages 57 and 61). It took the discovery of ripples in the cosmic microwave background radiation to explain exactly why matter is distributed in this way (see page 53).

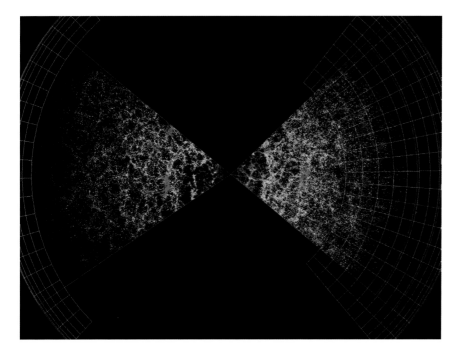

Extending our view

The initial CfA surveys were limited by technology to galaxies within about 700 million light years of Earth – still a relatively small region of the entire observable Universe, which stretches away to 13.7 billion light years in every direction (the maximum distance light can have travelled since the Big Bang). Since the 1980s, further surveys have improved our knowledge of the depths of the Universe, using electronic sensors and computerized analysis.

Between 1997 and 2002, the 2dF (2-degree field) Galaxy Redshift Survey measured more than 230,000 galaxies visible from Australian skies, using a camera that allowed it to record the spectra of 400 objects simultaneously. The 2dF Survey confirmed the 'Swiss cheese' structure of the Universe, but was also able to measure the density of the Universe with unprecedented precision, and to detect patterns generated by density waves ('sound') propagating through the early Universe. This in turn provides important clues to the nature of the Universe's invisible 'dark matter' (see page 397), and the way it interacts with 'normal' matter. A follow-up survey, known as 6dF, collected spectra for 125,000 galaxies, spread across a much larger area of the sky encompassing both the northern and southern hemispheres.

At the time of writing, the largest ongoing survey project of all is the Sloan Digital Sky Survey (SDSS), which began in 2000 and uses a dedicated telescope based in New Mexico. This project aims not only to collect spectra for galaxies, but also to image them at a variety of wavelengths. Data have been collected for more than a million objects (although not all of these are galaxies), including some of the most distant quasars known.

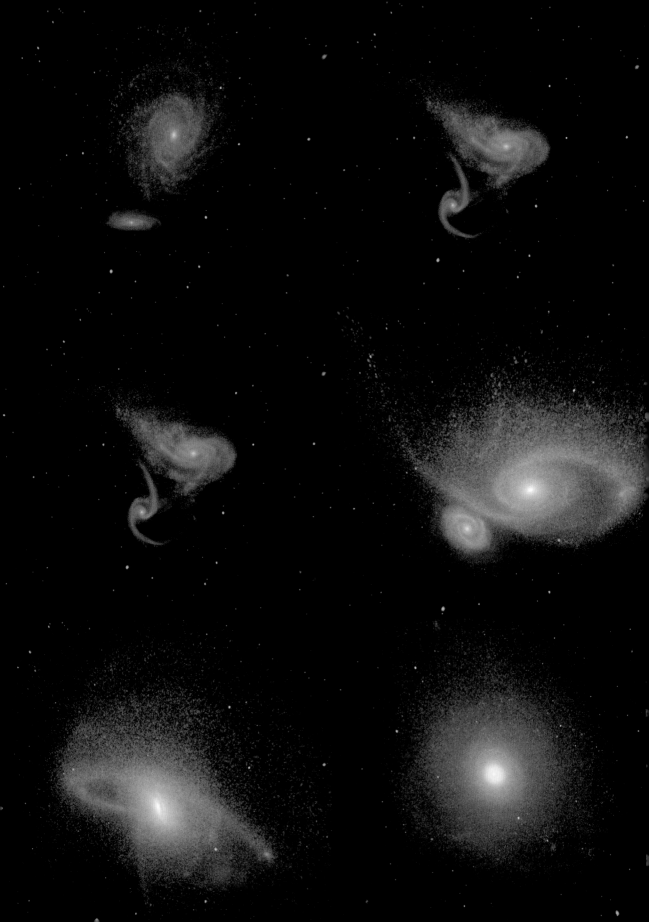

DEFINITION THEORIES DESCRIBING THE WAY IN WHICH GALAXIES EVOLVE FROM ONE TYPE TO ANOTHER.

DISCOVERY THE FIRST 'TOP-DOWN' THEORY OF GALAXY EVOLUTION WAS PROPOSED BY EGGEN, LYNDEN-BELL AND SANDAGE IN 1962.

KEY BREAKTHROUGH IN 1978, SEARLE AND ZINN PROPOSED A THEORY IN WHICH GALAXIES GROW BY SUCCESSIVE MERGERS.

IMPORTANCE MODELLING THE EVOLUTION OF GALAXIES IS VITAL IN ORDER TO COMPREHEND THE PAST AND FUTURE OF OUR OWN MILKY WAY STAR SYSTEM.

Astronomers now recognize that collisions and mergers between galaxies are a common and regular occurrence, and that the dominant types of galaxy in the Universe have changed significantly over time. Put together, these two facts produce a compelling picture of the way in which galaxies evolve.

Using modern telescope technology, astronomers can now observe galaxies whose light left on its journey to Earth when the Universe was much younger. Peering billions of years back through time, we find a population of galaxies that is quite different from that found today. Quasars and other active galaxies (see page 369) become far more common, while elliptical galaxies are less widespread, and (despite the general 'redshift' of light from these distant regions) galaxies are notably bluer in colour than they are in the nearby Universe. All these changes suggest that galaxies have evolved over time, but it has taken the better part of a century for astronomers to approach a workable theory of how this process happens.

Collapse from above

Early theories, inspired by Edwin Hubble's 'tuning fork' classification of galaxies, envisaged spiral galaxies developing from ellipticals. As early as 1919, British physicist James Jeans explained how the collapse of a massive gas cloud could create a spiral-shaped system with a central bulge surrounded by a flattened disc in which stars would continue to form, although it was not until the 1960s that the mechanism responsible for the spiral arms was explained (see page 366). However, at the time of Jeans' work, he was still thinking in terms of the spiral nebulae as large systems within or very close to our galaxy, and his theories ran into problems when the reality of galaxies as much more distant and slowly rotating objects became clear.

OPPOSITE A series of frames from a computer simulation model the approach and interaction of two different-sized spiral galaxies, and their eventual coalescence into a single larger elliptical galaxy. Based on Hubble Space Telescope observations, astronomers believe that such mergers between large galaxies happen just once every 9 billion years on average, but larger systems absorb smaller ones much more frequently.

Nevertheless, the basics of Jeans' model were resurrected in the first detailed theory of spiral galaxy formation, published by Olin J. Eggen, Donald Lynden-Bell and Allan Sandage in 1962. In the 'ELS' model, galaxies collapsed from a single cloud of gas in a relatively short period of time, triggering a burst of starbirth in the core which rapidly used up its star-forming material. Starbirth in the surrounding disc, in contrast, proceeded more slowly, with the result that the disc remained an active region of starbirth long after the core's short-lived massive stars had burnt out, leaving only sedate red and yellow stars behind. This theory neatly explained the two distinct populations of stars found in spiral galaxies (and British astronomer Lynden-Bell went on to predict correctly that many, if not all, galaxies would contain a supermassive black hole in their core). Further evidence came from the discovery of 'high-velocity clouds' (HVCs) – clumps of neutral hydrogen gas moving in and around the Milky Way at speeds that are much higher than could be explained by our galaxy's general rotation. Many HVCs appeared to be falling onto our galaxy as might be explained if this 'top-down' theory was correct.

Piece by piece

However, the ELS model had little to say on the subject of how ellipticals formed. It was not until 1977 that Estonian-born Alar Toomre suggested that ellipticals were the end result of mergers between spirals (see page 382). Along with increasing evidence that galaxy collisions were commonplace, this inspired the development of a rival hierarchical or 'bottom-up' theory of galaxy formation, published in 1978 by Leonard Searle and Robert Zinn. In this model, galaxies coalesce through the piecemeal merger of smaller

RIGHT This detail from a Hubble Space Telescope survey of the Coma Galaxy Cluster, some 320 million light years from Earth, shows lenticular and elliptical galaxies concentrated near the cluster's centre.

units, developing more complex forms as they grow from irregulars (rich in star-forming gas and dust but with little structure), into spirals. When large spirals collide, shock waves heat their star-forming gas clouds to such a degree that they can no longer collapse to create new stars, but instead the gas escapes to form a halo around the galaxy (a process called 'ram pressure stripping'). Star formation ceases and the surviving stars coalesce into a ball-shaped elliptical galaxy.

Since the 1980s, numerous lines of evidence have emerged to show that the hierarchical model is largely correct: the tendency for the largest giant elliptical galaxies to lie at the centre of galaxy clusters; the presence of hot X-ray emitting gas, dissociated from the galaxies, at the centre of clusters; and the discovery of numerous small blue irregulars, the building blocks of today's galaxies, in the early Universe. Studies of the way invisible dark matter is distributed in relation to galaxies support the hierarchical theory, as do individual galaxy mergers that have been studied in detail (see page 383).

> 'In the "ELS" model, galaxies collapsed from a single cloud of gas in a relatively short period of time, triggering a burst of starbirth in the core which rapidly used up its star-forming material.'

A hybrid theory

Despite this, hierarchy cannot be the end of the story – on its own it struggles to explain the lenticulars and other galaxies that seem to be ellipticals transforming back into spirals. In 2002, German astronomer Matthias Steinmetz of the Steward Observatory, Arizona, and his Argentinian colleague Julio Navarro of the University of Victoria, British Columbia, presented evidence that the 'top-down' model may also have a part to play. Using computer simulations, they showed how clouds of cool neutral hydrogen in the intergalactic medium continuously supply new gas to galaxies in the form of HVCs. This infalling gas allows spirals such as our own to maintain their high rates of star formation, and also allows ellipticals to 'regenerate' their discs (passing through a lenticular phase) and ultimately recreate their spiral arms. As a result, it may only be after several generations of mergers and regenerations, once all the nearby cool intergalactic gas has been exhausted, that merged galaxies finally settle into a last giant elliptical state.

Convincing though this 'hybrid hierarchical' model seems, it still leaves some significant questions unanswered. For instance, no one knows quite what process slows and halts the collapse of a galaxy before it becomes too dense – suggestions range from the radiation pressure produced by its individual stars, to the gravitational 'tug' of dark matter that remains in the galaxy's halo region. A more direct challenge to the current paradigm has come from the 2011 discovery of large numbers of elliptical galaxies in the very early Universe. The stars within these galaxies appear to be relatively young, but producing ellipticals so soon after the Big Bang itself seems to require that newborn galaxies were merging together at a furious, perhaps unsustainable, rate. It may be that the saga of galaxy evolution has a few more surprises in store.

97

Gravitational lensing

DEFINITION THE DEFLECTION OF LIGHT FROM DISTANT OBJECTS, CAUSED BY ITS PASSAGE CLOSE TO LARGE MASSES, CREATING MULTIPLE OR DISTORTED IMAGES.

DISCOVERY THE THEORY OF LENSING WAS EXPLORED BY EINSTEIN AS EARLY AS 1912, BUT HE DID NOT PUBLISH HIS IDEAS UNTIL 1936.

KEY BREAKTHROUGH IN 1979, ASTRONOMERS DETECTED THE FIRST GRAVITATIONALLY LENSED QUASAR.

IMPORTANCE LENSING PROVIDES AN IMPORTANT MECHANISM FOR IDENTIFYING EXTREMELY DISTANT GALAXIES, AND ALSO FOR MAPPING DARK MATTER IN INTERVENING OBJECTS.

The deflection of light rays as they pass through strong gravitational fields is a natural consequence of Einstein's general theory of relativity – but it took some time for astronomers to realize that it could also offer a powerful tool for spotting faint galaxies in the early Universe.

In 1919, Arthur Eddington famously used the deflection of starlight around the Sun during a total solar eclipse to prove Einstein's general theory of relativity (see page 45). According to classical physics, light rays, since they are massless, should be unaffected by gravitational fields, but Einstein's theory described how large masses 'warp' the space around them, creating a distortion that even deflects the path of light. The effect, known as a 'gravitational lens', would not be seen elsewhere in the Universe for 60 years.

From theory to practice

Einstein had recorded the possibility of the gravitational lens effect in his private notes as early as 1912 – all it requires is a large concentration of mass at a suitable distance between an observer and a distant source of radiation. Since electromagnetic rays spread out from the source in all directions, some may travel directly to the observer, while others may begin their journey on a quite different path, only to pass through the region of space distorted by the mass and be deflected. As a result, the observer sees radiation from the same object coming from two (or more) different parts of the sky.

At first, Einstein and other astronomers viewed the phenomenon as little more than a curious side-effect of relativity. They were thinking mostly in terms of starlight being distorted by other stars, and the distances between stars are so great in relation to their size that the chances of such a perfect

OPPOSITE This Hubble Space Telescope view targets Abell 1689, a dense cluster of galaxies some 2.2 billion light years from Earth. Lensed images of more distant bluish-white galaxies can clearly be seen around the yellowish cluster galaxies.

alignment were negligible. It was not until 1936 that a Czech amateur scientist called Rudi Mandl persuaded Einstein to formally publish his ideas.

In the intervening decades, astronomy had changed beyond recognition thanks to the implication of Einstein's own work, and Edwin Hubble's confirmation of galaxies beyond the Milky Way. As a result, while Einstein himself still limited his description of lensing to stars, there was another far more suitable candidate for creating an observable effect. Galaxies and galaxy clusters are far more massive than individual stars, and are far more closely packed, relative to their size, than stars within a galaxy. As a result, the chance alignments required to producing lensing are inevitable, and the strength of the effect is far greater. Within a year, Swiss astronomer Fritz Zwicky had published the first prediction of lensing on a galactic scale.

'Where lensing is caused by a foreground galaxy cluster, the pattern of lensed images can be used to probe the distribution of mass within the cluster, revealing the presence of unseen dark matter.'

Despite this breakthrough, technological limitations still put galactic lenses beyond the reach of observation. It was only in the 1960s, with the discovery of quasars (see page 369), that astronomers began to seriously search for signs of the phenomenon. Various geometric configurations, such as the 'Einstein cross' (with four lensed images around the central intervening mass) and the 'Einstein ring' (in which the image of the distant object is spread out in a perfect circle around the foreground object) were predicted. Eventually in 1979 Dennis Walsh, Robert Carswell and Ray Weymann of Kitt Peak National Observatory in Arizona showed that a 'double quasar' called SBS 0857+561 was actually two lensed images of the same distant object. The next decade saw the discovery of several more lensed quasars, including the first Einstein cross in 1985, and the first Einstein ring in 1988.

Putting lenses to work

However, it is only with advances in telescope technology since the 1990s that gravitational lensing has gone from a scientific curiosity to a valuable astronomical research tool. Dozens of lensed systems are now known, with background objects ranging from quasars to normal galaxies and even galaxy clusters, and foreground objects also ranging from individual galaxies to clusters. The Hubble Space Telescope has even revealed cases in which the light from one galaxy cluster is distorted by its passage through another. These systems, in which the distortion of the background object is easily visible, are examples of 'strong' lensing, and can reveal features of both the foreground and background object. For instance, where the lensing is caused by a foreground galaxy cluster, the pattern of lensed images can be used to probe the distribution of mass within the cluster, revealing for example the presence of unseen dark matter (see page 397).

In some circumstances, lensing can also intensify the light from a more distant object, bringing it within range of telescopes when it would otherwise

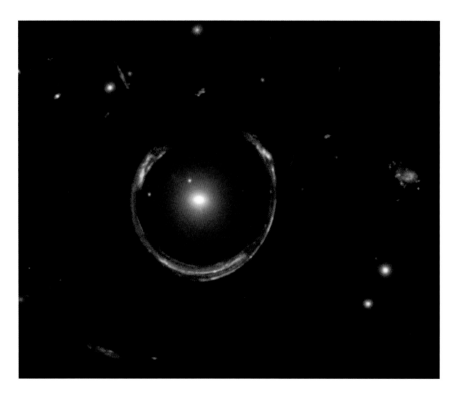

LEFT This horseshoe-like structure is a near-perfect Einstein Ring, in which a distant galaxy has had its light deflected very evenly back towards Earth. The more distant galaxy is thought to be around 10.7 billion light years away.

be invisible. This technique has allowed astronomers to identify the most distant galaxies yet seen within images such as the Hubble Ultra-Deep Field (see page 49). Using sophisticated modelling techniques, astronomers can also 'reconstruct' the original lensed object to learn more about it.

In addition to traditional 'strong' lensing, astronomers now recognize two other important effects. 'Weak' lensing, as its name suggests, does not create visibly warped images of distant galaxies, but instead creates much weaker distortions that can only be found by analysing the images of large numbers of galaxies and looking for unexpected patterns in their apparent shapes. Weak lensing is a powerful tool for measuring the distribution of mass in intergalactic space, and potentially discovering more about both dark matter and dark energy (see page 401).

'Microlensing', meanwhile, is a transient effect that alters the brightness of the lensed object, by temporarily deflecting more of its light towards Earth. This effect usually involves small bodies such as stars, and is essentially the type of lensing first noted by Einstein in 1912 and dismissed as statistically improbable. Today, it is used to detect extrasolar planets passing in front of their parent stars (see page 287). Microlensing in the light from stars in the Magellanic Clouds has also been used to detect possible 'Massive Compact Halo Objects' (MACHOs). These dense, dark objects are thought to lurk in the halo regions around our galaxy and others, and could make an important contribution to dark matter.

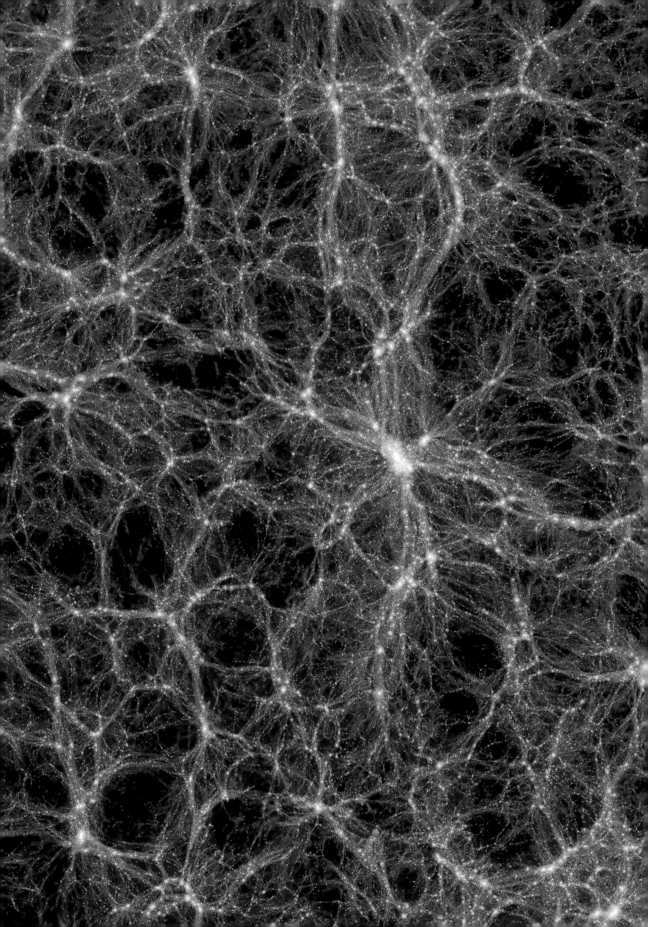

98

Dark matter

DEFINITION MATTER IN THE UNIVERSE THAT EMITS NO RADIATION, REVEALING ITSELF ONLY THROUGH GRAVITATIONAL EFFECTS.

DISCOVERY FRITZ ZWICKY INFERRED THE PRESENCE OF DARK MATTER IN THE COMA GALAXY CLUSTER IN 1933.

KEY BREAKTHROUGH THE ICECUBE NEUTRINO OBSERVATORY HAS HELPED TO CONFIRM THE TRUE COMPOSITION OF DARK MATTER IN THE UNIVERSE.

IMPORTANCE DARK MATTER HAS A HUGE EFFECT ON THE DEVELOPMENT OF THE UNIVERSE AT ALL SCALES.

With a hundred billion galaxies or more, the Universe might seem pretty crowded. But everywhere we look, there's evidence that the visible matter accounts for only a small proportion of the Universe's overall mass. The rest, an estimated 95 percent, is invisible, elusive 'dark matter'.

At first, it might seem unsurprising that much of the cosmos is 'dark' – after all, stars are just about the only objects capable of emitting their own light, and everything else merely shines by reflection of, or excitation from, stellar light sources. However, when astronomers talk of dark matter, they are not merely talking about material too faint or cold to shine in visible light – such objects always emit radiation of some sort (either infrared or radio waves), and they take this into account in their estimates of the overall amount of detectable or 'baryonic' matter. True dark matter simply does not interact with light or other electromagnetic radiations at all. The evidence for dark matter comes from a range of sources. Theoretical cosmologists point to a woeful mismatch between the amounts of matter predicted to have formed in the Big Bang and that observed in reality. Astronomers, meanwhile, find galaxies rotating in ways that contradict their distribution of baryonic matter, and see galaxy clusters produce lensing effects (see page 393) that suggest huge amounts of unaccounted-for mass within them.

The nature of dark matter

But what exactly is dark matter? Rather than seeking a single solution, most astronomers believe there are several different types contributing to the total enormous mass. A small proportion may in fact be relatively normal, but hard-to-detect objects such as stray planets, 'black dwarfs' (the cold remains of a white dwarf star) or even black holes. Lurking in the halos of spiral

OPPOSITE This supercomputer simulation shows the distribution of dark matter in the local Universe. The region shown is around 200 million light years distance across. Cold dark matter forms vast halos (bright yellow) around visible matter such as galaxies (coloured pink).

galaxies, these objects are often known as MACHOs (Massive Compact Halo Objects), and a few have been observed through their effects on the light of other stars.

The vast majority of dark matter, however, is thought to consist of huge amounts of subatomic particles. Cosmologists often make distinctions between cold dark matter (which moves at 'classical' speeds similar to normal objects in the Universe), warm dark matter, which moves at speeds approaching that of light and is therefore affected by special relativity (see page 43), and hot dark matter which moves at even faster speeds.

Hot and cold

The constraints of physics mean that warm and hot dark matter particles are likely to be extremely light, and therefore are unlikely to contribute much to the overall quantity of dark matter unless they are present in truly enormous quantities. For a long time, cosmologists hoped that neutrinos – the tiny and apparently massless particles created in huge numbers by the nuclear fusion process within stars, would prove to have a mass after all, and that this might solve the dark matter problem. In 1998, scientists at Japan's Super-Kamiokande detector established that neutrinos do indeed have a mass, but it turned out to be even less than expected. These particles contribute a

BELOW This composite image shows the pattern of light and dark matter in a cluster known as 'the Bullet'. The cluster lies 3.4 billion light years away, and is the result of a collision between two original clusters. A map of X-ray emission is overlaid on a Hubble image in pink, while the distribution of dark matter, calculated from lensing effects, is shown in blue. While the cluster collision has stripped the hot gas away from the galaxies, the dark matter and individual galaxies have been largely unaffected.

small amount to the Universe's overall mass, and thus they cannot explain the entire discrepancy between visible matter and gravitational behaviour.

Assuming they exist, most hot dark matter particles are thought to be so lightweight and fast-moving that they are barely influenced by gravity on the local scale (that of galaxies and galaxy clusters) at all. Instead cosmologists believe that this matter permeates the cosmos uniformly, with most of it actually lying far from the luminous parts of the Universe, lurking undetected in the huge voids that lie between filaments and sheets of galaxy clusters (see page 386).

'When astronomers talk of dark matter, they are not merely talking about material too faint or cold to shine in visible light. True dark matter simply does not interact with light or other electromagnetic radiations at all.'

While hot dark matter offers a solution to cosmological problems with the overall mass of the Universe, the relatively localized effects seen in galaxies and galaxy clusters require a different form of matter that remains in fairly close association with the visible mass of the Universe. This is cold dark matter – particles whose mass and relatively slow motion allow them to be influenced by local gravitational effects.

MACHOs are one component of cold dark matter whose existence has been confirmed, even if their abundance and contribution to the overall 'missing mass' has not been. However, even here astronomers are largely forced to rely on hypothetical particles, nicknamed WIMPs (Weakly Interactive Massive Particles).

Observing on ice

In the past few years, scientists have begun to get a more detailed picture of dark matter using a unique new observatory deep within the ice of Antarctica. The IceCube Neutrino Observatory consists of 'strings' of particle detectors deployed in shafts drilled to depths of 1,450–2,450 m (4,750–8,000 ft). Neutrinos are able to pass through this thick layer of ice largely unaffected (just as they pass through the entire planet Earth in huge numbers every second), while other types of particle from space are unable to penetrate this far down. Very occasionally, a neutrino will interact with molecules in the ice, creating particles of normal matter that emit a burst of light called 'Cerenkov radiation' (see page 42), and the depth and direction of travel of the radiation, recorded by the detectors, can reveal information about the neutrino that created it.

But how does this help to detect dark matter? According to theoretical models, the Sun's gravity should be enough to attract some WIMPs, causing them to collect in its core and occasionally 'annihilate' one another, producing a burst of particles including neutrinos with distinctive properties. IceCube has detected an excess of these neutrinos coming from the direction of the Sun, and calculations suggest that WIMPs are annihilating in such numbers that they are probably the dominant element of dark matter.

99 | Dark energy

DEFINITION THE RECENT IDENTIFICATION OF A PREVIOUSLY UNKNOWN FORCE THAT IS DRIVING COSMIC EXPANSION.

DISCOVERY DARK ENERGY WAS IDENTIFIED THROUGH OBSERVATIONS OF DISTANT SUPERNOVAE IN THE LATE 1990s.

KEY BREAKTHROUGH IN 2008, DATA FROM THE WMAP PROBE CONFIRMED THAT DARK ENERGY ACCOUNTS FOR 72.8 PERCENT OF ALL ENERGY IN THE UNIVERSE.

IMPORTANCE UNDERSTANDING DARK ENERGY IS VITAL TO IMPROVING OUR KNOWLEDGE OF THE PAST AND FUTURE OF THE UNIVERSE.

The fact that the expansion of the Universe is accelerating rather than slowing down has been one of the biggest cosmological discoveries of the past century, but astronomers are still struggling to understand the true nature of this mysterious 'dark energy'.

In the late 1990s, while work on the Hubble Space Telescope Key Project to measure the rate of cosmic expansion was underway (see page 51), two teams set out to double-check its results by an ingenious technique. No one expected to find evidence that the Universe today is expanding more rapidly than it did in earlier times, but this discovery, today known as 'dark energy', has revolutionized our ideas about the evolution and fate of the Universe.

Supernova cosmology

The main Hubble project to measure the expansion of the Universe relied on the detection of Cepheid variable stars in relatively nearby galaxies (out to around 200 million light years away). Because the periodic pulsations of these stars are linked to their intrinsic brightness, they can be used as 'standard candles' – objects whose true luminosity is known, and whose apparent brightness therefore indicates their distance from Earth (see page 31). However, independent verification of results is a key scientific principle, and in the late 1990s two independent teams – the international 'High-Z Supernova Search Team' (High-Z being a shorthand for high-redshift), and the Supernova Cosmology Project based at Lawrence Berkeley National Laboratory planned to cross-check the Cepheid results.

In order to do this, they used another standard candle, known as a Type 1a supernova. While most supernovae are caused by the deaths of massive

OPPOSITE In 2010, astronomers used the Hubble Space Telescope to measure the 'dark energy' across a small area of space. By measuring the gravitational lensing effect around galaxy cluster Abell 1689, they were able to calculate its dark matter distribution (overlaid in blue). Once this is known, the distortions seen in the background galaxies can be used to probe the strength of dark energy across the intervening space.

stars, and therefore release varying amounts of energy depending on the mass of material involved and the type of supernova remnant created, Type 1a explosions are different – they occur in nova systems (see page 315) where a white dwarf of 1.4 solar masses is tipped over the 'Chandrasekhar limit' by accumulation of material from a companion star. Above this limit, the stellar remnant is no longer able to support its own weight, and collapses violently to create a neutron star. Because the process is essentially the same in every case, the amount of energy released in a Type 1a supernova should also be the same, and so the apparent brightness of the explosion is a direct indicator of its distance. Like all supernovae, Type 1a explosions are quite rare, but fortunately they are bright enough to briefly outshine entire galaxies, and modern telescopes can spot them over enormous distances.

By measuring the intensity of distant supernovae and the redshifts of their host galaxies, the astronomers hoped to not only confirm the Cepheid-based measurements of cosmic expansion, but also to measure the rate at which the expansion was slowing down. At the time, it was an unspoken assumption that the gravity of the Universe would be gradually slowing its expansion, and cosmologists were keen to measure the exact speed of this deceleration in order to understand the possible destiny of the cosmos (see page 405). The deceleration should show its presence through a discrepancy in the most distant galaxies, where the supernovae would be brighter (and therefore closer) than their redshifts suggested.

Dark energy uncovered

But by the late 1990s, after several years of work, both teams had reached the same extraordinary conclusion: far from appearing brighter than expected, the distant supernovae actually looked fainter. The conclusion was inescapable – something was causing the expansion of the Universe to accelerate. In 1998, cosmologist Michael Turner argued that some kind of universal energy field, spread throughout the Universe, must be at work: he named it 'dark energy' as a counterpart to Fritz Zwicky's 'dark matter' (see page 397).

'It's only in relatively recent times, as normal and dark matter have become more thinly spread, that dark energy has begun to exert its influence.'

For such a controversial discovery, dark energy was accepted by the scientific community with surprising speed. This was partly due to the strong evidence gathered by two independent teams, but also because dark energy helped to resolve some other major problems. In particular, analysis of the cosmic microwave background radiation (see page 53) had suggested that the Universe was essentially 'flat', implying that it must contain a great deal more energy than accounted for by either 'normal' or dark matter. Dark energy, although undetectable, can account for the huge amounts of missing energy. According to data from the Wilson Microwave Anisotropy Probe published in 2008, energy in the Universe is probably distributed between 22.7 percent dark matter, 72.8 percent dark energy, and just 4.6 percent ordinary matter.

Properties and theories

Since the initial discovery, the existence of dark energy has been confirmed by several other techniques. It has yet to be detected in any laboratory-based experiment, and appears to make its presence felt only through its 'antigravity' effect. According to some estimates, its density is equivalent to one hundred-thousand-billionth of a gram per cubic kilometre (0.24 cubic miles) of space. Nevertheless, some of the new experiments have revealed tantalising hints, such as the fact that until around 5 billion years ago the expansion of the Universe was decelerating in the expected manner. It's only in relatively recent times, as normal and dark matter have become more thinly spread, that dark energy has begun to exert its influence.

But are scientists any closer to understanding exactly what it is? At present there are two leading theories, known as the 'cosmological constant' and 'quintessence'. The cosmological constant traces its origins back for almost a century to an idea abandoned by Albert Einstein. Prior to the discovery of cosmic expansion, he introduced it to general relativity as a means to reconcile his theory's prediction of a collapsing Universe with what seemed at the time to be a uniform cosmos. Some cosmologists now believe that the constant, essentially an energy field embedded within the fabric of space itself, provides an ideal candidate for dark energy. Quintessence, in contrast, is another kind of energy field independent of spacetime and capable of varying its distribution through space and over time. In some theories, the amount of quintessence increases exponentially over time, with potentially disastrous consequences (see page 407).

ABOVE Type 1a supernova explosions in distant galaxies (shown here in visible, ultraviolet and X-ray wavelengths) led to the surprising discovery that the expansion of the Universe is accelerating, driven by the mysterious force of dark energy.

The fate of the Universe

DEFINITION MODELS OF THE POSSIBLE FUTURE EVOLUTION OF THE UNIVERSE, AND ITS ULTIMATE DESTINY.

DISCOVERY WILLIAM THOMSON DEVELOPED THE IDEA OF 'HEAT DEATH' IN AN ETERNAL UNIVERSE DURING THE 1850s.

KEY BREAKTHROUGH IN THE 1920s, ALEXANDER FRIEDMANN WAS THE FIRST TO PROPOSE THE POSSIBILITY OF A 'CLOSED' UNIVERSE.

IMPORTANCE UNDERSTANDING THE END OF THE UNIVERSE APPEALS TO OUR PHILOSOPHICAL, AS WELL AS SCIENTIFIC, CURIOSITY.

Speculations about the way the Universe will end are almost as popular as theories about its origin, and exert a strong fascination for both cosmologists and lay people. While there are several competing scientific theories, the discovery of dark energy may have tilted the playing field decisively.

In the early 20th century, most astronomers believed that the Universe was infinite in both space and time – it had existed forever, and would continue to exist into the indefinite future. What happened to the material within it, however, was another matter – the laws of thermodynamics developed by French scientist Nicolas Sadi Carnot and German physicist Rudolf Clausius in the early 19th century appeared to doom the Universe to a slow decline.

Thermodynamics describes the way in which energy is transferred within a system, and in particular defines the fact that, while orderly structure can only be maintained using energy, energy itself has a tendency to become less concentrated and more widely distributed between particles – a phenomenon known as entropy. Based on these ideas, in the 1850s English scientist William Thomson, Lord Kelvin, developed the idea of 'heat death' in which all structure in the Universe will eventually disintegrate and the average temperature of the Universe will slowly decline.

A finite Universe

It was against this background that 20th-century cosmologists developed the Big Bang theory, with its implication of a definite beginning to the Universe in the relatively recent past (see page 57). And along with a finite beginning came the prospect of a potential end of the Universe. Since the Universe was still expanding from the initial explosion, it made sense to

OPPOSITE In one possible scenario for the end of the Universe, cosmic expansion is reversed (either by the pull of gravity or by a change in the behaviour of dark energy), and the Universe collapses back to a 'Big Crunch'.

consider whether this expansion would continue forever, or whether the Universe's own gravity would slow the expansion and perhaps eventually reverse it. Soviet cosmologist Alexander Friedmann, one of the pioneers of the Big Bang theory in the 1920s, was perhaps the first to identify this possibility, postulating an 'oscillating Universe' that passed through successive phases of expansion and contraction (see page 57).

Once the Big Bang theory was fully established in the later 20th century, astronomers concluded that measuring the density of matter in the Universe, through a quantity known as Ω (Omega), the density parameter, was crucial to understanding its possible fate. Theoreticians predicted three possible scenarios: a closed Universe in which gravity would overcome expansion, causing the Universe to collapse back into a cataclysmic 'Big Crunch'; an open Universe in which expansion continued forever without significantly slowing down; and an intermediate flat Universe in which gravity slows down the rate of expansion until it is negligible, but never quite reverses it. In both the open and flat scenarios, Kelvin's heat death may ultimately come into play after trillions of years.

Attempts to measure Ω between the 1970s and 1990s all appeared to suggest that the density of matter was close to the critical value required for a flat Universe, but then in 1998, cosmologists announced the discovery of dark energy, an unexpected force that is actually accelerating the expansion of the cosmos (see page 401). This discovery meant that the 'dust solutions' previously used (in which gravitational collapse is the only significant factor to be considered) were dramatically overturned. It also appeared to settle the debate conclusively in favour of an 'open' Universe.

BELOW Possible fates of the Universe. The Universe today is expanding at an increasing rate, powered by the initial impetus of the Big Bang and the subsequent influence of dark energy. In the future the expansion may slow down gradually, accelerate further, or reverse, giving rise to a 'Big Chill', a 'Big Rip', or a 'Big Crunch'.

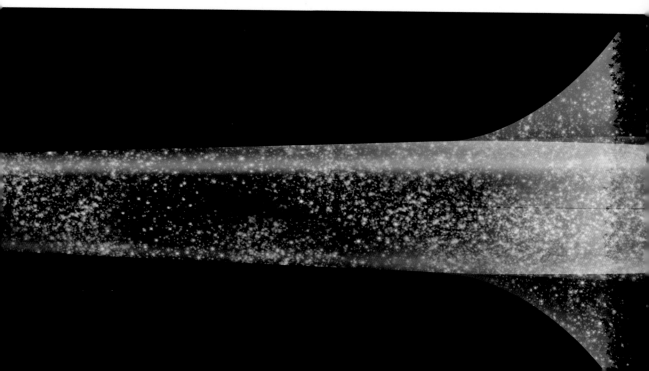

Modern theories

But there are other factors to consider. Recent measurements show that effects of dark energy have not always been constant, and that acceleration only began to take effect around 5 billion years ago. According to the 'cosmological constant' theory of dark energy, this is a natural consequence of the changing balance between dark energy and normal and dark matter in an expanding Universe, but there are other possibilities. American cosmologist Robert Caldwell has suggested a form of dark energy known as 'phantom energy', which could grow stronger exponentially over time until eventually both space and the matter within it are torn apart in a so-called 'Big Rip'. Conversely, Andrei Linde of California's Stanford University has suggested dark energy might one day reverse its effect, pulling the Universe back together and dooming it to a Big Crunch, perhaps on a relatively short timescale of another 10–20 billion years.

'In the 1850s English scientist Lord Kelvin developed the idea of "heat death", in which all structure in the Universe will disintegrate and its average temperature will slowly decline.'

Of course, some other cosmological theories suggest that the fate of the Universe might not be as simple as choosing between open, closed and flat scenarios. Some of the characteristics of Friedmann's oscillating Universe have recently been revived in theories such as loop quantum cosmology (see page 62), predicting the possibility of a rebounding Universe or 'Big Bounce'. Even if expansion does continue without end, dooming the cosmos to a cold 'heat death' or a violent Big Rip, brane theory (see page 63) suggests that another force acting in unseen dimensions could ultimately trigger the creation of a new Universe. Finally Linde's chaotic inflation theory (see page 62) suggests that, whatever the fate of our Universe, it may ultimately be just one small bubble among an infinite number, and that new Universes, giving rise to new species of stargazers, are constantly being born.

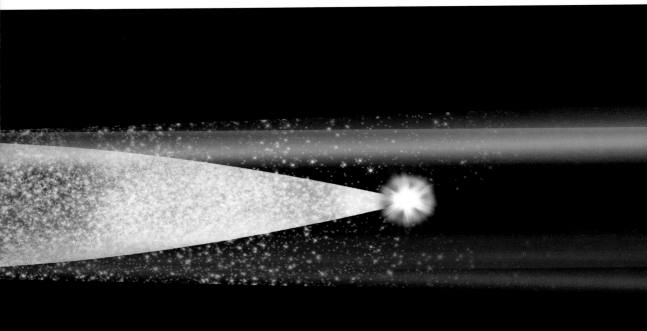

Glossary

Accretion disc
A flattened disc of material spiralling onto a dense object at its centre under the influence of gravity. Accretion discs are a common feature of many astronomical systems – heated by extreme tidal forces around superdense objects such as neutron stars and black holes, they can often emit X-rays and other radiation.

Active galaxy
A galaxy that emits large amounts of energy from its central regions, probably generated as matter falls into a supermassive black hole at its heart.

Antimatter
A form of matter in which elementary particles are identical to their 'normal matter' counterparts, but have opposite electrical charge.

Asteroid
One of countless small rocky worlds in the inner solar system, largely confined to the asteroid belt beyond the orbit of Mars.

Astronomical unit
A unit of measurement widely used in astronomy, equivalent to Earth's average distance from the Sun – roughly 150 million km or 93 million miles.

Atmosphere
A shell of gases held around a planet or star by its gravity.

Barred spiral galaxy
A spiral galaxy in which the arms are linked to the hub by a straight bar of stars and other material.

Big Bang
An enormous explosion 13.7 billion years ago that created time, space and all the energy and matter in the Universe.

Binary star
A pair of stars in orbit around one another. Because the stars in a binary pair were usually born at the same time, they allow a direct comparison of the way that stars with different properties evolve.

Black hole
A superdense point in space formed by a collapsing stellar core more than five times the mass of the Sun. A black hole's gravity is so powerful that even light cannot escape from it.

Boson
A massless elementary particle responsible for transferring forces between matter particles. Bosons include the photon, which transfers electromagnetic force, the gluon, which transfers the strong nuclear force, and the W and Z particles, which transmit the weak nuclear force. Gravity-carrying gravitons remain hypothetical.

Brown dwarf
A so-called 'failed star' that never gains enough mass to begin the fusion of hydrogen in its core and start to shine properly. Instead, brown dwarfs radiate low-energy radiation (mostly infrared) through gravitational contraction and a more limited form of fusion.

Centaur
An icy body that orbits the Sun between the paths of the outer planets.

Cepheid variable
An important class of variable stars, consisting of brilliant, pulsating yellow supergiants. The rate of pulsation in Cepheids is related to their intrinsic luminosity, allowing them to be used as 'standard candles' for intergalactic distance measurements.

Chondrite
A meteorite of the most common type, composed of chondrules – condensed nodules of primitive material from the early solar system.

Comet
A chunk of rock and ice from the outer reaches of the solar system. When comets fall into orbits that bring them close to the Sun, they heat up and their surface ices evaporate, forming a coma and a tail.

Cosmic microwave background radiation (CMBR)
Weak radiation from all over the sky, reaching us from the edge of the visible Universe. The CMBR is redshifted light from the Universe's 'last scattering surface', and allows us to see back to the era when the Universe became transparent.

Cosmic ray
A high-energy particle entering Earth's atmosphere from space. Cosmic rays have a variety of origins, from the surface of the Sun to the regions around supermassive black holes.

Cryovolcanism
A strange form of geological activity found on some of the icy moons of the outer solar system. Cryovolcanism typically involves eruptions of runny ice, kept 'molten' by the presence of significant amounts of ammonia.

Dark energy
A recently discovered force that appears to be accelerating the expansion of the cosmos. The true nature of dark energy, and its long-term consequences for the evolution of the Universe, are still unknown.

Dark matter
The dominant form of matter in the Universe, a substance that does not emit or interact with electromagnetic radiation and so far can be detected only through its gravitational effects. Dark matter is thought to be dominated by hitherto undiscovered types of particle, but massive dark objects such as burnt-out stellar remnants and planets may make a significant contribution.

Dark nebula
A cloud of interstellar gas and dust that absorbs light, and only becomes visible when silhouetted against a field of stars or other nebulae.

Doppler effect
The phenomenon by which the wavelengths of electromagnetic radiation from distant objects are compressed (blueshifted) or stretched (redshifted) when the object is approaching or receding relative to an observer. Redshift caused by the Doppler effect is the key evidence that the Universe is expanding.

Dwarf planet
Any object that is in an independent orbit around the Sun, and has sufficient gravity to pull itself into a roughly spherical shape, but which, unlike a true planet, has not cleared the region around it of other objects. Currently there are three known dwarf planets – Ceres, Pluto and Eris – but there are many more objects whose status is currently uncertain.

Eclipsing binary
A binary star in which one star regularly passes in front of another as seen from Earth, causing a drop in the overall brightness of the system.

Electromagnetic radiation

A form of energy consisting of combined electric and magnetic waves, able to propagate itself across a vacuum at the speed of light. The energy or temperature of the object emitting radiation affects its wavelength and other characteristics.

Electron

A lightweight elementary particle with negative electric charge. Electrons orbit in shells around an atomic nucleus, and the number of electrons in the outermost shell of an atom governs its chemical behaviour.

Elementary particle

Any particle that cannot be subdivided into smaller fragments. According to current models of the structure of matter, the major families of elementary particles are the quarks, leptons and bosons.

Elliptical galaxy

A galaxy consisting of stars in orbits that have no particular orientation, and generally lacking in star-forming gas. Ellipticals are among the smallest and largest galaxies known.

Emission nebula

A cloud of gas in space that glows at very specific wavelengths, producing a spectrum full of emission lines. These nebulae are usually energized by the high-energy light of nearby stars, and are often associated with regions of star formation.

Flare

A huge release of superheated particles above the surface of a star, caused by a short-circuit in its magnetic field.

Flare star

A small, low-mass star that is normally faint, but is prone to violent eruptions on its surface, similar to solar flares.

Fusion shell

A spherical shell of nuclear fusion spreading out through a star after it exhausts a particular fuel supply in its core.

Galaxy

An independent system of stars, gas and other material with a size measured in thousands of light years.

Gamma rays

The highest-energy forms of electromagnetic radiation, with extremely short wavelengths, generated by the hottest objects and most energetic processes in the Universe.

Giant planet

A planet comprising a huge envelope of gas, liquid, or slushy ice (various frozen chemicals), perhaps around a relatively small rocky core.

Globular cluster

A dense ball of ancient, long-lived stars, in orbit around a galaxy such as the Milky Way.

Gravitational lens

A large concentration of mass that bends the path of light rays passing near it, producing a distorted, and sometimes intensified, image of more distant objects. Dense galaxy clusters produce the most easily detected lensing effects.

Habitable zone

The region around a star where moderate temperatures allow water to exist in liquid form on the surface of any substantial planets that may orbit there. Because it is neither too hot, nor too cold, this region is often referred to as the 'Goldilocks zone'.

Helium fusion

Nuclear fusion of helium (formed by hydrogen fusion) into heavier elements (so-called metals). Most stars rely on helium fusion to keep on shining when they exhaust their supplies of hydrogen near the end of their lives.

Hydrogen fusion

The nuclear fusion of hydrogen, the lightest element, into helium, the next lightest. Hydrogen fusion is the main power source for all stars for the majority of their lives. It proceeds at different rates depending on conditions within a star.

Hypernova

A stellar explosion even more energetic than a supernova, in which the death of a massive star gives rise to a black hole. Astronomers believe that radiation and particles from the resulting explosion may be channelled along narrow beams, giving rise to intense bursts of gamma rays.

Infrared

Electromagnetic radiation with slightly less energy than visible light. Infrared radiation is typically emitted by warm objects too cool to glow visibly.

Inflation

An event that occurred a minute fraction of a second after the Big Bang itself, during which the infant Universe underwent a sudden and dramatic expansion.

Irregular galaxy

A galaxy with no obvious structure, generally rich in gas, dust and star-forming regions.

Kelvin–Helmholtz mechanism

A mechanism by which the slow condensation of denser material in the cores of giant planets and other dense gaseous bodies generates heat.

Kuiper Belt

A doughnut-shaped ring of icy worlds directly beyond the orbit of Neptune. The largest known Kuiper Belt Objects are Pluto and Eris.

Lagrangian point

One of several gravitational 'balance points' related to the orbit of one massive body around another (such as the Moon around the Earth, or the Earth around the Sun). The Lagrangian points mark spots where objects such as 'Trojan' moons or asteroids can orbit while avoiding disruption from either of the larger bodies.

Last scattering surface

The spherical surface marking the point where the early Universe became transparent, around 400,000 years after the Big Bang. Up until this point, space was so densely packed with particles that it was opaque and foggy, so the last scattering surface marks the earliest stage in cosmic history that we can observe, and the origin of the cosmic microwave background radiation.

Lepton

One of a group of lightweight elementary particles. According to the standard model of particle physics, there are six leptons: the electron, muon and tau particle, and matching electron, muon and tau neutrinos.

Light year

A common unit of astronomical measurement, equivalent to the distance travelled by light (or other electromagnetic radiation) in one year. A light year is equivalent to roughly 9.5 million million km (5.9 trillion miles).

Luminosity

A measure of the energy output of a star. Although luminosity is technically measured in watts, the stars are so luminous that it is simpler to compare them with the Sun. A star's visual luminosity (the energy it produces in visible light) is not necessarily equivalent to its overall luminosity in all radiations.

Main sequence

A term used to describe the longest phase in a star's life, during which it is relatively stable and shines by fusing hydrogen into helium at its core. During this period, the star obeys a general relationship that links its mass, size, luminosity and colour.

Multiple star

A system of two or more stars in orbit around one another (pairs of stars are also called binaries). Most of the stars in our galaxy are members of multiple systems rather than individuals like the Sun.

Nebula

Any cloud of gas or dust floating in space. Nebulae are the material from which stars are born, and into which they are scattered again at the end of their lives. The word means cloud in Latin, and was originally applied to any fuzzy object in the sky, including some we now know to be star clusters or distant galaxies.

Neutrino

A near-massless lepton particle produced by nuclear fusion in the Sun and other stars. Three types are known – the electron, muon and tau neutrinos.

Neutron

A subatomic particle found in the nuclei of atoms that possesses significant mass but no electric charge. Neutrons are composed of two down quarks and an up quark.

Neutron star

The collapsed core of a supermassive star, left behind by a supernova explosion. A neutron star consists of subatomic neutrons compressed to incredible density. Many neutron stars initially behave as pulsars.

Nova

A binary star system in which a white dwarf is pulling material from a companion star, building up a layer of gas around itself that then burns away in a violent nuclear explosion.

Nuclear fusion

The joining-together of light atomic nuclei (the central cores of atoms) to make heavier ones at very high temperatures and pressures, releasing excess energy in the process. Fusion is the process by which the stars shine.

Oort Cloud

A spherical shell of dormant comets, up to two light years across, surrounding the entire solar system.

Open cluster

A large group of bright young stars that have recently been born from the same star-forming nebula and may still be embedded in its gas clouds.

Planet

A world that follows its own orbit around the Sun or another star, is massive enough to pull itself into a spherical shape, and which has cleared the space around it of other objects (apart from satellites). According to this definition, there are eight planets in our solar system – Mercury, Venus, Earth, Mars, Jupiter, Saturn, Uranus and Neptune.

Planetary nebula

An expanding cloud of glowing gas sloughed off from the outer layers of a dying red giant star as it transforms into a white dwarf.

Population I

A population of stars with relatively high concentrations of heavy elements, similar to those in our Sun. Population I stars are typically found in the discs and spiral arms of spiral galaxies, and in irregular galaxies. Population I stars formed in the last few billion years of cosmic history, once the Universe had become enriched with heavier elements.

Population II

A population of stars with lower metal content than the Sun, found in globular star clusters, elliptical galaxies, and the central hub of spiral galaxies. Population II stars are thought to be remnants from the earlier Universe.

Population III

A hypothetical population of primitive stars with almost no metal content, thought to have been the first stars in the early Universe.

Proper motion

The movement of a star across the sky caused by its own motion across space, once effects caused by Earth's own movements have been removed.

Proton

A subatomic particle found in the nuclei of atoms that possesses significant mass and a positive electric charge. Protons are composed of two up quarks and a down quark, and the number of protons in an atomic nucleus determines its identity as an element.

Protoplanetary disc

A disc of gas and dust left in orbit around a newly formed star, out of which planets can form.

Pulsar

A rapidly spinning neutron star with an intense magnetic field that channels its radiation out along two narrow beams that sweep across the sky.

Quark

An elementary particle with substantial mass and electric charge, found in protons and neutrons – the subatomic particles that make up the nuclei of atoms.

Quark star

A hypothetical stellar remnant intermediate between a neutron star and a black hole, with a structure composed entirely of quarks.

Radar

A technique useful both in tracking objects such as aircraft and in mapping planetary surfaces. Radar (originally an acronym for Radio Detection and Ranging) involves sending a beam of radio waves towards a target and measuring the time for the echo to return in order to calculate the target's precise distance.

Radial velocity

The speed with which an object such as a star is moving towards or away from Earth. Detected through the Doppler effect, radial velocity is useful for measuring wobbles in the motion of stars that are linked to the influence of extrasolar planets.

Radio waves

The lowest-energy form of electromagnetic radiation, with the longest wavelengths. Radio waves are emitted by cool gas clouds in space, but also by violent active galaxies and pulsars.

Red dwarf

A star with considerably less mass than the Sun – small, faint and with a low surface temperature. Red dwarfs fuse hydrogen into helium in their cores very slowly, and live for much longer than Sun-like stars, despite their size.

Red giant

A star passing through a phase of its life where its luminosity has increased hugely, causing its outer layers to expand and its surface to cool. Stars usually enter red giant phases when they exhaust the fuel supplies in their core.

Reflection nebula

A cloud of interstellar gas and dust that shines through the reflection or scattering of light from nearby stars.

Rocky planet

A relatively small planet composed largely of rocks and minerals, perhaps surrounded by a thin envelope of gas and liquid.

Spectral lines

Dark or light bands in a spectrum of light. Bright emission lines indicate that an object is emitting certain wavelengths, while dark bands silhouetted against a broad background spectrum indicate that something is absorbing light before it reaches us. In both cases, the location of the lines offers information on which atoms or molecules are involved.

Spectroscopic binary

A binary star that can only be detected thanks to the shifting of the lines in its spectrum as its two components swing around one another.

Spectrum

The spread-out band of light created by passing light through a prism or similar device. The prism bends light by different amounts depending on its wavelength and colour, so the spectrum reveals the precise intensities of light at different wavelengths.

Spiral galaxy

A galaxy consisting of a hub of old yellow stars, surrounded by a flattened disk of younger stars, gas and dust, with spiral arms marking regions of current star formation.

Standard candle

Any astronomical object or event whose intrinsic luminosity can be calculated independently of assumptions about its distance. Standard candles such as Cepheid variables and certain supernovae provide an important way of directly estimating the distance of objects in remote parts of the Universe.

Star

A dense ball of gas that has collapsed under its own weight and become hot and dense enough to trigger nuclear fusion reactions in its core.

Stellar wind

A stream of high-energy particles blasted off the surface of a star by the pressure of its radiation, and spreading across the surrounding space.

Sun

The star at the centre of Earth's solar system. The Sun is a fairly average low-mass star, and a useful comparison for other stars. Its key properties include a diameter of 1.39 million kilometres, a mass of 2,000 trillion trillion tonnes, energy output of 380 trillion trillion watts, and a surface temperature of 5,500°C (9,900°F).

Sun-like star

A yellow star with roughly the same mass, luminosity and surface temperature as the Sun. Stars like this are of particular interest to astronomers because they are long-lived, stable, and any planets around them are potential havens for life.

Supergiant

A massive and extremely luminous star with between 10 and 70 times the mass of the Sun. Supergiants can have almost any colour, depending on how the balance of their energy output and their size affects their surface temperature.

Supermassive black hole

A black hole with the mass of millions of stars, believed to lie in the very centre of many galaxies. Supermassive black holes form from the collapse of huge gas clouds rather than the death of massive stars.

Supernova

A cataclysmic explosion marking the death of a star. Supernovae can be triggered when a heavyweight star exhausts the last of its fuel and its core collapses (forming either a neutron star or a black hole) or when a white dwarf in a nova system tips over its upper mass limit and collapses suddenly into a neutron star.

Supernova remnant

A cloud of superheated gas expanding from the site of a supernova explosion.

Tectonics

The geological process in which the crust of a planet or moon is broken into fragments that drift around on top of a semi-molten interior layer, leading to compression of the crust in some places, and stretching in others. In our solar system, Earth shows the most highly developed system of tectonics, but several other worlds show signs of tectonic activity in their past history.

Transit

The passage of one celestial body across the face of another – such as the movement of a planet across the face of a star.

Trojan

Any of a family of asteroids orbiting at the Lagrangian points of Jupiter's orbit, where the gravitational influences of the Sun and Jupiter are balanced. By extension, any object orbiting at a system's Lagrangian points.

Ultraviolet

Electromagnetic radiation with wavelengths slightly shorter than visible light, typically radiated by objects hotter than the Sun. The hottest stars give out much of their energy in the ultraviolet.

Variable star

Any star that changes its brightness. Some definitions include eclipsing binaries, but true variable stars undergo a physical change, such as cyclical or irregular pulsations in size, or cataclysmic explosions.

Visible light

Electromagnetic radiation with wavelengths between 400 and 700 nanometres (billionths of a metre), corresponding to the sensitivity of the human eye. Stars like the Sun emit most of their energy in the form of visible light.

White dwarf

A stellar remnant left behind by the death of a star with less than about eight times the Sun's mass. White dwarfs are the dense, slowly cooling cores of stars – typically very hot, but hard to see on account of their tiny size.

Wolf–Rayet star

A star with extremely high mass which develops such fierce stellar winds that it blows away most of its outer layers in a few million years, exposing the extremely hot interior.

X-rays

High-energy electromagnetic radiation emitted by extremely hot objects and violent processes in the Universe. Material heated as it is pulled towards a black hole is one of the strongest sources of astronomical X-rays.

Index

Quercus Editions Ltd.
55 Baker Street
7th floor, South Block
London
W1U 8EW

First published in 2012

Copyright © 2012 Giles Sparrow

UK and associated territories:
ISBN 978 1 78087 225 4

Design and editorial by Pikaia Imaging

Printed and bound in China

10 9 8 7 6 5 4 3 2 1

Giles Sparrow would like to thank Tim Brown at Pikaia, Dan Green for editorial assistance, and all the researchers who kindly shared their insight and provided images during the making of this book. And thanks, especially, to Katja Seibold for her constant inspiration and support.

2: NASA, ESA, and the Hubble Heritage (STScI/AURA)-ESA/Hubble Collaboration; 6-7: NASA, ESA, and F. Paresce (INAF-IASF, Bologna, Italy), R. O'Connell (University of Virginia, Charlottesville), and the Wide Field Camera 3 Science Oversight Committee; 8: Iztok Bon ina/ESO; 10: Pikaia Imaging; 12: Mark Garlick/Science Photo Library; 15: Tunç Tezel; 16: NASA, ESA and AURA/Caltech; 19: Pikaia Imaging; 20: NASA/DOE/Fermi LAT Collaboration, Capella Observatory, and Ilana Feain, Tim Cornwell, and Ron Ekers (CSIRO/ATNF), R. Morganti (ASTRON), and N. Junkes (MPIfR); 22: NASA/JPL-Caltech; 24: NSO/AURA/NSF; 27: NASA/JPL-Caltech/Univ.of Ariz.; 28: ESO/Y.Beletsky; 30: Bill Schoening, Vanessa Harvey/REU program/NOAO/AURA/NSF; 32: CERN; 35: Pikaia Imaging; 36: National Institute of Standards and Technology/Science Photo Library; 39: Guido Vrola/Shutterstock; 40: SuriyaPhoto/Shutterstock; 42: Argonne National Laboratory, U.S. Department of Energy; 44: Babak Trafreshi, TWAN/Science Photo Library; 46: Scientific Visualization by Werner Benger, Max-Planck-Institute for Gravitational Physics, Zuse-Institute Berlin, Center for Computation & Technology at Louisiana State University, University of Innsbruck. Scientific Computation by Ed Seidel / Numerical Relativity Group at Max-Planck-Institute for Gravitational Physics; 48: NASA, ESA, S. Beckwith (STScI) and the HUDF Team; 51: Pikaia Imaging; 52: NASA/WMAP Science Team/Science Photo Library; 54: NASA/COBE; 56: Michael Dunning/Science Photo Library; 58-9: Pikaia Imaging; 60: Detlev Van Ravenswaay/Science Photo Library; 63: Pikaia Imaging; 64: NASA/CXC/ASU/J. Hester et al.; 66: CERN; 68: Adolf Schaller for STScI; 71: NASA/JPL-Caltech/A. Kashlinsky (GSFC); 72: NASA, ESA, S. Gallagher (The University of Western Ontario), and J. English (University of Manitoba); 74: NASA, ESA, A. van der Wel (Max Planck Institute for Astronomy, Heidelberg, Germany), H. Ferguson and A. Koekemoer (Space Telescope Science Institute, Baltimore, Md.), and the CANDELS team; 76: NASA, ESA, and the Hubble Heritage Team (STScI/AURA); 78: NASA, ESA, and P. Hartigan (Rice University); 80: Courtesy of SOHO/LASCO consortium. SOHO is a project of international cooperation between ESA and NASA.; 83: Pikaia Imaging; 84: Royal Swedish Academy of Sciences/Göran Scharmer, Mats Löfdahl, ISP; 87: NASA/TRACE/NCAR; 88: Kamioka Observatory, ICRR (Institute for Cosmic Ray Research), The University of Tokyo; 90: Science Photo Library; 92: Landsat 7 Science Team and NASA; 95: ISAS/Lockheed Martin/NASA; 96: D. Ermakoff/Eurelios/Science Photo Library; 99: NASA/ESA and L. Ricci (ESO); 100: NASA/JPL; 103: Pikaia Imaging; 104: Image Science and Analysis Laboratory, NASA-Johnson Space Center.; 106: Oleg Abramov, University of Colorado, Boulder; 108: Ian Steele & Ian Hutcheon/Science Photo Library; 111: Science Source/Science Photo Library; 112: nikkytok/Shutterstock; 114: European Southern Observatory; 116: Dr. Terry Beveridge, Visuals Unlimited /Science Photo Library; 119: fotokik_dot_com/Shutterstock; 120: NASA/JPL/USGS; 123: NASA; 124: Robin Canup, Southwest Research Institute; 127: NASA; 128: ISRO/NASA/JPL-Caltech/Brown Univ./USGS; 130: NASA/GSFC/Arizona State University; 132: NASA/JPL; 134: NASA/Goddard; 136: NASA/Johns Hopkins University Applied Physics Laboratory/Carnegie Institution of Washington; 139: NASA/Johns Hopkins University Applied Physics Laboratory/Carnegie Institution of Washington; 140: NASA/JPL; 143: NASA/JPL-Caltech/ESA; 144: NASA/JPL/USGS; 147 l: ESA/VIRTIS/INAF-IASF/Obs. de Paris-LESIA; r: NASA/JPL; 148: US Geological Survey; 150: V.L. Sharpton, LPI; 152: Image by J.C. Casado © starryearth.com; 155: Image Science and Analysis Laboratory, NASA-Johnson Space Center; 156: NASA/JPL-Caltech/University of Arizona; 158-9: NASA/JPL/Cornell; 160: HiRISE, MRO, LPL (U. Arizona), NASA; 163: ESA/DLR/FU Berlin (G. Neukum); 164: NASA/USGS; 167: NASA/JPL-Caltech/Univ. of Arizona; 168: NASA/JPL/University of Arizona ; 170: NASA; 172: NASA/JPL/University of Arizona; 174: NASA/JPL/University of Arizona ; 176: NASA, ESA, J. Parker (Southwest Research Institute), P. Thomas (Cornell University), L. McFadden (University of Maryland, College Park), and M. Mutchler and Z. Levay (STScI); 179: Pikaia Imaging; 180: NASA/JPL-Caltech/UCLA/MPS/DLR/IDA; 182: NASA/JPL-Caltech/UCLA/MPS/DLR/IDA; 184: ESA 2010 MPS for OSIRIS Team MPS/UPD/LAM/IAA/RSSD/INTA/UPM/DASP/IDA; 187: NASA, ESA, and D. Jewitt (UCLA); 188: NASA/JPL/Space Science Institute; 190: NASA, ESA, IRTF, and A. Sánchez-Lavega and R. Hueso (Universidad del País Vasco, Spain); 192: NASA/JPL; 195: M. Wong and I. de Pater (University of California, Berkeley); 196: Hubble Space Telescope Comet Team; 199: R. Evans, J. Trauger, H. Hammel and the HST Comet Science Team and NASA; 200: NASA/JPL/University of Arizona; 202: NASA/JPL/USGS; 204: NASA/JPL/University of Arizona; 207: NASA/JPL/University of Arizona; 208: NASA/JPL; 211: NASA/JPL; 212: NASA/JPL/Space Science Institute; 214-5: NASA/JPL-Caltech/SSI; 216: NASA/JPL/Space Science Institute; 219: NASA/JPL-Caltech/Keck ; 220: NASA/JPL/Space Science Institute; 222: NASA/JPL/Space Science Institute; 224: NASA/JPL-Caltech/ASI/Space Science Institute; 227: NASA/JPL/Space Science Institute; 228: NASA/JPL/University of Arizona; 230: NASA/JPL/University of Arizona/DLR; 232: NASA/JPL/Space Science Institute; 235: NASA/JPL/Space Science Institute; 236: NASA/JPL; 238: Lawrence Sromovsky, University of Wisconsin-Madison/ W. M. Keck Observatory; 240: NASA/JPL; 243: VLT/ESO/NASA/JPL/Paris Observatory; 244: NASA/JPL/USGS; 247: NASA/JPL/Universities Space Research Association/Lunar & Planetary Institute; 248: NASA, ESA, H. Weaver (JHU/APL), A. Stern (SwRI), and the HST Pluto Companion Search Team; 251: NASA, ESA, and M. Buie (Southwest Research Institute); 252: NASA, ESA, J.E. Krist (STScI/JPL); D.R. Ardila (JHU); D.A. Golimowski (JHU); M. Clampin (NASA/Goddard); H.C. Ford (JHU); G.D. Illingworth (UCO-Lick); G.F. Hartig (STScI) and the ACS Science Team; 254: Pikaia Imaging; 256: R. Richins, enchantedskies.net; 259: NASA/JPL-Caltech/UMD; 260: McComas, et al., and Science; 262: Pikaia Imaging; 264: NASA, ESA, R. O'Connell (University of Virginia), F. Paresce (National Institute for Astrophysics, Bologna, Italy), E. Young (Universities Space Research Association/Ames Research Center), the WFC3 Science Oversight Committee, and the Hubble Heritage Team (STScI/AURA); 267: Pikaia Imaging; 268: NASA, ESA, and The Hubble Heritage Team (STScI/AURA); 270: NASA, ESA, STScI, J. Hester and P. Scowen (Arizona State University); 272: NASA, ESA, and M. Livio and the Hubble 20th Anniversary Team (STScI); 275: NASA, John Krist (Space Telescope Science Institute), Karl Stapelfeldt (Jet Propulsion Laboratory), Jeff Hester (Arizona State University), Chris Burrows (European Space Agency/Space Telescope Science Institute); 276: ESO; 279 l: T. Nakajima (Caltech), S. Durrance (JHU); r: S. Kulkarni (Caltech), D.Golimowski (JHU) and NASA; 280: NASA/SDO; 282: Casey Reed/NASA; 284: NASA/JPL-Caltech; 287: Pikaia Imaging; 288: NASA/JPL-Caltech/Palomar Observatory; 290: NASA/JPL-Caltech/J. Langton (UC Santa Cruz); 292: NASA, ESA, P. Kalas, J. Graham, E. Chiang, E. Kite (University of California, Berkeley), M. Clampin (NASA Goddard Space Flight Center), M. Fitzgerald (Lawrence Livermore National Laboratory), and K. Stapelfeldt and J. Krist (NASA Jet Propulsion Laboratory); 295: NASA/JPL-Caltech/K. Stapelfeldt (JPL), James Clerk Maxwell Telescope; 296: NASA; 298: NASA/Ames/JPL-Caltech ; 300: NASA/JPL-Caltech/R. Hurt (SSC/Caltech); 303: Research by Kloppenborg et al., Nature 464, 870-872 (8 April 2010). Image by John D. Monnier, University of Michigan; 304 t: Andrea Dupree (Harvard-Smithsonian CfA), Ronald Gilliland (STScI), NASA and ESA; b: ESO and P. Kervella; 306: Haubois et al., A&A, 508, 2, 923,2009, reproduced with permission © ESO/Observatoire de Paris; 308: NASA/JPL-Caltech/WISE Team; 311: NASA, ESA, and R. Sahai (NASA's Jet Propulsion Laboratory); 312: NASA, ESA, and the Hubble SM4 ERO Team; 314: NASA/ESA; 316: NASA/CXC/SAO/M. Karovska et al; 318-9: NASA/JPL-Caltech; 320: NASA, ESA, HEIC, and The Hubble Heritage Team (STScI/AURA); 322: NASA, ESA, and Z. Levay (STScI); 324: NASA, ESA, and Z. Levay (STScI); 327: NASA, ESA, and H. Bond (STScI); 328: Nathan Smith, University of Minnesota/NOAO/AURA/NSF; 330: ESO; 332: NASA, ESA, J. Hester and A. Loll (Arizona State University); 334: ORNL/Science Photo Library; 336: ESO/L.Calçada; 339: NASA, ESA, and the Hubble SM4 ERO Team; 340: Blundell & Bowler, NRAO/AUI/NSF; 342: Pikaia Imaging; 344: ESO; 346: NASA and The Hubble Heritage Team (STScI/AURA); 348: NASA/CXC/MIT/F. Baganoff, R. Shcherbakov et al. ; 350: A.Ghez, Keck/UCLA Galactic Center Group; 352: Purcell, Tollerud, & Bullock/UC Irvine; 355: Sharma, Johnston, & Bullock/UC Irvine; 356: The Hubble Heritage Team (AURA/STScI/NASA); 358: ESO/L. Calçada; 360: ESO; 362: NASA, ESA, and F. Paresce (INAF-IASF, Bologna, Italy), R. O'Connell (University of Virginia, Charlottesville), and the Wide Field Camera 3 Science Oversight Committee; 364: NASA, ESA, and the Hubble Heritage (STScI/AURA)-ESA/Hubble Collaboration; 367: NASA, ESA, and The Hubble Heritage Team (STScI/AURA); 368: Image courtesy of NRAO/AUI and J. M. Uson; 370: NASA, Andrew S. Wilson (University of Maryland); Patrick L. Shopbell (Caltech); Chris Simpson (Subaru Telescope); Thaisa Storchi-Bergmann and F. K. B. Barbosa (UFRGS, Brazil); and Martin J. Ward (University of Leicester, U.K.); 372: Tomasz Barszczak/Super-Kamiokande Collaboration/Science Photo Library; 375: Randy Landsberg, Dinoj Surendran, and Mark SubbaRao (U of Chicago / Adler Planetarium); 376: Andrew MacFadyen/Science Photo Library; 378: DANIEL PRICE/STEPHAN ROSSWOG/Science Photo Library; 380: NASA, ESA, SAO, CXC, JPL-Caltech, and STScI; 383: NASA, ESA, and The Hubble Heritage Team (STScI/AURA); 384: Visualisation by Christopher Fluke, Centre for Astrophysics & Supercomputing, Swinburne University of Technology, using data from the 6dF Galaxy Survey (courtesy H.Jones et al.) ; 387: The 2dF Galaxy Redshift Survey Team, http://www2.aao.gov.au/2dFGRS/; 388: P. Jonsson (Harvard-Smithsonian Center for Astrophysics), G. Novak (Princeton University), and T.J. Cox (Carnegie Observatories, Pasadena, Calif.); 390: NASA, ESA, and the Hubble Heritage Team (STScI/AURA); 392: NASA, N. Benitez (JHU), T. Broadhurst (Racah Institute of Physics/The Hebrew University), H. Ford (JHU), M. Clampin (STScI), G. Hartig (STScI), G. Illingworth (UCO/Lick Observatory), the ACS Science Team and NASA; 395: ESA/Hubble & NASA; 396: Volker Springel/Max Planck Institute for Astrophysics/Science Photo Library; 398: X-ray: NASA/CXC/CfA/M.Markevitch et al.; Optical: NASA/STScI; Magellan/U.Arizona/D.Clowe et al.; Lensing Map: NASA/STScI; ESO WFI; Magellan/U.Arizona/D.Clowe et al.; 400: NASA, ESA, E. Jullo (Jet Propulsion Laboratory), P. Natarajan (Yale University), and J.-P. Kneib (Laboratoire d'Astrophysique de Marseille, CNRS, France); 403: NASA/Swift/S. Immler; 404: Mark Garlick/Science Photo Library; 406-7: Pikaia Imaging.